2020

The ARRL
HANDBOOK
FOR RADIO COMMUNICATIONS

NINETY-SEVENTH EDITION

Volume 1: Introduction and Fundamental Theory — Ch. 1-4

Volume 2: Practical Design and Principles Part 1 — Ch. 5-11

Volume 3: Practical Design and Principles Part 2 — Ch. 12-18

Volume 4: Antenna Systems and Radio Propagation — Ch. 19-21

▶ **Volume 5:** Equipment Construction and Station Accessories — Ch. 22-24

Volume 6: Test Equipment, Troubleshooting, RFI, and Index — Ch. 25-28

Editor
H. Ward Silver, NØAX

Contributing Editors
Steven R. Ford, WB8IMY
Mark J. Wilson, K1RO

Editorial Assistant
Maty Weinberg, KB1EIB

Technical Consultants
Bob Allison, WB1GCM
Edward F. Hare, Jr., W1RFI
Zachary H.J. Lau, W1VT

Cover Design
Sue Fagan, KB1OKW
Bob Inderbitzen, NQ1R

Production
Michelle Bloom, WB1ENT
Jodi Morin, KA1JPA
David F. Pingree, N1NAS

Additional Contributors to the 2020 Edition
John Brooks, N9ZL
Jim Brown, K9YC
Glen Brown, W6GJB
Ralph Crumrine, NØKC

Don Daso, K4ZA
Joel Hallas, W1ZR
Bill Koch, W2RMA
Rick Lindquist, WW1ME
Glenn Loake, GØGBI
Helmut Berka, DL2MAJ
Oliver Micic, DG7XO
Carl Luetzelschwab, K9LA
Phil Salas, AD5X
Rob Sherwood, NCØB
Cory Sickles, WA3UVV
George Steber, WB9LVI
Jim Tonne, W4ENE
Paul Wade, W1GHZ

Published by:
ARRL The national association for **AMATEUR RADIO**®
225 Main Street, Newington, CT 06111-1400 USA
www.arrl.org

Copyright © 2019 by
The American Radio Relay League, Inc.

Copyright secured under the Pan-American Convention

International Copyright secured

All rights reserved. No part of this work may be reproduced in any form except by written permission of the publisher. All rights of translation are reserved.

Printed in the USA

Quedan reservados todos los derechos

ISBN: 978-1-62595-107-6 Softcover
ISBN: 978-1-62595-113-7 Six-Volume Set

Kindle eBook Editions
 ISBN: 978-1-62595-091-8 — Volume 1
 ISBN: 978-1-62595-092-5 — Volume 2
 ISBN: 978-1-62595-093-2 — Volume 3
 ISBN: 978-1-62595-094-9 — Volume 4
 ISBN: 978-1-62595-095-6 — Volume 5
 ISBN: 978-1-62595-096-3 — Volume 6

Ninety-Seventh Edition

About the cover:
The collection of components comprises the HF Packer miniHFPA2 amplifier kit. Although the kit is not featured in this 2020 edition of the ARRL Handbook, its components represent the spirit of project design and craftsmanship that has been part of Amateur Radio from the beginning.

Contents

A more detailed Table of Contents is included at the beginning of each chapter.

VOLUME 1

INTRODUCTION AND FUNDAMENTAL THEORY

1 **What is Amateur (Ham) Radio?**
1.1 Do-It-Yourself Wireless
1.2 Joining the Ham Radio Community
1.3 Your Ham Radio Station
1.4 Getting on the Air
1.5 Your Ham Radio "Lifestyle"
1.6 Public Service
1.7 Ham Radio in the Classroom
1.8 Resources
1.9 Glossary

2 **Electrical Fundamentals**
2.1 Introduction to Electricity
2.2 Resistance and Conductance
2.3 Basic Circuit Principles
2.4 Power and Energy
2.5 Circuit Control Components
2.6 Capacitance and Capacitors
2.7 Inductance and Inductors
2.8 Semiconductor Devices
2.9 References and Bibliography

3 **Radio Fundamentals**
3.1 AC Waveforms
3.2 Measuring AC Voltage, Current and Power
3.3 Effective Radiated Power
3.4 AC in Capacitors and Inductors
3.5 Working with Reactance
3.6 Impedance
3.7 Quality Factor (Q) of Components
3.8 Resonant Circuits
3.9 Analog Signal Processing
3.10 Electromagnetic Waves
3.11 References and Bibliography

4 **Circuits and Components**
4.1 Practical Resistors
4.2 Practical Capacitors
4.3 Practical Inductors
4.4 Transformers
4.5 Practical Semiconductors
4.6 Amplifiers
4.7 Operational Amplifiers
4.8 Miscellaneous Analog ICs
4.9 Analog-Digital Interfacing
4.10 Analog Device and Circuits Glossary
4.11 Heat Management
4.12 References and Bibliography

VOLUME 2

PRACTICAL DESIGN AND PRINCIPLES — PART 1

5 RF Techniques
5.1 Introduction
5.2 Lumped-Element versus Distributed Characteristics
5.3 Effects of Parasitic (Stray) Characteristics
5.4 Semiconductor Circuits at RF
5.5 Ferrite Materials
5.6 Impedance Matching Networks
5.7 RF Transformers
5.8 Noise
5.9 Two-Port Networks
5.10 RF Design Techniques Glossary
5.11 References and Bibliography

6 Computer-Aided Circuit Design
6.1 Circuit Simulation Overview
6.2 Simulation Basics
6.3 Limitations of Simulation at RF
6.4 Electromagnetic Analysis of RF Circuits
6.5 References and Bibliography

7 Power Sources
7.1 Power Processing
7.2 AC-AC Power Conversion
7.3 Power Transformers
7.4 AC-DC Power Conversion
7.5 Voltage Multipliers
7.6 Current Multipliers
7.7 Rectifier Types
7.8 Power Filtering
7.9 Power Supply Regulation
7.10 "Crowbar" Protective Circuits
7.11 DC-DC Switchmode Power Conversion
7.12 High-Voltage Techniques
7.13 Batteries
7.14 Glossary of Power Source Terms
7.15 References and Bibliography
7.16 Power Supply Projects

8 DSP and SDR Fundamentals
8.1 Introduction to DSP
8.2 Introduction to SDR
8.3 Analog-Digital Conversion
8.4 Data Converters for SDR and DSP
8.5 Digital Signal Processors
8.6 Digital (Discrete-time) Signals
8.7 The Fourier Transform
8.8 Glossary of DSP and SDR Terms
8.9 References and Bibliography

9 Oscillators and Synthesizers
9.1 How Oscillators Work
9.2 LC Variable Frequency Oscillator (VFO) Circuits
9.3 Building an Oscillator
9.4 Crystal Oscillators
9.5 Oscillators at UHF and Above
9.6 Frequency Synthesizers
9.7 Phase Noise
9.8 Glossary of Oscillator and Synthesizer Terms
9.9 References and Bibliography

10 Analog and Digital Filtering
10.1 Introduction
10.2 Filter Basics
10.3 Passive LC Filters
10.4 Active Audio Filters
10.5 Digital Filters
10.6 Quartz Crystal Filters
10.7 SAW Filters
10.8 Transmission Line VHF/UHF/Microwave Filters
10.9 Helical Resonators
10.11 Filter Projects
10.12 Glossary of Filter Terms
10.13 References and Bibliography

11 Modulation
11.1 Introduction
11.2 Amplitude Modulation (AM)
11.3 Angle Modulation
11.4 FSK and PSK
11.5 Quadrature Modulation
11.6 Analytic Signals and Modulation
11.7 Image Modulation
11.8 Spread Spectrum Modulation
11.9 Pulse Modulation
11.10 Modulation Bandwidth and Impairments
11.11 Glossary of Modulation Terms
11.12 References and Further Reading

VOLUME 3

PRACTICAL DESIGN AND PRINCIPLES — PART 2

12 **Receiving**
   12.1 Characterizing Receivers
   12.2 Heterodyne Receivers
   12.3 SDR Receivers
   12.4 Mixing and Mixers
   12.5 Demodulation and Detection
   12.6 Automatic Gain Control (AGC)
   12.7 Noise Management
   12.8 References and Bibliography

13 **Transmitting**
   13.1 Characterizing Transmitters
   13.2 Transmitter Architecture
   13.3 Modulators
   13.4 Transmitting CW
   13.5 Transmitting AM and SSB
   13.6 Transmitting Angle Modulation
   13.7 Effects of Transmitted Noise
   13.8 Microphones and Speech Processing
   13.9 Voice Operation
   13.10 Transmitter Power Stages
   13.11 References and Bibliography

14 **Transceiver Design Topics**
   14.1 Signal Chains in SDR Transceivers
   14.2 User Interfaces
   14.3 Configuration and Control Interfaces
   14.4 SDR Design Tools

15 **Digital Protocols and Modes**
   15.1 Digital "Modes"
   15.2 Unstructured Digital Modes
   15.3 Fuzzy Modes
   15.4 Structured Digital Modes
   15.5 Networking Modes
   15.6 Digital Mode Table
   15.7 Glossary of Digital Protocol and Mode Terms
   15.8 References and Bibliography

16 **Amateur Radio Data Platforms**
   16.1 Platform Overview
   16.2 Sensors
   16.3 Navigation Data and Telemetry
   16.4 Payloads
   16.5 High Altitude Balloon Platforms
   16.6 Unmanned Aerial Vehicles (UAVs)
   16.7 Rockets
   16.8 Robotics
   16.9 Fixed Stations
   16.10 References and Bibliography

17 **RF Power Amplifiers**
   17.1 High Power, Who Needs It?
   17.2 Types of Power Amplifiers
   17.3 Vacuum Tube Basics
   17.4 Tank Circuits
   17.5 Transmitting Tube Ratings
   17.6 Sources of Operating Voltages
   17.7 Tube Amplifier Cooling
   17.8 Vacuum Tube Amplifier Stabilization
   17.9 MOSFET Design for RF Amplifiers
   17.10 Solid-State RF Amplifiers
   17.11 Solid State Amplifier Projects
   17.12 Tube Amplifier Projects
   17.13 References and Bibliography

18 **Repeaters**
   18.1 A Brief History
   18.2 Repeater Overview
   18.3 FM Voice Repeaters
   18.4 D-STAR Repeater Systems
   18.5 System Fusion Repeater Systems
   18.6 Digital Mobile Radio (DMR)
   18.7 Other Digital Voice Repeater Technologies
   18.8 Glossary of FM and Repeater Terminology
   18.9 References and Bibliography

VOLUME 4

ANTENNA SYSTEMS AND RADIO PROPAGATION

19 **Propagation of Radio Signals**
   19.1 Fundamentals of Radio Waves
   19.2 Sky-Wave Propagation and the Sun
   19.3 MUF Predictions
   19.4 Propagation in the Troposphere
   19.5 VHF/UHF Mobile Propagation
   19.6 Propagation for Space Communications
   19.7 Noise and Propagation
   19.8 Propagation Below the AM Broadcast Band
   19.9 Glossary of Radio Propagation Terms
   19.10 References and Bibliography

20 **Transmission Lines**
   20.1 Transmission Line Basics
   20.2 Choosing a Transmission Line
   20.3 The Transmission Line as Impedance Transformer
   20.4 Matching Impedances in the Antenna System
   20.5 Baluns and Transmission-Line Transformers
   20.6 PC Transmission Lines
   20.7 Waveguides
   20.8 Glossary of Transmission Line Terms
   20.9 References and Bibliography

21 **Antennas**
   21.1 Antenna Basics
   21.2 Dipoles and the Half-Wave Antenna
   21.3 Vertical (Ground-Plane) Antennas
   21.4 T and Inverted-L Antennas
   21.5 Slopers and Vertical Dipoles
   21.6 Yagi Antennas
   21.7 Quad and Loop Antennas
   21.8 HF Mobile Antennas
   21.9 VHF/UHF Mobile Antennas
   21.10 VHF/UHF Antennas
   21.11 VHF/UHF Beams
   21.12 Radio Direction Finding Antennas
   21.13 Rotators
   21.13 Glossary
   21.14 References and Bibliography

VOLUME 5

EQUIPMENT CONSTRUCTION AND STATION ACCESSORIES

22 **Component Data and References**
22.1 Component Data
22.2 Resistors
22.3 Capacitors
22.4 Inductors
22.5 Transformers
22.6 Semiconductors
22.7 Tubes, Wire, Materials, Attenuators, Miscellaneous
22.8 Computer Connectors
22.9 RF Connectors and Transmission Lines
22.10 Reference Tables

23 **Construction Techniques**
23.1 Electronic Shop Safety
23.2 Tools and Their Use
23.3 Soldering Tools and Techniques
23.4 Surface Mount Technology (SMT)
23.5 Constructing Electronic Circuits
23.6 CAD for PCB Design
23.7 Microwave Construction
23.8 Mechanical Fabrication

24 **Assembling a Station**
24.1 Fixed Stations
24.2 Mobile Installations
24.3 Portable Installations
24.4 Remote Stations

VOLUME 6

TEST EQUIPMENT, TROUBLESHOOTING, RFI, AND INDEX

25 **Test Equipment and Measurements**
25.1 Introduction
25.2 DC Measurements
25.3 AC Measurements
25.4 RF Measurements
25.5 Receiver Measurements
25.6 Transmitter Measurements
25.7 Antenna System Measurements
25.8 Miscellaneous Measurements
25.9 Construction Projects
25.10 References and Further Reading
25.11 Glossary of Test Equipment and Measurement Terms

26 **Troubleshooting and Maintenance**
26.1 Test Equipment
26.2 Components
26.3 Getting Started
26.4 Inside the Equipment
26.5 Testing at the Circuit Level
26.6 After the Repairs
26.7 Professional Repairs
26.8 Typical Symptoms and Faults
26.9 Radio Troubleshooting Hints
26.10 Antenna Systems
26.11 Repair and Restoration of Vintage Equipment
26.12 References and Bibliography

27 **RF Interference**
27.1 Managing Radio Frequency Interference
27.2 FCC Rules and Regulations
27.3 Elements of RFI
27.4 Identifying the Type of RFI Source
27.5 Locating Sources of RFI
27.6 Power-Line Noise
27.7 Elements of RFI Control
27.8 Troubleshooting RFI
27.9 Automotive RFI
27.10 RFI Projects
27.11 Glossary of RFI Terms
27.12 References and Bibliography

28 **Safety**
28.1 Electrical Safety
28.2 Antenna and Tower Safety
28.3 RF Safety

Advertiser's Index
Index
Project Index
Author's Index

DOWNLOADABLE CONTENT AND TOOLS

Space Communications
Digital Communications
Image Communications
Digital Basics
Station Accessories and Projects
2020 HF Transceiver Survey
Radio Mathematics

Contents

22.1 Component Data
   22.1.1 EIA and Industry Standards
   22.1.2 Other Sources of Component Data
   22.1.3 The ARRL Technical Information Service (TIS)
   22.1.4 Definitions
   22.1.5 Surface-Mount Technology (SMT)
22.2 Resistors
   22.2.1 Resistor Types
   22.2.2 Resistor Identification
22.3 Capacitors
   22.3.1 Capacitor Types
   22.3.2 Electrolytic Capacitors
   22.3.3 Surface Mount Capacitors
   22.3.4 Capacitor Voltage Ratings
   22.3.5 Capacitor Identification
22.4 Inductors
22.5 Transformers
22.6 Semiconductors
   22.6.1 Diodes
   22.6.2 Transistors
   22.6.3 Voltage Regulators
   22.6.4 Analog and Digital Integrated Circuits
   22.6.5 MMIC Amplifiers
22.7 Tubes, Wire, Materials, Attenuators, Miscellaneous
22.8 Computer Connectors
22.9 RF Connectors and Transmission Lines
   22.9.1 UHF Connectors
   22.9.2 BNC, N, and F Connectors
   22.9.3 Connector Identifier and Range Chart
22.10 Reference Tables

List of Figures

Fig 22.1 — Resistor wattages and sizes
Fig 22.2 — Surface mount resistors
Fig 22.3 — Power resistors
Fig 22.4 — Resistor value identification
Fig 22.5 — Common capacitor types and package styles
Fig 22.6 — Aluminum and tantalum electrolytic capacitors
Fig 22.7 — Aluminum electrolytic capacitor dimensions
Fig 22.8 — Surface-mount capacitor packages
Fig 22.9 — Surface-mount electrolytic packages
Fig 22.10 — Abbreviated EIA capacitor identification
Fig 22.11 — Obsolete capacitor color codes
Fig 22.12 — Complete EIA capacitor labeling scheme
Fig 22.13 — Obsolete JAN "postage stamp" capacitor labeling
Fig 22.14 — Color coding for cylindrical encapsulated RF chokes
Fig 22.15 — Color-coding for semiconductor diodes
Fig 22.16 — Axial-leaded diode packages and pad dimensions
Fig 22.17 — MMIC application
Fig 22.18 — MMIC package styles
Fig 22.19 — Installing PL-259 on RG-8 cable
Fig 22.20 — Installing PL-259 on RG-58 or RG-59 cable
Fig 22.21 — Installing crimp-on UHF connectors
Fig 22.22 — Installing BNC connectors
Fig 22.23 — Installing Type N connectors
Fig 22.24 — Installing Type F connectors

List of Tables

Resistors
Table 22.1 — Resistor Wattages and Sizes
Table 22.2 — SMT Resistor Wattages and Sizes
Table 22.3 — Power Resistors
Table 22.4 — Resistor Color Codes
Table 22.5 — EIA Standard Resistor Values
Table 22.6 — Mil–Spec Resistors

Capacitors
Table 22.7 — EIA Standard Capacitor Values
Table 22.8 — Ceramic Temperature Characteristics
Table 22.9 — Aluminum Electrolytic Capacitors Standard Sizes (Radial Leads)
Table 22.10 — Aluminum Electrolytic Capacitors EIA ±20%Standard Values
Table 22.11 — SMT Capacitor Two-Character Labeling
Table 22.12 — Surface Mount Capacitors EIA Standard Sizes
Table 22.13 — Capacitor Standard Working Voltages
Table 22.14 — European Marking Standards for Capacitors

Inductors
Table 22.15 — EIA Standard Inductor Values
Table 22.16 — Powdered-Iron Toroidal Cores: Magnetic Properties
Table 22.17 — Powdered-Iron Toroidal Cores: Dimensions
Table 22.18 — Ferrite Toroids: A_L Chart (mH per 1000 turns) Enameled Wire

Transformers
Table 22.19 — Power-Transformer Wiring Color Codes
Table 22.20 — IF Transformer Wiring Color Codes
Table 22.21 — IF Transformer Slug Color Codes
Table 22.22 — Audio Transformer Wiring Color Codes

Semiconductors
Table 22.23 — Semiconductor Diode Specifications
Table 22.24 — Package dimensions for small signal, rectifier and Zener diodes
Table 22.25 — Common Zener Diodes
Table 22.26 — Voltage-variable Capacitance Diodes
Table 22.27 — Three-terminal Voltage Regulators
Table 22.28 — Monolithic 50-Ω Amplifiers (MMIC gain blocks)
Table 22.29 — Small-Signal FETs
Table 22.30 — Low-Noise Bipolar Transistors
Table 22.31 — General-Purpose Bipolar Transistors
Table 22.32 — General-Purpose Silicon Power Bipolar Transistors
Table 22.33 — Power FETs or MOSFETs
Table 22.34 — RF Power Transistors — By Part Number
Table 22.35 — RF Power Transistors — By Power Output
Table 22.36 — RF Power Amplifier Modules
Table 22.37 — Digital Logic Families
Table 22.38 — Operational Amplifiers (Op Amps)

Tubes, Wire, Materials, Attenuators, Miscellaneous
Table 22.39 — Triode Transmitting Tubes
Table 22.40 — Tetrode Transmitting Tubes
Table 22.41 — EIA Vacuum Tube Base Diagrams
Table 22.42 — Metal-oxide Varistor (MOV) Transient Suppressors
Table 22.43 — Crystal Holders
Table 22.44 — Copper Wire Specifications
Table 22.45 — Standard vs American Wire Gauge
Table 22.46 — Antenna Wire Strength
Table 22.47 — Guy Wire Lengths to Avoid
Table 22.48 — Aluminum Alloy Specifications
Table 22.49 — Impedance of Two-Conductor Twisted Pair Lines
Table 22.50 — Attenuation per foot of Two-Conductor Twisted Pair Lines
Table 22.51 — Large Machine-Wound Coil Specifications
Table 22.52 — Inductance Factor for Large Machine-Wound Coils
Table 22.53 — Small Machine-Wound Coil Specifications
Table 22.54 — Inductance Factor for Small Machine-Wound Coils
Table 22.55 — Measured Inductance for #12 Wire Windings
Table 22.56 — Relationship Between Noise Figure and Noise Temperature
Table 22.57 — Pi-Network Resistive Attenuators (50-Ω Impedance)
Table 22.58 — T-Network Resistive Attenuators (50-Ω Impedance)

Computer Connectors
Table 22.59 — Computer Connector Pin Outs

RF Connectors and Transmission Lines
Table 22.60 — Nominal Characteristics of Commonly Used Transmission Lines
Table 22.61 — Coaxial Cable Connectors

Reference Tables
Table 22.62 — US Customary Units and Conversion Factors
Table 22.63 — Metric System — International System of Units (SI)
Table 22.64 — Voltage-Power Conversion Table
Table 22.65 — Reflection Coefficient, Attenuation, SWR, and Return Loss
Table 22.66 — Abbreviations List

Chapter 22

Component Data and References

Radio amateurs are known for electronic experimentation and homebrew building. Using the wide variety of components available, they design and build impressive radio equipment. With the industry growth of components for wireless communications and surface mount technology (SMT), the choices available seem endless and selecting the proper component can seem a daunting task.

Fortunately, most amateurs tend to use a limited number of component types that have "passed the test of time," making component selection in many cases easy and safe. Others are learning to design and build using the vast array of SMT parts.

Dick Frey, K4XU, updated the RF power semiconductor tables for the 2019 edition.

Chapter 22 — Downloadable Supplemental Content

Supplemental Files
- BNC Crimp Installation Instructions
- N Crimp Installation Instructions
- Miniature Lamp Guide
- Thermoplastics Properties
- TV Deflection Tube Guide
- Obsolete RF Power Semiconductor Tables
- F Compression Installation Instructions

22.1 Component Data

This section provides reference information on the old and new components most often used by the Amateur Radio experimenter and homebrewer, and information for those wishing to learn more about component performance and selection.

22.1.1 EIA and Industry Standards

The American National Standards Institute (ANSI), the Electronic Industries Alliance (EIA), and the Electronic Components Association (ECA) establish the US standards for most electronic components, connectors, wire and cables. These standards establish component sizes, wattages, "standard values," tolerances and other performance characteristics. A branch of the EIA sets the standards for Mil-spec (standard military specification) and special electronic components used by defense and government agencies. The Joint Electron Devices Engineering Council (JEDEC), another branch of the EIA, develops the standards for the semiconductor industry. The EIA cooperates with other standards agencies such as the International Electrotechnical Commission (IEC), a worldwide standards agency. You can often find published EIA standards in the engineering library of a college or university.

And finally, the International Organization of Standardization (ISO), headquartered in Geneva, Switzerland, sets the global standards for nearly everything from paper sizes to photographic film speeds. ANSI is the US representative to the ISO.

These organizations, or their acronyms, are familiar to most of us. They are much more than a label on a component. EIA and other industry standards are what mark components for identification, establishes the "preferred standard values" and ensures their reliable performance from one unit to the next, regardless of their source. Standards require that a 1.2 kΩ 5% resistor from Ohmite Corp. has the same performance as a 1.2 kΩ 5% resistor from Vishay-Dale, or a 2N3904 to have the same performance characteristics and physical packaging whether from ON Semi or Gold Star.

Much of the component data in this chapter is devoted to presenting these component standards, physical dimensions and the various methods of component identification and marking. By selecting components manufactured under these industry standards, building a project from the *Handbook* or other source will ensure nearly identical performance to the original design.

22.1.2 Other Sources of Component Data

There are many sources you can consult for detailed component data but the best source of component information and data sheets is the Internet. Most manufacturers maintain extensive websites with information and data on their products. Often, the quickest route to detailed product information is to enter "data sheet" and the part number into an Internet search engine. Distributors such as Digi-Key and Mouser include links to useful information in their online catalogs as well. Some manufacturers still publish data books for the components they make, and parts catalogs themselves are often good sources of component data and application notes and bulletins.

Some of the tables printed in previous editions of this book have been moved to the downloadable supplemental content to make room for new material. If a table or figure you need is missing, check the downloadable supplemental content!

22.1.3 The ARRL Technical Information Service (TIS)

The ARRL Technical Information Service on the ARRL website (**www.arrl.org/technical-information-service**) provides technical assistance to members and nonmembers, including information about components and useful references. The TIS includes links to detailed, commonly needed information in many technical areas. Questions may also be submitted via email (**tis@arrl.org**); fax (860-594-0259); or mail (TIS, ARRL, 225 Main St, Newington, CT 06111).

22.1.4 Definitions

Electronic components such as resistors, capacitors, and inductors are manufactured with a *nominal* value — the value with which they are labeled. The component's *actual* value is what is measured with a suitable measuring instrument. If the nominal value is given as text characters, an "R" in the value (for example "4R7") stands for *radix* and is read as a decimal point, thus "4.7".

Tolerance refers to a range of acceptable values above and below the nominal component value. For example, a 4700-Ω resistor rated for ±20% tolerance can have an actual value anywhere between 3760 Ω and 5640 Ω. You may always substitute a closer-tolerance device for one with a wider tolerance. For most Amateur Radio projects, assume a 10% tolerance if none is specified.

The *temperature coefficient* or *tempco* of a component describes its change in value with temperature. Tempco may be expressed as a change in unit value per degree (ohms per degree Celsius) or as a relative change per degree (parts per million per degree). Except for temperature sensing components that may use Fahrenheit or Kelvin, Celsius is almost always used for the temperature scale. Temperature coefficients may not be linear, such as those for capacitors, thermistors, or quartz crystals. In such cases, tempco is specified by an identifier such as Z5U or C0G and an equation or graph of the change with temperature provided by the manufacturer.

22.1.5 Surface-Mount Technology (SMT)

"SMT" is used throughout this book to refer to components, printed-circuit boards or assembly techniques that involve surface-mount technology. SMT components are often referred to by the abbreviations "SMD" and "SMC," but all three abbreviations are considered to be effectively equivalent. *Through-hole* or *leaded* components are those with wire leads intended to be inserted into holes in printed-circuit boards or used in point-to-point wiring.

Many different types of electronic components, both active and passive, are now available in surface-mount packages. Each package is identified by a code, such as 1802 or SOT. Resistors in SMT packages are referred to by package code and not by power dissipation, as through-hole resistors are. The very small size of these components leaves little space for marking with conventional codes, so brief alphanumeric codes are used to convey the most information in the smallest possible space. You will need a magnifying glass to read the markings on the bodies of SMT components.

In many cases, vendors will deliver SMT components packaged in tape from master reels and the components will not be marked. This is often the case with SMT resistors and small capacitors. However, the tape will be marked or the components are delivered in a plastic bag with a label. Take care to keep the components separated and labeled or you'll have to measure their values one by one!

HAMCALC Calculators

The *HAMCALC* package of software calculators by George Murphy, VE3ERP, is very handy. Covering dozens of topics from antenna lengths to impedance matching, the package can be downloaded free of charge from **www.cq-amateur-radio.com**. *HAMCALC* utilities were written in GWBASIC. *Windows 7* and later users may not be able to run *HAMCALC* software depending on the version and configuration of their operating system.

22.2 Resistors

Most resistors are manufactured using EIA standards to establish common ratings for wattage, resistor values and tolerance regardless of the manufacturer. EIA marking methods for resistors utilize either an alphanumeric scheme or a color code to denote the value and tolerance.

In the earlier days of electronics, 10% and 20% tolerance resistors were the common and inexpensive varieties used by most amateurs. 1% tolerance resistors were considered the "precision resistors" and seldom used by the amateur due to their significantly higher cost.

Today, with improved manufacturing techniques, both 5% and 1% tolerance resistors are commonly available *and* inexpensive, with precision resistors to 0.1% not uncommon.

22.2.1 Resistor Types

The major resistor types are carbon composition, carbon film, metalized film and wire-wound, as described below. (For additional discussion of the characteristics of the different types of resistors, see the **Electrical Fundamentals** chapter.)

Carbon composition resistors are made from a slurry of carbon and binder material formulated to achieve the desired resistance when compressed into a cylinder and encapsulated. This yields a resistor with tolerances in the 5% to 20% range. "Carbon comp" resistors have a tendency to absorb moisture over time and to change value, but can withstand temporary "pulse" overloads that would damage or destroy a film-type resistor.

Carbon film resistors are made from a layer of carbon deposited on a dielectric film or substrate. The thickness of the carbon film is controlled to form the desired resistance with greater accuracy than for carbon composition. They are low cost alternatives to carbon composition resistors and are available with 1% to 5% tolerances.

Metalized film resistors replace carbon films with metal films deposited onto the dielectric using sputtering techniques to achieve very accurate resistances to 0.1% tolerances. Metal film resistors also generate less thermal noise than carbon resistors.

All three of these resistor types are normally available with power ratings from ¹⁄₁₀ W to 2 W. **Figure 22.1** and **Tables 22.1** and **22.2** provide the body sizes and lead or pad spacing for through-hole and SMT resistors.

For new designs, carbon film and metalized film resistors should be used for their improved characteristics and lower cost compared to the older carbon composition resistors. Metalized films have lower residual inductance and often preferred at VHF. Most surface mount resistors (shown in **Figure 22.2**) are metalized films.

Wire-wound resistors, as the name implies, are made from lengths of wire wound around an insulating form to achieve the desired resistance for power ratings above 2 W. Wire-wound resistors have high parasitic inductance, caused by the wire wrapped around a form similar to a coil, and thus should not be used at RF frequencies. **Figure 22.3** (A, B and D) show three types of wire-wound resistors with wattage ranges in **Table 22.3**.

An alternative to wire-wound resistors is the new generation of resistors known as *thick-film power resistors*. They are rated up to 100 W and packaged in a TO-220 or similar case which makes it easy to mount them on heat sinks and printed-circuit boards. Most varieties are non-inductive and suitable for RF use. Metal-oxide ("cement") resistors are also available in packages similar to that of Figure 22.3B. Similar to carbon composition resistors, metal-oxide resistors are non-inductive and useful at RF.

22.2.2 Resistor Identification

Resistors are identified by the IEC 60062:2016 standard as shown in **Figure 22.4**. The IEC numerical code is used worldwide. The IEC numerical code for resistor identification is widely used in industry. The nominal resistance, expressed in ohms, is identified by three digits for 2% (and greater) tolerance devices. The first two digits represent the significant figures; the last digit specifies the multiplier as the exponent of 10. (The multiplier is simply the number of zeros following the significant numerals.) For values less than 100 Ω, the letter R is substituted for one of the significant digits and represents a decimal point. An alphabetic character indicates the tolerance as shown in Table 22.2

For example, a resistor marked with "122J" would be a 1200 Ω, or a 1.2 kΩ 5% resistor. A resistor containing four digits, such as "1211," would be a 1210 Ω, or a 1.21 kΩ 1% precision resistor.

If the tolerance of the unit is narrower than ±2%, the code used is a four-digit code where the first three digits are the significant figures and the last is the multiplier. The

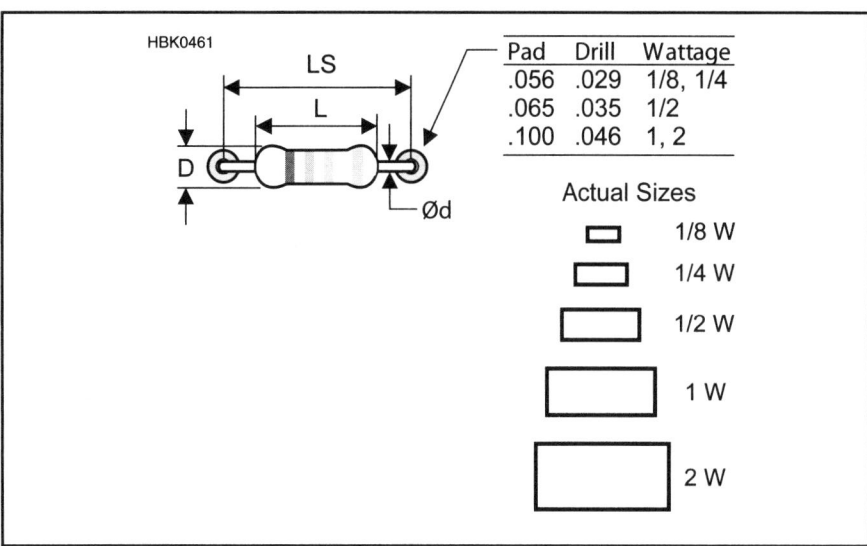

Figure 22.1 — Resistor wattages and sizes.

Table 22.1
Resistor Wattages and Sizes

Size	L	D	LS*	Ød	PCB Pad Size and Drill
⅛ W	0.165	0.079	0.25	0.020	0.056 round, 0.029 hole
¼ W	0.268	0.098	0.35	0.024	0.056 round, 0.029 hole
½ W	0.394	0.138	0.60	0.029	0.065 round, 0.035 hole
1 W	0.472	0.197	0.70	0.032	0.100 round, 0.046 hole
2 W	0.687	0.300	0.90	0.032	0.100 round, 0.046 hole

Dimensions in inches.
*LS = Recommended PCB lead bend

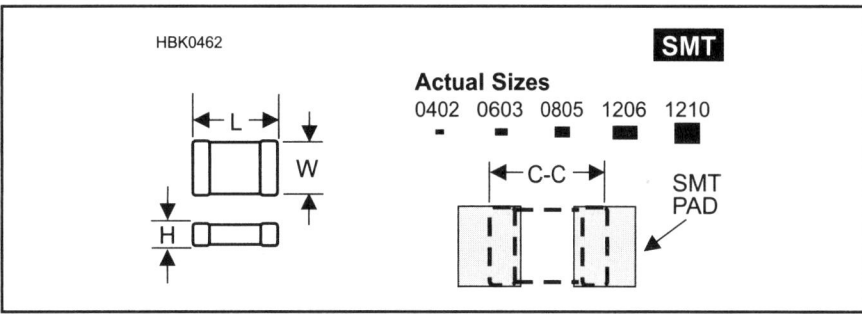

Figure 22.2 — Surface mount resistors.

Table 22.2
SMT Resistor Wattages and Sizes

Body Size	L	W	H	SMT Pad	C-C*
0402	0.039	0.020	0.014	0.025 × 0.035	0.050
0603	0.063	0.031	0.018	0.030 × 0.030	0.055
0805	0.079	0.049	0.020	0.040 × 0.050	0.075
1206	0.126	0.063	0.024	0.064 × 0.064	0.125
1210	0.126	0.102	0.024	0.070 × 0.100	0.150

Dimensions in inches.
*C-C is SMT pad center-to-center spacing

SMT Resistor Tolerance Codes

Letter	Tolerance
D	±0.5%
F	±1.0%
G	±2.0%
J	±5.0%

Component Data and References   22.3

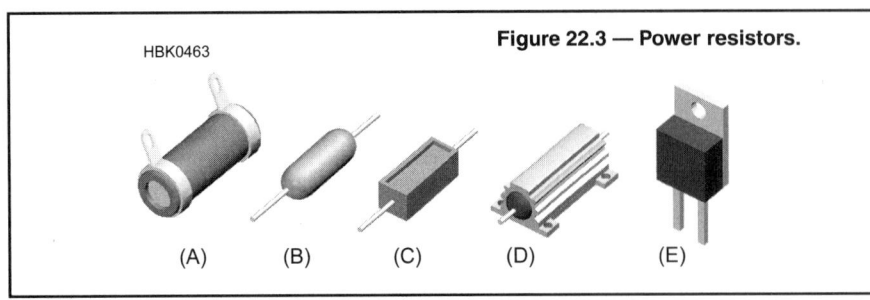

Figure 22.3 — Power resistors.

Table 22.3
Power Resistors

Figure 22.3	Power Resistor Type	Wattage Range
A	Wire-wound, ceramic core	10-300 W
B	Wire-wound, axial	3-10 W
C	Metal-oxide	5-25 W
D	Wire-wound, aluminum housing	3-50 W
E	Thick-film resistors*	15-100 W

*Wire-wound resistors are inductive, though seldom noted as such on the data sheets, and are not recommended for RF. Thick-film and metal-oxide power resistors are low inductance or noninductive.

IEC 60062:2016 Identification and Marking Standard

5–20% Resistors: 132J
- 1st digit, 2nd digit, multiplier
- tolerance: J ± 5%, K ±10%, G ±20%

"Precision" Resistors: 2491B
- 1st digit, 2nd digit, 3rd digit, multiplier
- tolerance: B ±0.1%, D ±0.5%, F ± 1%

Examples:
"132J"=1300=1.3KΩ 5%
"510K"=51 =51Ω 10%
"2R2G"=2.2Ω 20%

"2491B"=2490=2.49K 0.1%
"5110D"=511 =511Ω 0.5%
"51R1F" =51.1=51.1Ω 1%

EIA Resistor Color Codes

Color Codes

Digit	Color	
0	black	(blk)
1	brown	(brn)
2	red	(red)
3	orange	(org)
4	yellow	(ylw)
5	green	(grn)
6	blue	(blu)
7	violet	(vio)
8	gray	(gry)
9	white	(wht)

5–20% Resistors (4-band color code)
- 1st digit, 2nd digit, multiplier
- tolerance: gold ± 5%, silver ±10%, none ±20%

"Precision" Resistors (5-band color code)
- 1st digit, 2nd digit, 3rd digit, multiplier
- tolerance: vio ±0.1%, grn ±0.5%, brn ± 1%

Examples:
brn-org-org-gold = 13KΩ 5%
grn-brn-blk-silver = 51Ω 10%
brn-org-org-brn-brn = 1.33KΩ

letter R is used in the same way to represent a decimal point. For example, 1001 indicates a 1000-Ω unit, and 22R0 indicates a 22-Ω unit.

Here are some additional examples of resistor value markings:

Code	Value
101	10 and 1 zero = 100 Ω
224	22 and 4 zeros = 220,000 Ω
1R0	1.0 and no zeros = 1 Ω
22R	22.0 and no zeros = 22 Ω
R10	0.1 and no zeros = 0.1 Ω

The resistor color code, used only with through-hole components, assigns colors to the numerals one through nine and zero, as shown in **Table 22.4**, to represent the significant numerals, the multiplier and the tolerance. The color code is often memorized with a mnemonic such as "Big boys race our young girls, but Violet generally wins" to represent the colors black (0), brown (1), red (2), orange (3), yellow (4), green (5), blue (6), violet (7), gray (8) and white (9). You will no doubt discover other versions of this memory aid made popular over the years.

For example, a resistor with color bands black (1), red (2), red (2) and gold would be a 1200 Ω, or 1.2 kΩ 5% resistor, with the gold band signifying 5% tolerance.

The resistor color code should be memorized as it is also used for identifying capacitors, and inductors. It is also handy to use when connecting multi-conductor or ribbon cables.

Resistors are also identified by an "E" series classification, such as E12 or E48. The number following the letter E signifies the number of logarithmic steps per decade. The more steps per decade, the more choices of resistor values and tighter the tolerances can be. For example, in the E12 series, there are twelve resistor values between 1 kΩ and 10 kΩ with 10% tolerance; E48 provides 48 values between 1 kΩ and 10 kΩ at 1% tolerance. This system is often used with online circuit calculators to indicate the resistor accuracy and tolerance desired. The standard resistor values of the E12 (±10%), E24 (±5%), E48 (±2%) and E96 (±1%) series are listed in **Table 22.5**.

Resistors used in military electronics (Mil-spec) use the type identifiers listed in **Table 22.6**. In addition, Mil-spec resistors with paint-stripe value bands have an extra band indicating the reliability level to which they are certified.

Surface-mount resistors are labeled with an alphanumeric code. There are several identification conventions, including the three-digit and four-digit value-and-exponent and an EIA-96 labeling standard described at **www.hobby-hour.com/electronics/smd-calc.php**.

Figure 22.4 — Resistor value identification.

Table 22.4
Resistor Color Codes

Color	Significant Figure	Decimal Multiplier	Tolerance (%)
Black	0	1	
Brown	1	10	1
Red	2	100	2
Orange	3	1,000	
Yellow	4	10,000	
Green	5	100,000	0.5
Blue	6	1,000,000	0.25
Violet	7	10,000,000	0.1
Gray	8	100,000,000	0.05
White	9	1,000,000,000	
Gold		0.1	5
Silver		0.01	10
No color			20

Table 22.5
EIA Standard Resistor Values

±10% (E12)	±5% (E24)	±2% (E48)		±1% (E96)			
100	100	100	316	100	178	316	562
120	110	105	332	102	182	323	576
150	120	110	348	105	187	332	590
180	130	115	365	107	191	340	604
220	150	121	383	110	196	348	619
270	160	127	402	113	200	357	634
330	180	133	422	115	205	365	649
390	200	140	442	118	210	374	665
470	220	147	464	121	215	383	681
560	240	154	487	124	221	392	698
680	270	162	511	127	226	402	715
820	300	169	536	130	232	412	732
	330	178	562	133	237	422	750
	360	187	590	137	243	432	768
	390	196	619	140	249	442	787
	430	205	649	143	255	453	806
	470	215	681	147	261	464	825
	510	226	715	150	267	475	845
	560	237	750	154	274	487	866
	620	249	787	158	280	499	887
	680	261	825	162	287	511	909
	750	274	866	165	294	523	931
	820	287	909	169	301	536	953
	910	301	953	174	309	549	976

Use Table 22.5 values for each decade.
Example: 133 = 13.3 Ω, 133 Ω, 1.33 kΩ, 13.3 Ω, 133 kΩ, 1.33MΩ

Table 22.6
Mil-Spec Resistors

Wattage	Metal Film Types	Fixed Film Types	Composition Types	
1/10 W	RN50			
1/8 W	RN55	RL05	RLR05	RCR05
1/4 W	RN60	RL07	RLR07	RCR07
1/2 W	RN65	RL20	RLR20	RCR20
1 W	RN75	RL32	RLR32	RCR32
2 W	RN80	RL42	RLR62	RCR42

Examples:
RN60D-2202F = 22 kΩ 1%
RL07S-471J = 470 Ω ±5%
RLR07C-471J = 470 Ω ±5%

Note: The RN Mil-Spec was discontinued in 1996 Still used by some manufacturers such as Vishay-Dale.

Tolerance Codes
B	±0.1%
C	±0.25%
D	±0.5%
F	±1%
G	±2%
J	±5%
K	±10%

22.3 Capacitors

Capacitors exhibit the largest variety of electronic components. So many varieties and types are available that selecting the proper capacitor for a particular application can be overwhelming. Ceramic and film capacitors are the two most common types used by the amateur. (For additional information on the characteristics of the different types of capacitors, see the **Electrical Fundamentals** chapter.)

Though capacitors are classified by dozens of characteristics, the EIA has simplified the selection process by organizing ceramic capacitors into four categories called Class 1, 2, 3 and 4. Class 1 capacitors are the most stable and Class 4 the least preferred. Many catalogs now list ceramic capacitors by their class, greatly simplifying component selection.

For capacitors used in frequency-sensitive circuits, such as the frequency determining capacitors in oscillators or tuned circuits, select a Class 1 capacitor (C0G or NP0). For other applications, such as interstage coupling or bypass capacitors, components from Class 2 or Class 3 (X7R or Z5U) are usually sufficient. With modern manufacturing techniques, it is rare to find a Class 4 capacitor today.

Like resistors, capacitors are available in EIA standard series of values, E6 and E12, shown in **Table 22.7**. Most capacitors have a tolerance of 5% or greater. High-value capacitors used for filtering may have asymmetric tolerances, such as −5% and +10%, since the primary concern is for a guaranteed minimum value of capacitance.

22.3.1 Capacitor Types

Capacitor types can be grouped into ceramic dielectrics, film dielectrics and electrolytics. The type of capacitor can often be determined by their appearance, as shown in **Figs 22.5** and **22.6**. Capacitors with wire leads have two lead styles: *axial* and *radial*. Axial leads are aligned in opposite directions along a common axis, usually the largest dimension of the capacitor. Radial leads leave the capacitor body in the same direction and are usually arranged radially about the center of the capacitor body.

Disc (or *disk*) *ceramic* capacitors consist of two metal plates separated by a ceramic dielectric that establishes the desired capacitance. Due to their low cost, they are the most common capacitor type. The main disadvantage is their sensitivity to temperature changes (that is, a high temperature coefficient).

Monolithic ceramic capacitors are made by sandwiching layers of metal electrodes and ceramic layers to form the desired capacitance. "Monolithics" are physically smaller than disc ceramics for the same value of capacitance and cost, but exhibit the same high temperature coefficients.

Polyester film capacitors use layers of metal and polyester (Mylar) to make a wide

Table 22.7
EIA Standard Capacitor Values

±20% Capacitors (E6)

pF	pF	pF	µF	µF	µF	µF
1.0	10	100	0.001	0.01	0.1	1
1.5	15	150	0.0015	0.015	0.15	1.5
2.2	22	220	0.0022	0.022	0.22	2.2
3.3	33	330	0.0033	0.033	0.33	3.3
4.7	47	470	0.0047	0.047	0.47	4.7
6.8	68	680	0.0068	0.068	0.68	6.8

±10%, ±5% Capacitors (E12)

pF	pF	pF	µF	µF	µF	µF
1.0	10	100	0.001	0.01	0.1	1
1.2	12	120	0.0012	0.012	0.12	
1.5	15	150	0.0015	0.015	0.15	
1.8	18	180	0.0018	0.018	0.18	
2.2	22	220	0.0022	0.022	0.22	2.2
2.7	27	270	0.0027	0.027	0.27	
3.3	33	330	0.0033	0.033	0.33	3.3
3.9	39	390	0.0039	0.039	0.39	
4.7	47	470	0.0047	0.047	0.47	4.7
5.6	56	560	0.0056	0.056	0.56	
6.8	68	680	0.0068	0.068	0.68	
8.2	82	820	0.0082	0.082	0.82	

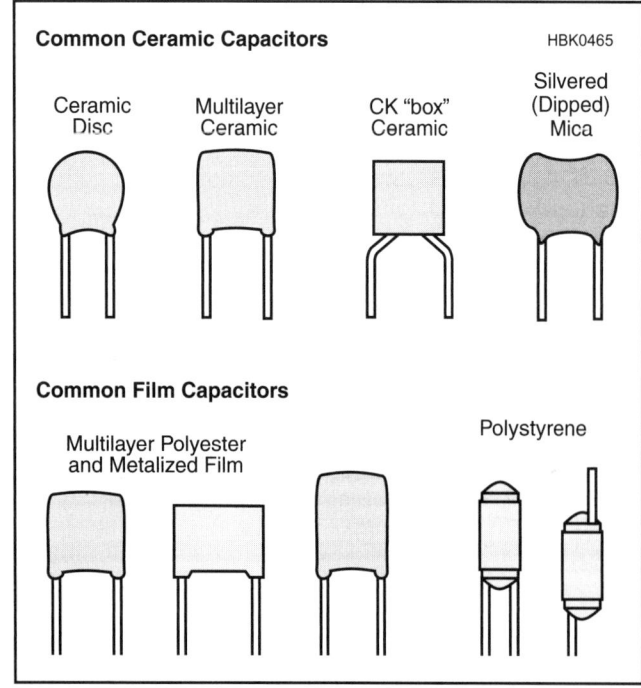

Figure 22.5 — Common capacitor types and package styles.

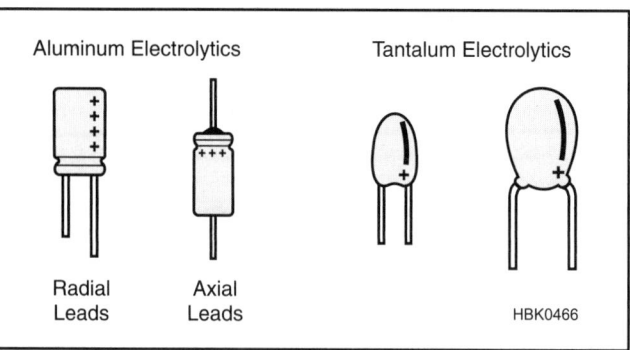

Figure 22.6 — Aluminum and tantalum electrolytic capacitors.

range of capacitances. They have poor temperature coefficients and are not recommended for high frequency use, but are suitable for low frequency and audio circuits.

To improve the performance of film capacitors, other dielectrics are used, such as polypropylene, polystyrene or polycarbonate film, or silvered-mica. These are very stable capacitors developed for RF use. Their main disadvantages are higher cost and lower working voltages than other varieties.

Capacitors are particularly sensitive to temperature changes because the physical dimensions of the capacitor determine its value. Standard temperature coefficient codes are shown in **Table 22.8**. Each code is made up of one character from each column in the table. For example, a capacitor marked Z5U is suitable for use between +10 and +85°C, with a maximum change in capacitance of –56% or +22%.

Capacitors with highly predictable temperature coefficients of capacitance are sometimes used in circuits whose performance must remain stable with temperature. If an application called for a temperature coefficient of –750 ppm/°C (N750), a capacitor marked U2J would be suitable. The older industry code for these ratings is being replaced with the EIA code shown in Table 22.8. NP0 (that is, N-P-zero) means "negative, positive, zero." It is a characteristic often specified for RF circuits requiring temperature stability, such as VFOs. A capacitor of the proper value marked C0G is a suitable replacement for an NP0 unit.

22.3.2 Electrolytic Capacitors

Aluminum electrolytic capacitors use aluminum foil "wetted" with a chemical agent and formed into layers to increase the effective area, and therefore the capacitance. Aluminum electrolytics provide high capacitance in small packages at low cost. Most varieties are polarized, that is, voltage should only be applied in one "direction." Polarized capacitors have a negative (–) and positive (+) lead. Standard dimensions of aluminum electrolytics are shown in **Figure 22.7** and **Table 22.9**. EIA standard values for aluminum electrolytics are given in **Table 22.10**.

Very old electrolytic capacitors should be used with care or, preferably, replaced. The wet dielectric agent can dry out during prolonged periods of non-use, causing the internal capacitor plates to form a short circuit when energized. Applying low voltage and gradually increasing it over a period of time may restore the capacitor to operation, but if the dielectric agent has dried out, the capacitor will have lost some or most of its value and will likely be lossy and prone to failure.

Tantalum electrolytic capacitors consist of a tantalum pentoxide powder mixed with a wet or dry electrolyte, then formed into a pellet or slug for a large effective area. Tantalums also provide high capacitance values in very small packages. Tantalums tend to be more expensive than aluminum electrolytic capacitors. Like the aluminum electrolytic capacitor, tantalum capacitors are also polarized for which care should be exercised. Some varieties of tantalums can literally explode or burst open if voltage is applied with reverse polarity or the voltage rating is exceeded. Tantalum electrolytics are used almost exclusively as high-value SMT components due to their small sizes. Capacitance values up to 1000 μF at 4 V are available with body sizes about a quarter-inch square.

Identifying the polarity markings of aluminum and tantalum electrolytics (shown in Figure 22.6) can be confusing. Most tantalum electrolytics are marked with a solid band indicating the positive lead. Aluminum electrolytics are available with bands or symbols

Table 22.8
Ceramic Temperature Characteristics
Common EIA Types:

EIA Class	EIA Code	Characteristics	Temp. Range*
1	C0G	0 ± 30 ppm/°C	–55 °C to +125 °C
2	Y5P	±10%	–30 °C to + 85 °C
2	X7R	±15%	–55 °C to +125 °C
2	Y5U	±20%	–10 °C to + 85 °C
2	Z5U	±20%	+10 °C to + 85 °C
2	Z5V	+80%, –20%	–30 °C to + 85 °C
3	Y5V	+80%, –20%	–10 °C to + 85 °C

Common Industry Types:

EIA Class	EIA Code	Characteristics	Temp. Range*
1	NP0	0 ± 30 ppm/°C	–55 °C to +125 °C
2	CK05	±10%	–55 °C to +125 °C

*Temp. range for which characteristics are specified and may vary slightly between different manufacturers

Temperature Coefficient Codes

Minimum Temperature	Maximum Temperature	Maximum capacitance change over temp range
X –55 °C	2 +45°C	A ±1.0%
Y –30 °C	4 +65°C	B ±1.5%
Z +10 °C	5 +85°C	C ±2.2%
6 +105 °C		D ±3.3%
7 +125 °C		E ±4.7%
		F ±7.5%
		P ±10%
		R ±15%
		S ±22%
		T –33%, +22%
		U –56%, +22%
		V –82%, +22%

Table 22.9
Aluminum Electrolytic Capacitors Standard Sizes (Radial Leads)

H	Dia	LS	Pad Size and Drill*
0.44	0.20	0.08	0.056 round, 0.029 hole
0.44	0.25	0.10	0.056 round, 0.029 hole
0.44	0.32	0.14	0.065 round, 0.029 hole
0.52	0.40	0.20	0.080 round, 0.035 hole
0.78	0.50	0.20	0.080 round, 0.035 hole
1.00	0.63	0.30	0.100 round, 0.035 hole
1.42	0.72	0.30	0.100 round, 0.035 hole
1.60	0.88	0.40	0.100 round, 0.035 hole

Dimensions in inches.
*Customary to make "+" lead square pad on PCB

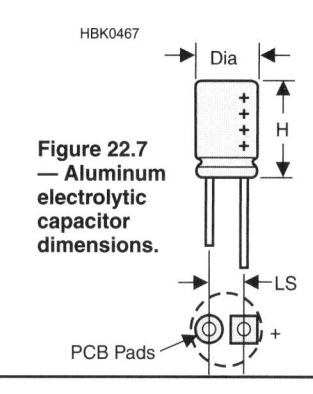

Figure 22.7 — Aluminum electrolytic capacitor dimensions.

Table 22.10
Aluminum Electrolytic Capacitors
EIA ±20% Standard Values

μF	μF	μF	μF	μF
0.1	1.0	10	100	1000
0.22	2.2	22	220	2200
0.33	3.3	33	330	3300
0.47	4.7	47	470	4700
0.68	6.8	68	680	6800
0.82	8.2	82	820	8200

marking *either* the negative or positive lead. The positive lead of axial-lead electrolytic capacitors is usually manufactured to be longer than the negative lead and often enters the capacitor through fiber or plastic insulating material while the negative lead is connected directly to the metallic case of the capacitor. Misidentifying the polarity of capacitors is a common error during assembly or repair.

22.3.3 Surface Mount Capacitors

SMT capacitors are generally film, ceramic or tantalum electrolytics. Body sizes are shown in **Figure 22.8** and **22.9**. Although the IEC scheme is the standard method of labeling capacitor value, you may encounter a two-character alphanumeric code (see **Table 22.11**) consisting of a letter indicating the significant digits and a number indicating the multiplier. The code represents the capacitance in picofarads. For example, a chip capacitor marked "A4" would have a capacitance of 10,000 pF, or 0.01 µF. A unit marked "N1" would be a 33-pF capacitor. If there is sufficient space on the device package, a tolerance code may be included. The standard SMT body sizes and pad spacing are provided in **Table 22.12**.

Table 22.11
SMT Capacitor Two-Character Labeling
Significant Figure Codes

Character	Significant Figures	Character	Significant Figures
A	1.0	T	5.1
B	1.1	U	5.6
C	1.2	V	6.2
D	1.3	W	6.8
E	1.5	X	7.5
F	1.6	Y	8.2
G	1.8	Z	9.1
H	2.0	a	2.5
J	2.2	b	3.5
K	2.4	d	4.0
L	2.7	e	4.5
M	3.0	f	5.0
N	3.3	m	6.0
P	3.6	n	7.0
Q	3.9	t	8.0
R	4.3	y	9.0
S	4.7		

Multiplier Codes

Numeric Character	Decimal Multiplier
0	1
1	10
2	100
3	1,000
4	10,000
5	100,000
6	1,000,000
7	10,000,000
8	100,000,000
9	0.1

Table 22.12
Surface Mount Capacitors — EIA Standard Sizes

Size	Length	Width	Height	C	SMT Pad	C-C*
0402	0.039	0.020	0.014	0.010	0.025 × 0.035	0.050
0603	0.063	0.031	0.018	0.014	0.030 × 0.030	0.055
0805	0.079	0.049	0.020	0.016	0.040 × 0.050	0.075
1206	0.126	0.063	0.024	0.020	0.064 × 0.064	0.125
1210	0.126	0.102	0.024	0.020	0.070 × 0.100	0.150

Surface Mount Electrolytic Capacitors — EIA Standard Sizes

Size	Length	Width	Height	C-C*	SMT Pad
A (1206)	0.126	0.063	0.063	0.110	0.055 × 0.060
B (1411)	0.138	0.110	0.075	0.136	0.075 × 0.090
C (2412)	0.236	0.126	0.098	0.265	0.090 × 0.120
D (2916)	0.287	0.169	0.110	0.250	0.100 × 0.100
E (2924)	0.287	0.236	0.142	0.250	0.100 × 0.100

Dimensions in inches.
*C-C is SMT pad center-to-center spacing

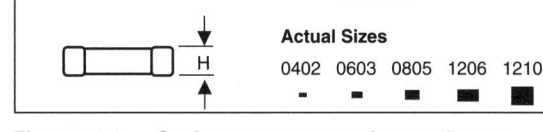

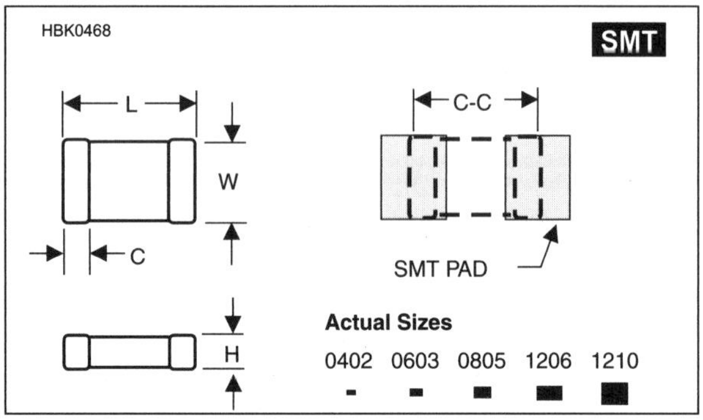

Figure 22.8 — Surface-mount capacitor packages.

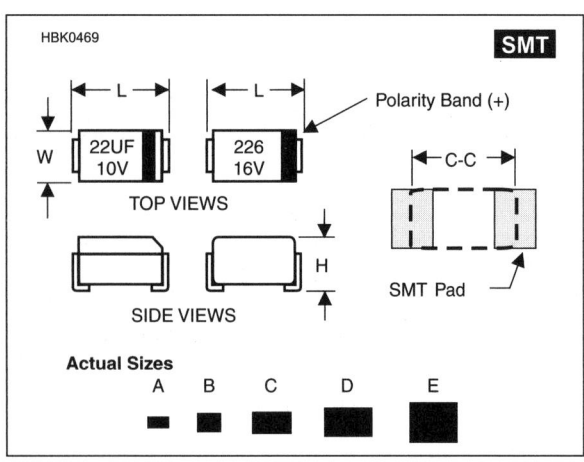

Figure 22.9 — Surface-mount electrolytic packages.

22.3.4 Capacitor Voltage Ratings

Capacitors are also rated by their maximum operating voltage. The importance of selecting a capacitor with the proper voltage rating is often overlooked. Exceeding the voltage rating, even momentarily, can cause excessive heating, a permanent shift of the capacitance value, a short circuit, or outright destruction. As a result, the voltage rating should be at least 25% higher than the working voltage across the capacitor; many designers use 50-100%.

Following the 25% guideline, filter capacitors for a 12-V system should have at least a 15-V rating (12 V × 1.25). However, 12-V systems such as 12-V power supplies and automotive 12-V electrical systems actually operate near 13.8 V and in the case of automotive systems, as high as 15 V. In such cases, capacitors rated for 15 V would be an insufficient margin of safety; 20 to 25-V capacitors should be used in such cases.

In large signal ac circuits, the maximum voltage rating of the capacitor should be based on the peak-to-peak voltages present. For example, the output of a 5-W QRP transmitter is 16 V_{RMS}, or about 45 V_{P-P}. Capacitors exposed to the 5 W RF power, such as in the output low-pass filter, should be rated well above 50 V for the 25% rule. A 100 W transmitter produces RF voltages of about 200 V_{P-P}.

Capacitors that are to be connected to primary ac circuits (directly to the ac line) for filtering or coupling *must* be rated for ac line use. These capacitors are listed as such in catalogs and are designed to minimize fire and other hazards in case of failure. Remember, too, that ac line voltage is given as RMS, with peak-to-peak voltage 2.83 times higher: 120 V_{RMS} = 339 V_{P-P}.

Applying peak-to-peak voltages approaching the maximum voltage rating will cause excessive heating of the capacitor. This, in turn, will cause a permanent shift in the capacitance value. This could be undesirable in the output low pass filter example cited above in trying to maintain the proper impedance match between transmitter and antenna.

Exceeding the maximum voltage rating can also cause a breakdown of the dielectric material in the capacitor. The voltage can jump between the plates causing momentary or permanent electrical shorts between the capacitor plates.

In electrolytic and tantalum capacitors, exceeding the voltage rating can produce extreme heating of the oil or wetting agent used as the dielectric material. The expanding gases can cause the capacitor to burst or explode.

These over-voltage problems are easily avoided by selecting a capacitor with a voltage rating 25-50% above the normal peak-to-peak

Table 22.13
Capacitor Standard Working Voltages

Ceramic	Polyester	Electrolytic	Tantalum
		6.3 V	6.3 V
		10 V	10 V
16 V		16 V	16 V
			20 V
25 V		25 V	25 V
		35 V	35 V
50 V	50 V	50 V	50 V
		63 V	63 V
100 V	100 V	100 V	
	150 V	150 V	
200 V	200 V		
	250 V	250 V	

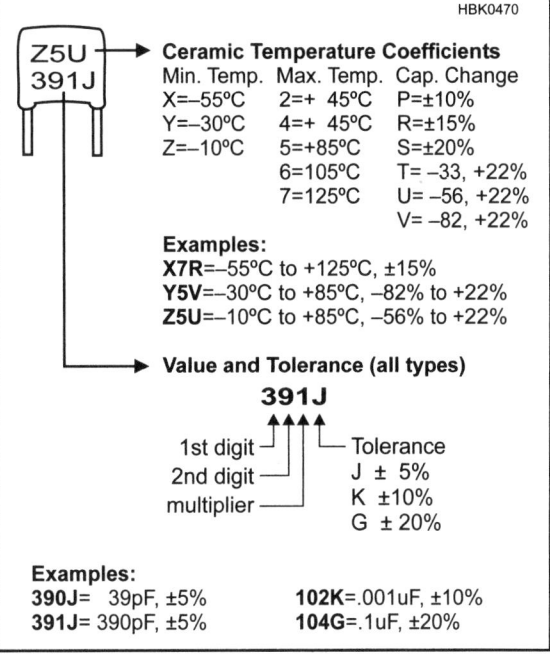

Figure 22.10 — Abbreviated IEC capacitor identification. This method is used on SMT capacitors. An "R" in the numeric field stands for "radix" and represents a decimal point, so that "4R7" indicates "4.7" for example.

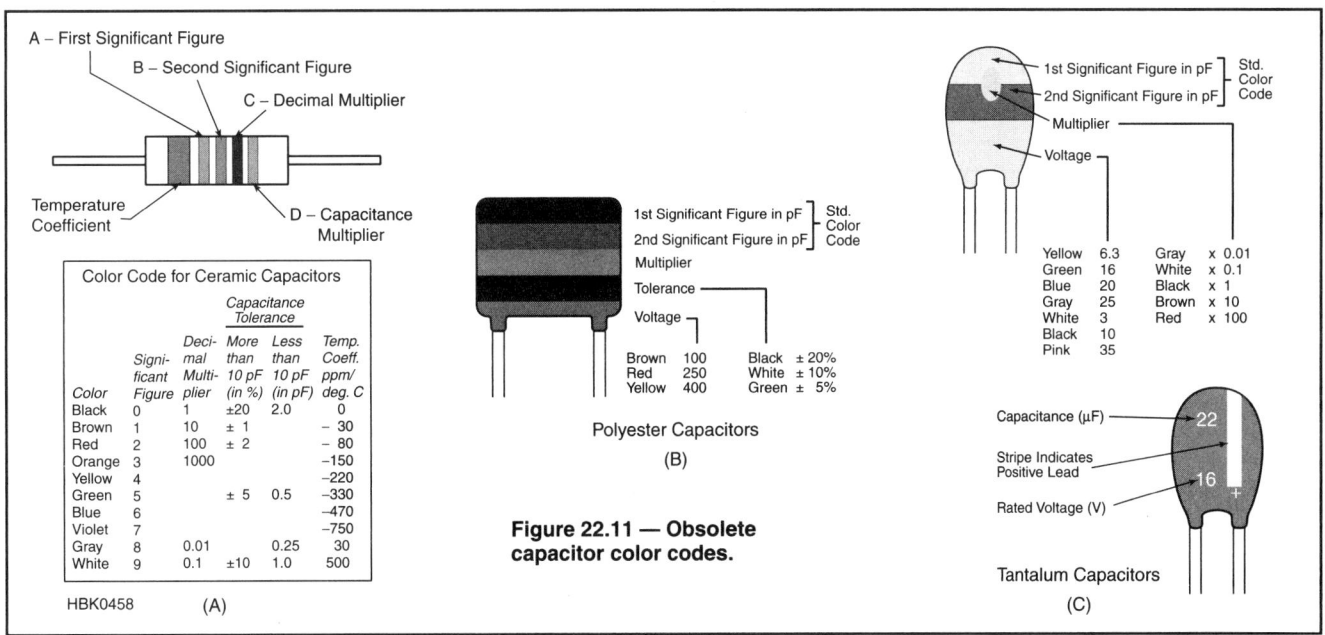

Figure 22.11 — Obsolete capacitor color codes.

operating voltage. **Table 22.13** lists standard working voltages for common capacitor types.

22.3.5 Capacitor Identification

Capacitors are identified by the numerical or color code standard as shown in **Figure 22.10**. Since 2000, the IEC numerical code is the most dominant form of capacitor identification and is used on all capacitor types and body styles. Color coding schemes are becoming rare, used only by a few non-US manufacturers. Some thru-hole "gum drop" tantalum capacitors also still use the color codes of **Figure 22.11**. Electrolytic and tantalum capacitors are often labeled with capacitance and working voltage in µF and V as in Figure 22.11C.

Similar to the resistor IEC code, numerals are used to indicate the significant numerals and the multiplier, followed by an alphabetic character to indicate the tolerance. The multiplier is simply the number of zeros following the significant numerals. For example, a capacitor marked with "122K" would be a 1200 pF 10% capacitor. The use of R to denote a decimal point in a value can be confusing if pF or µF are not specified. Generally, an inspection of the capacitor will determine which is correct but a capacitance meter may be required. Additional digits and codes may be encountered as shown in **Figure 22.12**.

Military-surplus equipment using the obsolete "postage stamp" capacitors is still encountered in Amateur Radio. These capacitors used the colored dot method of value identification shown in **Figure 22.13**.

European manufacturers often use nanofarads or nF, such that 10 nF, or simply 10N, indicates 10 nanofarads. This is equivalent to 10,000 pF or 0.01 µF. This notational scheme, shown in **Table 22.14**, is more commonly found on schematic diagrams than actual part markings.

Table 22.14
European Marking Standards for Capacitors

Marking	Value
1p	1 pF
2p2	2.2 pF
10p	10 pF
100p	100 pF
1n	1 nF (= 0.001 µF)
2n2	2.2 nF (= 0.0022 µF)
10n	10 nF (= 0.01 µF)
100n	100 nF (= 0.1 µF)
1u	1 µF
5u6	5.6 µF
10u	10 µF
100u	100 µF

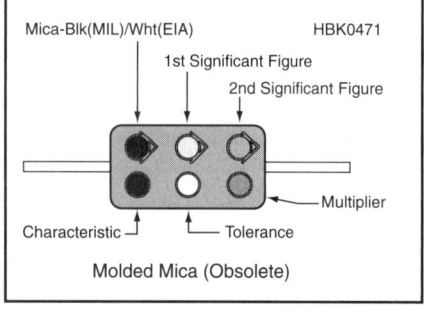

Figure 22.13 — Obsolete JAN "postage stamp" capacitor labeling.

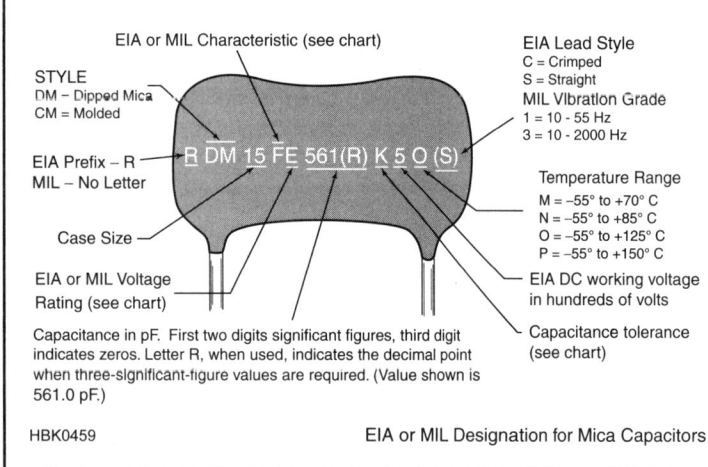

Figure 22.12 — Complete capacitor labeling scheme.

22.4 Inductors

Inductors, both fixed and variable are available in a wide variety of types and packages, and many offer few clues as to their values. Some coils and chokes are marked with the EIA color code shown in Table 22.4. See **Figure 22.14** for another marking system for cylindrical encapsulated RF chokes. The body of these components is often green to identify them as inductors and not resistors. Measure the resistance of the component with an ohmmeter if there is any doubt as to the identity of the component. **Table 22.15** is a list of the EIA standard inductor values.

Table 22.16 lists the properties of common powdered-iron cores. Formulas are given for calculating the number of required turns based on a given inductance and for calculating the inductance given a specific number of turns. Most powdered-iron toroid cores that amateurs use are manufactured by Micrometals (**www.micrometals.com**). Paint is used to identify the material used in the core. The Micrometals color code is part of Table 22.16. **Table 22.17** gives the physical dimensions of powdered-iron toroids.

An excellent design resource for ferrite-based components is the Fair-Rite Materials Corp on-line catalog at **www.fair-rite.com**. The Fair-Rite website's Technical section also has free papers on the use of ferrites for EMI suppression and broadband transformers. The

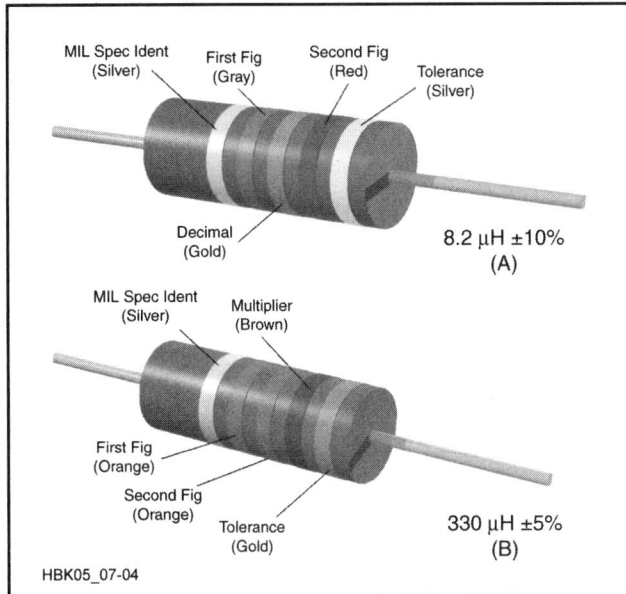

Figure 22.14 — Color coding for cylindrical encapsulated RF chokes. At A, an example of the coding for an 8.2-µH choke is given. At B, the color bands for a 330-µH inductor are illustrated. The color code is given in Table 22.4.

Table 22.15
EIA Standard Inductor Values

µH	µH	µH	mH	mH	mH
1.0	10	100	1.0	10	100
1.2	12	120	1.2	12	120
1.5	15	150	1.5	15	150
2.2	22	220	2.2	22	220
2.7	27	270	2.7	27	270
3.3	33	330	3.3	33	330
3.9	39	390	3.9	39	390
4.7	47	470	4.7	47	470
5.6	56	560	5.6	56	560
6.8	68	680	6.8	68	680
8.2	82	820	8.2	82	820

following list presents the general characteristics (material and composition and intended application) of Fair-Rite's ferrite materials:

• Type 31 (MnZn) — EMI suppression applications from 1 MHz up to 500 MHz.

• Type 43 (NiZn) — Suppression of conducted EMI, inductors and HF common-mode chokes from 20 MHz to 250 MHz.

• Type 44 (NiZn) — EMI suppression from 30 MHz to 500 MHz.

• Type 61 (NiZn) — Inductors up to 25 MHz and EMI suppression above 200 MHz.

• Type 67 (NiZn) — Broadband transformers, antennas and high-Q inductors up to 50 MHz.

• Type 73 (MnZn) — Suppression of conducted EMI below 50 MHz.

• Type 75 (MnZn) — Broadband and pulse transformers.

See **Table 22.18** for information about the magnetic properties of ferrite cores. Ferrite cores are not typically painted, so identification is often difficult. More information about the use of ferrites at RF is provided in the **RF Techniques** chapter.

Table 22.16
Powdered-Iron Toroidal Cores: Magnetic Properties

There are differing conventions for referring to the type of core material: #, mix and type are all used. For example, all of the following designate the same material: #12, Mix 12, 12-Mix, Type 12 and 12-Type.

Inductance and Turns Formula

The turns required for a given inductance or inductance for a given number of turns can be calculated from:

$$N = 100\sqrt{\frac{L}{A_L}} \quad L = A_L\left(\frac{N^2}{10,000}\right) \quad \text{(Amidon cores)} \qquad N = \sqrt{\frac{L}{A_L}} \quad L = A_L \times N^2 \quad \text{(Non-Amidon cores)}$$

where N = number of turns; L = desired inductance; A_L = inductance index (µH per 100 turns-squared for Amidon cores; nH or µH per turns-squared for non-Amidon cores; see core data sheet)

Amidon Associates literature gives the value of A_L as inductance per 100 turns but the correct units are inductance per 100 turns-squared. The units of inductance are generally in nH but may also be mH. Make sure you understand which units apply and use the A_L value and formula provided by the manufacturer of the core to calculate number of turns or inductance.

Toroid diameter is indicated by the number following "T" — T-200 is 2.00 in. dia; T-68 is 0.68 in. diameter, etc.

AL Values

Size	26*	3	15	1	2	7	6	10	12	17	0
T-12	na	60	50	48	20	18	17	12	7.5	7.5	3.0
T-16	145	61	55	44	22	na	19	13	8.0	8.0	3.0
T-20	180	76	65	52	27	24	22	16	10.0	10.0	3.5
T-25	235	100	85	70	34	29	27	19	12.0	12.0	4.5
T-30	325	140	93	85	43	37	36	25	16.0	16.0	6.0
T-37	275	120	90	80	40	32	30	25	15.0	15.0	4.9
T-44	360	180	160	105	52	46	42	33	18.5	18.5	6.5
T-50	320	175	135	100	49	43	40	31	18.0	18.0	6.4
T-68	420	195	180	115	57	52	47	32	21.0	21.0	7.5
T-80	450	180	170	115	55	50	45	32	22.0	22.0	8.5
T-94	590	248	200	160	84	na	70	58	32.0	na	10.6
T-106	900	450	345	325	135	133	116	na	na	na	19.0
T-130	785	350	250	200	110	103	96	na	na	na	15.0
T-157	870	420	360	320	140	na	115	na	na	na	na
T-184	1640	720	na	500	240	na	195	na	na	na	na
T-200	895	425	na	250	120	105	100	na	na	na	na

*Mix-26 is similar to the older Mix-41, but can provide an extended frequency range.

Magnetic Properties Iron Powder Cores

Mix	Color	Material	µ	Temp stability (ppm/°C)	f (MHz)	Notes
26	Yellow/white	Hydrogen reduced	75	825	dc - 1	Used for EMI filters and dc chokes
3	Gray	Carbonyl HP	35	370	0.05 - 0.50	Excellent stability, good Q for lower frequencies
15	Red/white	Carbonyl GS6	25	190	0.10 - 2	Excellent stability, good Q
1	Blue	Carbonyl C	20	280	0.50 - 5	Similar to Mix-3, but better stability
2	Red	Carbonyl E	10	95	2 - 30	High Q material
7	White	Carbonyl TH	9	30	3 - 35	Similar to Mix-2 and Mix-6, but better temperature stability
6	Yellow	Carbonyl SF	8	35	10 - 50	Very good Q and temperature stability for 20-50 MHz
10	Black	Powdered iron W	6	150	30 - 100	Good Q and stability for 40 - 100 MHz
12	Green/white	Synthetic oxide	4	170	50 - 200	Good Q, moderate temperature stability
17	Blue/yellow	Carbonyl	4	50	40 - 180	Similar to Mix-12, better temperature stability, Q drops about 10% above 50 MHz, 20% above 100 MHz
0	Tan	phenolic	1	0	100 - 300	Inductance may vary greatly with winding technique

Courtesy of Amidon Assoc and Micrometals
Note: Color codes hold only for cores manufactured by Micrometals, which makes the cores sold by most Amateur Radio distributors.

Table 22.17

Powdered-Iron Toroidal Cores: Dimensions

Toroid diameter is indicated by the number following "T" — T-200 is 2.00 in. dia; T-68 is 0.68 in. diameter, etc.
See Table 22.16 for a core sizing guide.

Red E Cores—500 kHz to 30 MHz ($\mu = 10$)

No.	OD (in)	ID (in)	H (in)
T-200-2	2.00	1.25	0.55
T-94-2	0.94	0.56	0.31
T-80-2	0.80	0.50	0.25
T-68-2	0.68	0.37	0.19
T-50-2	0.50	0.30	0.19
T-37-2	0.37	0.21	0.12
T-25-2	0.25	0.12	0.09
T-12-2	0.125	0.06	0.05

Black W Cores—30 MHz to 200 MHz ($\mu=6$)

No.	OD (In)	ID (In)	H (In)
T-50-10	0.50	0.30	0.19
T-37-10	0.37	0.21	0.12
T-25-10	0.25	0.12	0.09
T-12-10	0.125	0.06	0.05

Yellow SF Cores—10 MHz to 90 MHz ($\mu=8$)

No.	OD (In)	ID (In)	H (In)
T-94-6	0.94	0.56	0.31
T-80-6	0.80	0.50	0.25
T-68-6	0.68	0.37	0.19
T-50-6	0.50	0.30	0.19
T-26-6	0.25	0.12	0.09
T-12-6	0.125	0.06	0.05

Number of Turns vs Wire Size and Core Size

Approximate maximum number of turns—single layer wound—enameled wire.

Wire Size	T-200	T-130	T-106	T-94	T-80	T-68	T-50	T-37	T-25	T-12
10	33	20	12	12	10	6	4	1		
12	43	25	16	16	14	9	6	3		
14	54	32	21	21	18	13	8	5	1	
16	69	41	28	28	24	17	13	7	2	
18	88	53	37	37	32	23	18	10	4	1
20	111	67	47	47	41	29	23	14	6	1
22	140	86	60	60	53	38	30	19	9	2
24	177	109	77	77	67	49	39	25	13	4
26	223	137	97	97	85	63	50	33	17	7
28	281	173	123	123	108	80	64	42	23	9
30	355	217	154	154	136	101	81	54	29	13
32	439	272	194	194	171	127	103	68	38	17
34	557	346	247	247	218	162	132	88	49	23
36	683	424	304	304	268	199	162	108	62	30
38	875	544	389	389	344	256	209	140	80	39
40	1103	687	492	492	434	324	264	178	102	51

Actual number of turns may differ from above figures according to winding techniques, especially when using the larger size wires. Chart prepared by Michel J. Gordon, Jr, WB9FHC.
Courtesy of Amidon Assoc.

Table 22.18
Ferrite Toroids: A_L Chart (mH per 1000 turns-squared) Enameled Wire

There are differing conventions for referring to the type of ferrite material: #, mix and type are all used. For example, all of the following designate the same ferrite material: #43, Mix 43, 43-Mix, Type 43, and 43-Type.

Fair-Rite Corporation (www.fair-rite.com) and Amidon (www.amidoncorp.com) ferrite toroids can be cross-referenced as follows:

For Amidon toroids, "FT-XXX-YY" indicates a ferrite toroid, with XXX as the OD in hundredths of an inch and YY the mix. For example, an FT-23-43 core has an OD of 0.23 inch and is made of type 43 material. Additional letters (usually "C") are added to indicate special coatings or different thicknesses.

For Fair-Rite toroids, digits 1 and 2 of the part number indicate product type (59 indicates a part for inductive uses), digits 3 and 4 indicate the material type, digits 5 through 9 indicate core size, and the final digit indicates coating (1 for Paralene and 2 for thermo-set). For example, Fair-Rite part number 5943000101 is equivalent to the Amidon FT-23-43 core.

Ferrite Toroids: A_L Chart (mH per 1000 turns-squared)
Toroid diameter is specified as the outside diameter of the core. See Table 22.16 for a core sizing guide.

Core Size (in)	63/67-Mix $\mu = 40$	61-Mix $\mu = 125$	43-Mix $\mu = 850$	77 (72)-Mix $\mu = 2000$	J (75)-Mix $\mu = 5000$
0.23	7.9	24.8	188	396	980
0.37	19.7	55.3	420	884	2196
0.50	22.0	68.0	523	1100	2715
0.82	22.4	73.3	557	1170	NA
1.14	25.4	79.3	603	1270	3170
1.40	45	140	885	2400	5500
2.40	55	170	1075	2950	6850

31-Mix is an EMI suppression material and not recommended for inductive use.

Inductance and Turns Formula
The turns required for a given inductance or inductance for a given number of turns can be calculated from:

$$N = 100\sqrt{\frac{L}{A_L}} \quad L = A_L\left(\frac{N^2}{10,000}\right) \quad \text{(Amidon cores)} \qquad N = \sqrt{\frac{L}{A_L}} \quad L = A_L \times N^2 \quad \text{(Non-Amidon cores)}$$

where N = number turns; L = desired inductance; A_L = inductance index. Amidon specifies A_L as mH per 1000 turns-squared. See non-Amidon manufacturer's core data sheet to determine appropriate units for L and A_L, usually nH and nH/turns-squared. Make sure you understand which units apply and use the A_L value appropriate for your core.

Ferrite Magnetic Properties

Property	Unit	63/67-Mix	61-Mix	43-Mix	77 (72)-Mix	J (75)-Mix	31-Mix
Initial perm.	(μ_i)	40	125	850	2000	5000	1500
Max. perm.		125	450	3000	6000	8000	Not spec.
Saturation flux density @ 10 oe	gauss	1850	2350	2750	4600	3900	3400
Residual flux density	gauss	750	1200	1200	1150	1250	2500
Curie temp.	°C	450	350	130	200	140	>130
Vol. resistivity	ohm/cm	1×10^8	1×10^8	1×10^5	1×10^2	5×10^2	3×10^3
Resonant circuit frequency	MHz	15-25	0.2-10	0.01-1	0.001-1	0.001-1	*
Specific gravity		4.7	4.7	4.5	4.8	4.8	4.7
Loss factor	$\frac{1}{\mu_i Q}$	110×10^{-6} @25 MHz	32×10^{-6} @2.5 MHz	120×10^{-6} @1 MHz	4.5×10^{-6} @0.1 MHz	15×10^{-6} @0.1 MHz	20×10^{-6} @0.1 MHz
Coercive force	Oe	2.40	1.60	0.30	0.22	0.16	0.35
Temp. Coef. of initial perm.	%/°C (20°-70°)	0.10	0.15	1.0	0.60	0.90	1.6

*31-Mix is an EMI suppression material and not recommended for inductive uses.

Ferrite Toroids—Physical Properties
All physical dimensions in inches.

OD (in)	ID (in)	Height (in)	A_e	ℓ_e	V_e
0.230	0.120	0.060	0.00330	0.529	0.00174
0.375	0.187	0.125	0.01175	0.846	0.00994
0.500	0.281	0.188	0.02060	1.190	0.02450
0.825	0.520	0.250	0.03810	2.070	0.07890
1.142	0.750	0.295	0.05810	2.920	0.16950
1.400	0.900	0.500	0.12245	3.504	0.42700
2.400	1.400	0.500	0.24490	5.709	1.39080

Different height cores may be available for each core size.
A_e — Effective magnetic cross-sectional area (in)^2
ℓ_e — Effective magnetic path length (inches)
V_e — Effective magnetic volume (in)^3
To convert from (in)^2 to (cm)^2, divide by 0.155
To convert from (in)^3 to (cm)^3, divide by 0.0610
Courtesy of Amidon Assoc. and Fair-Rite Corp.

22.5 Transformers

Many transformers, including power transformers, IF transformers, and audio transformers, are made to be installed on PC boards, and have terminals designed for that purpose. Some transformers are manufactured with wire leads that are color-coded to identify each connection. When colored wire leads are present, the color codes in **Tables 22.19, 22.20** and **22.21** usually apply. In addition, many miniature IF transformers are tuned with slugs, color-coded to signify their application. **Table 22.22** lists application versus slug color.

Table 22.20
IF Transformer Wiring Color Codes

Plate lead:	Blue
B+ lead:	Red
Grid (or diode) lead:	Green
Grid (or diode) return:	Black

Note: If the secondary of the IF transformer is center-tapped, the second diode plate lead is green-and-black striped, and black is used for the center-tap lead.

Table 22.21
IF Transformer Slug Color Codes

Frequency	Application	Slug color
455 kHz	1st IF	Yellow
	2nd IF	White
	3rd IF	Black
	Osc tuning	Red
10.7 MHz	1st IF	Green
	2nd or 3rd IF	Orange, Brown or Black

Table 22.19
Power-Transformer Wiring Color Codes

Non-tapped primary leads:	Black
Tapped primary leads:	Common: Black
	Tap: Black/yellow striped
	Finish: Black/red striped
High-voltage plate winding:	Red
Center tap:	Red/yellow striped
Rectifier filament winding:	Yellow
Center tap:	Yellow/blue striped
Filament winding 1:	Green
Center tap:	Green/yellow striped
Filament winding 2:	Brown
Center tap:	Brown/yellow striped
Filament winding 3:	Slate
Center tap:	Slate/yellow striped

Table 22.22
Audio Transformer Wiring Color Codes

Plate lead of primary	Blue
B+ lead (plain or center-tapped)	Red
Plate (start) lead on center-tapped primaries	Brown (or blue if polarity is not important)
Grid (finish) lead to secondary	Green
Grid return (plain or center tapped)	Black
Grid (start) lead on center tapped secondaries	Yellow (or green if polarity not important)

Note: These markings also apply to line-to-grid and tube-to-line transformers.

22.6 Semiconductors

Most semiconductors are labeled with industry standard part numbers, such as 1N4148 or 2N3904, and possibly a date or batch code. You will also encounter numerous manufacturer-specific part numbers and the so-called "house numbers" (marked with codes used by an equipment manufacturer instead of the standard part numbers). In such cases, it is often possible to find the standard equivalent or a suitable replacement by using one of the semiconductor cross-reference directories available from various replacement-parts distributors. If you look up the house number and find the recommended replacement part, you can often find other standard parts that are replaced by that same part.

Information on the use of semiconductors, common design practices, and the necessary circuit design equations can be found in the **Circuits and Components** chapter. Manufacturer websites are often a rich source of information on applying semiconductors, both in general and the specific devices they offer.

22.6.1 Diodes

The diode parameters of most importance are maximum forward current or power handling capacity, reverse leakage current, maximum peak inverse voltage (PIV), maximum reverse voltage and the forward voltage. (See **Table 22.23**) For switching or high-speed rectification applications, the time response parameters are also important.

Power dissipation in a diode is equal to the diode's forward voltage drop multiplied by the average forward current. Although fixed voltages are often used for diodes in small-signal applications (0.6 V for silicon PN-junction diodes, 0.3 V for germanium, for example), the actual forward voltage at higher currents can be significantly higher and must be taken into account for high-current applications, such as power supplies.

Most diodes are marked with a part number and some means of identifying the anode or cathode. A thick band or stripe is commonly used to identify the cathode lead or terminal. Stud-mount diodes are usually labeled with a small diode symbol to indicate anode and cathode. Diodes in axial lead packages are sometimes identified with a color scheme as shown in **Figure 22.15**. The common diode packaging standards are illustrated in **Figure 22.16** and the dimensions listed in **Table 22.24**. Many surface mount diodes are packaged in the same SMT packages as resistors.

Packages containing multiple diodes and rectifier bridge configurations are also

Table 22.23
Semiconductor Diode Specifications†
Listed numerically by device

Device	Type	Material	Peak Inverse Voltage, PIV (V)	Average Rectified Current Forward (Reverse) $I_O(A)(I_R(A))$	Peak Surge Current, I_{FSM} 1 s @ 25°C (A)	Average Forward Voltage, VF (V)
1N34	Signal	Ge	60	8.5 m (15.0 μ)		1.0
1N34A	Signal	Ge	60	5.0 m (30.0 μ)		1.0
1N67A	Signal	Ge	100	4.0 m (5.0 μ)		1.0
1N191	Signal	Ge	90	15.0 m		1.0
1N270	Signal	Ge	80	0.2 (100 μ)		1.0
1N914	Fast Switch	Si	75	75.0 m (25.0 n)	0.5	1.0
1N1183	RFR	Si	50	40 (5 m)	800	1.1
1N1184	RFR	Si	100	40 (5 m)	800	1.1
1N2071	RFR	Si	600	0.75 (10.0 μ)		0.6
1N3666	Signal	Ge	80	0.2 (25.0 μ)		1.0
1N4001	RFR	Si	50	1.0 (0.03 m)		1.1
1N4002	RFR	Si	100	1.0 (0.03 m)		1.1
1N4003	RFR	Si	200	1.0 (0.03 m)		1.1
1N4004	RFR	Si	400	1.0 (0.03 m)		1.1
1N4005	RFR	Si	600	1.0 (0.03 m)		1.1
1N4006	RFR	Si	800	1.0 (0.03 m)		1.1
1N4007	RFR	Si	1000	1.0 (0.03 m)		1.1
1N4148	Signal	Si	75	10.0 m (25.0 n)		1.0
1N4149	Signal	Si	75	10.0 m (25.0 n)		1.0
1N4152	Fast Switch	Si	40	20.0 m (0.05 μ)		0.8
1N4445	Signal	Si	100	0.1 (50.0 n)		1.0
1N5400	RFR	Si	50	3.0 (500 μ)	200	
1N5401	RFR	Si	100	3.0 (500 μ)	200	
1N5402	RFR	Si	200	3.0 (500 μ)	200	
1N5403	RFR	Si	300	3.0 (500 μ)	200	
1N5404	RFR	Si	400	3.0 (500 μ)	200	
1N5405	RFR	Si	500	3.0 (500 μ)	200	
1N5406	RFR	Si	600	3.0 (500 μ)	200	
1N5408	RFR	Si	1000	3.0 (500 μ)	200	
1N5711	Schottky	Si	70	1 m (200 n)	15 m	0.41 @ 1 mA
1N5767	Signal	Si		0.1 (1.0 μ)		1.0
1N5817	Schottky	Si	20	1.0 (1 m)	25	0.75
1N5819	Schottky	Si	40	1.0 (1 m)	25	0.9
1N5821	Schottky	Si	30	3.0		
ECG5863	RFR	Si	600	6	150	0.9
1N6263	Schottky	Si	70	15 m	50 m	0.41 @ 1 mA
5082-2835	Schottky	Si	8	1 m (100 n)	10 m	0.34 @ 1 mA

Si = Silicon; Ge = Germanium; RFR = rectifier, fast recovery.
†For package shape, size and pin-connection information see manufacturers' data sheets. Many retail suppliers offer data sheets to buyers free of charge on request. Data books are available from many manufacturers and retailers.

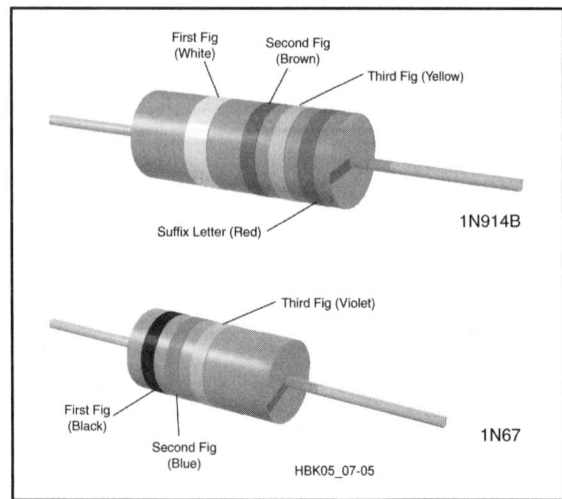

Figure 22.15 — Color-coding for semiconductor diodes. At A, the cathode is identified by the double-width first band. At B, the bands are grouped toward the cathode. Two-Figure designations are signified by a black first band. The color code is given in Table 22.4. The suffix-letter code is A-Brown, B-red, C-orange, D-yellow, E-green, F-blue. The 1N prefix is assumed.

Table 22.24
Package Dimensions for Small Signal, Rectifier and Zener diodes

Case	L	D	Ød	LS	PCB Pads*	Hole	Example
DO-35	0.166	0.080	0.020	0.30	0.056 dia	0.029	1N4148
DO-41	0.205	0.107	0.034	0.40	0.074 dia	0.040	1N4001
DO-201	0.283	0.189	0.048	0.65	0.150 dia	0.079	1N5401
DO-204	0.205	0.106	0.034	0.40	0.074 dia	0.040	1N4001

Dimensions in inches.
*Customary to make cathode lead square.

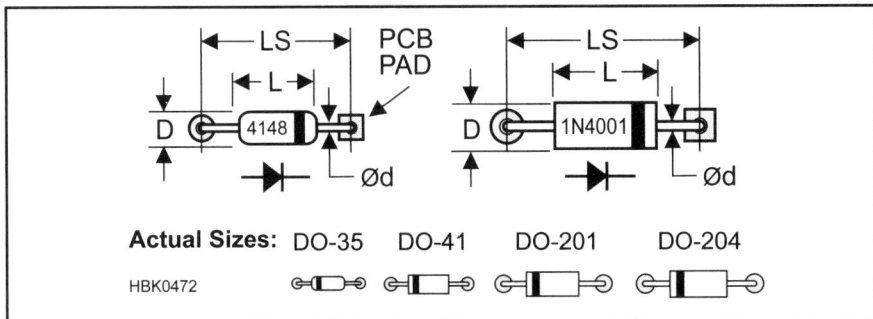

Figure 22.16 — Axial-leaded diode packages and pad dimensions.

commonly available. Full-wave bridge packages are labeled with tildes (~) for the ac inputs and + and – symbols for the rectifier outputs. High-power diodes are often packaged in TO-220 packages with two leads. The package may be labeled with a diode symbol, but if not you will have to obtain the manufacturer's data sheet to identify the anode and cathode leads.

The common 1N914, 1N4148, and 1N5767 switching diodes are suitable for most all small signal applications. The 1N4000 family is commonly used for ac voltage rectification up to 1000 volts PIV. Schottky diodes are used when low forward voltages are required, particularly at high-currents, and exhibit voltages of 0.1-0.2 V at low currents.

Zener diodes, used as voltage references, are manufactured in a wide range of voltages and power handling capacities. Power dissipation in a Zener diode is equal to the Zener voltage multiplied by the average reverse current. The Zener voltage has a significant temperature coefficient and also varies with reverse current. To avoid excessive variations in Zener voltage, limit the diode's power dissipation to no more than ½ of the rated value and for precision uses, ⅕ to ⅒ of the rated power dissipation is recommended. Common varieties of Zener diodes are listed in **Table 22.25**.

Voltage-variable capacitance diodes, also called Varicaps, varactors or tuning diodes, are used in oscillator and tuned circuits where a variable capacitor is needed. Operated with reverse bias, the depletion region forms a capacitor of variable width with a fairly linear voltage vs. capacitance function. Standard tuning diodes produce capacitances in the range of 5 to 40 pF. Hyper-abrupt tuning diodes produce variable capacitances to 100 pF or more for low frequency or wide tuning range applications. Some of the common voltage variable capacitance diodes are listed in **Table 22.26**.

Maximum capacitance occurs with minimum reverse voltage. As the reverse voltage is increased, the capacitance decreases. Tuning diodes are specified by the capacitance produced at two reverse voltages, usually 2 and 30 V. This is called the capacitance ratio and is specified in units of pF per volt. Beyond this range, capacitance change with voltage can become non-linear and may cause signal distortion.

All diodes exhibit some capacitance when reversed biased. Amateurs have learned to use reverse biased Zener and rectifier diodes to form tuning diodes with 20-30 pF maximum capacitance. These "poor man's" tuning diodes are widely used in homebrew projects. However, because the capacitance ratio varies widely from one diode to the next, requiring experimentation to find a suitable diode, they are seldom used in published construction articles.

Light emitting diodes (LED) are another common type of diode. The primary application is that of an illuminated visual indicator when forward biased. LEDs have virtually replaced miniature lamp bulbs for indicators and illumination. LED's are specified primarily by their color, size, shape and output light intensity.

The "standard" size LED is the T-1¾; 5 mm or 0.20 in. diameter. The "miniature" size is the T-1; 3 mm or 0.125 in. diameter. Today, the "standard" and "miniature" size is a bit of a misnomer due to the wide variety of LED sizes and shapes, including SMT varieties. However, the T-1 and T-1¾ remain the most common for homebrew projects due to their inexpensive availability and ease of mounting with a simple panel hole. Their long leads are ideal for prototyping.

22.6.2 Transistors

The information in the tables of transistor data includes the most important parameters for typical applications of transistors of that type. The meaning of the parameters and their relationship to circuit design is covered in the **Circuits and Components** chapter or in the references listed at the end of that chapter.

The tables are organized by application; small-signal, general-purpose, RF power, and so on. Some obsolete parts are listed in these tables for reference in repair and maintenance of older equipment. Before using a device in a new design, it is recommended that you check the manufacturer's website to be sure that the device has not been replaced by a more capable part and that it is available for future orders.

22.6.3 Voltage Regulators

For establishing a well-regulated fixed voltage reference, the linear voltage regular ICs are often preferred over the Zener diode. Three-terminal voltage regulators require no external components and most have internal current limiting and thermal shutdown circuitry, making them virtually indestructible. (Three-terminal regulators are described in the **Circuits and Components** chapter.) The specifications and packages for common voltage regulators are listed in **Table 22.27**.

For fixed-voltage positive regulators, the 7800 family in the TO-220 package is the most common and reasonably priced. They are available in a variety of voltages and supply up to 1 A of current or more, depending on the input voltage. The part number identifies the voltage. For example, a 7805 is a 5-V regulator and a 7812 is a 12-V regulator. The 78L00 low-power versions in the TO-98 package or SOT-89 surface-mount package provide load currents up to 100 mA. The 317 and 340 are the most common adjustable-voltage regulators. Integrated voltage regulators can be used with a pass transistor to extend their load current capability as described in the device data sheets.

Three-terminal regulators are selected primarily for output voltage and maximum load

Table 22.25
Common Zener Diodes
Power dissipation and (package style)

Voltage (V)	¼ W (DO-35)	0.35 W (SOT-23)	½ W (SOD-123)	½ W (DO-35)	1 W (DO41)
2.7	1N4618	MMBZ5223B	MMSZ5223B	1N5223B	—
3.3	1N4620	MMBZ5226B	MMSZ5226B	1N5226B	1N4728A
3.6	1N4621	MMBZ5227B	MMSZ5227B	1N5227B	1N4729A
3.9	1N4622	MMBZ5228B	MMSZ5228B	1N5228B	1N4730A
4.3	1N4623	MMBZ5229B	MMSZ5229B	1N5229B	1N4731A
4.7	1N4624	MMBZ5230B	MMSZ5230B	1N5230B	1N4732A
5.1	1N4625	MMBZ5231B	MMSZ5231B	1N5231B	1N4733A
5.6	1N4626	MMBZ5232B	MMSZ5232B	1N5232B	1N4734A
6.0	— —	MMBZ5233B	MMSZ5233B	1N5233B	—
6.2	1N4627	MMBZ5234B	MMSZ5234B	1N5234B	1N4735A
6.8	1N4099	MMBZ5235B	MMSZ5235B	1N5235B	1N4736A
7.5	1N4100	MMBZ5236B	MMSZ5236B	1N5236B	1N4737A
8.2	1N4101	MMBZ5237B	MMSZ5237B	1N5237B	1N4738A
9.1	1N4103	MMBZ5239B	MMSZ5239B	1N5239B	1N4739A
10	1N4104	MMBZ5240B	MMSZ5240B	1N5240B	1N4740A
11	1N4105	MMBZ5241B	MMSZ5241B	1N5241B	1N4741A
12	— —	MMBZ5242B	MMSZ5242B	1N5242B	1N4742A
13	1N4107	MMBZ5243B	MMSZ5243B	1N5243B	1N4743A
15	1N4109	MMBZ5245B	MMSZ5245B	1N5245B	1N4744A
18	1N4112	MMBZ5248B	MMSZ5248B	1N5248B	1N4746A
20	1N4114	MMBZ5250B	MMSZ5250B	1N5250B	1N4747A
22	1N4115	MMBZ5251B	MMSZ5251B	1N5251B	1N4748A
24	1N4116	MMBZ5252B	MMSZ5252B	1N5252B	1N4749A
27	1N4118	MMBZ5254B	MMSZ5254B	1N5254B	1N4750A
28	1N4119	MMBZ5255B	MMSZ5255B	1N5255B	—
30	1N4120	MMBZ5256B	MMSZ5256B	1N5256B	1N4751A
33	1N4121	MMBZ5257B	MMSZ5257B	1N5257B	1N4752A
36	1N4122	MMBZ5258B	MMSZ5258B	1N5258B	1N4753A
39	1N4123			1N5259B	1N4754A
43	—			1N5260B	1N4755A
47	1N4125			1N5261B	1N4756A
51	1N4126			1N5262B	1N4757A
56				1N5263B	1N4758A
60				1N5264B	—
62				1N5265B	1N4759A
68				1N5266B	1N4760A
75				1N5267B	1N4761A
82					1N4762A
91					1N4763A
100					1N4764A

current. Dropout voltage — the minimum voltage between input and output for which regulation can be maintained — is also very important. For example, the dropout voltage for the 5-V 78L05 is 1.7 V. Therefore, the input voltage must be at least 6.7 V (5 + 1.7 V) to ensure output voltage regulation. The maximum input voltage should also not be exceeded.

Make sure to check the pin assignments for all voltage regulators. While the fixed-voltage positive regulators generally share a common orientation of input, output, and ground, negative-voltage and adjustable regulators do not. Installing a regulator with the wrong connections will usually destroy it and may allow excessive voltage to be applied to the circuit it supplies.

22.6.4 Analog and Digital Integrated Circuits

Integrated circuits (ICs) come in a variety of packages, including transistor-like metal cans, dual and single in-line packages (DIPs and SIPs), flat-packs and surface-mount packages. Most are marked with a part number and a four-digit manufacturer's date code indicating the year (first two digits) and week (last two digits) that the component was made. As mentioned in the introduction to this chapter, ICs are frequently house-marked and cross-reference directories can be helpful in identification and replacement.

IC part numbers provide a complete description of the device's function and ratings. For example, a 4066 IC contains four independent CMOS SPST switches. The 4066 is a CMOS device available from a number of different manufacturers in different package styles and ratings. The two- or three-letter prefix of the part number is generally associated with the part manufacturer. Next, the part type (4066 in this case) shows the function and pin assignments or "pin outs." Following the part type is an alphabetic suffix that describes the version of the part, package code, temperature range, reliability rating and possibly other information. For complete information on the part — any or all of which may be significant to circuit function — use the websites of the various manufacturers or enter "data sheet" and the part number into an Internet search engine.

When choosing ICs that are not exact re-

Table 22.26
Voltage-Variable Capacitance Diodes[†]

Listed numerically by device

Device	Nominal Capacitance pF ±10% @ $V_R = 4.0$ V $f = 1.0$ MHz	Capacitance Ratio 2-30 V Min.	Q @ 4.0 V 50 MHz Min.	Case Style
1N5441A	6.8	2.5	450	
1N5442A	8.2	2.5	450	
1N5443A	10	2.6	400	DO-7
1N5444A	12	2.6	400	
1N5445A	15	2.6	450	
1N5446A	18	2.6	350	
1N5447A	20	2.6	350	
1N5448A	22	2.6	350	DO-7
1N5449A	27	2.6	350	
1N5450A	33	2.6	350	
1N5451A	39	2.6	300	
1N5452A	47	2.6	250	
1N5453A	56	2.6	200	DO-7
1N5454A	68	2.7	175	
1N5455A	82	2.7	175	
1N5456A	100	2.7	175	
1N5461A	6.8	2.7	600	
1N5462A	8.2	2.8	600	
1N5463A	10	2.8	550	DO-7
1N5464A	12	2.8	550	
1N5465A	15	2.8	550	
1N5466A	18	2.8	500	
1N5467A	20	2.9	500	
1N5468A	22	2.9	500	DO-7
1N5469A	27	2.9	500	
1N5470A	33	2.9	500	

Device	Nominal Capacitance pF ±10% @ $V_R = 4.0$ V $f = 1.0$ MHz	Capacitance Ratio 2-30 V Min.	Q @ 4.0 V 50 MHz Min.	Case Style
1N5471A	39	2.9	450	
1N5472A	47	2.9	400	
1N5473A	56	2.9	300	DO-7
1N5474A	68	2.9	250	
1N5475A	82	2.9	225	
1N5476A	100	2.9	200	
MV2101	6.8	2.5	450	TO-92
MV2102	8.2	2.5	450	
MV2103	10	2.0	400	
MV2104	12	2.5	400	
MV2105	15	2.5	400	
MV2106	18	2.5	350	TO-92
MV2107	22	2.5	350	
MV2108	27	2.5	300	
MV2109	33	2.5	200	
MV2110	39	2.5	150	
MV2111	47	2.5	150	TO-92
MV2112	56	2.6	150	
MV2113	68	2.6	150	
MV2114	82	2.6	100	
MV2115	100	2.6	100	

[†]For package shape, size and pin-connection information, see manufacturers' data sheets.

---

placements, be wary of substituting "similar" devices, particularly in demanding applications, such as high-speed logic, sensitive receivers, precision instrumentation and similar devices. In particular, substitution of one type of logic family for another — even if the device functions and pin outs are the same — can cause a circuit to not function or function erratically, particularly at temperature extremes. For example, substituting LS TTL devices for HCMOS devices will result in mismatches between logic level thresholds. Substituting a lower-power IC may result in problems supplying enough output current. Even using a faster or higher clock-speed part can cause problems if signals change faster or propagate more quickly than the circuit was designed for. Problems of this sort can be extremely difficult to troubleshoot unless you are skilled in circuit design. When necessary, you can add interface circuits or buffer amplifiers that improve the input and output capabilities of replacement ICs, but auxiliary circuits cannot improve basic device ratings, such as speed or bandwidth. Whenever possible, substitute ICs that are guaranteed or "direct" replacements and that are listed as such by the manufacturer.

ICs are available in different operating temperature ranges. Three standard ranges are common:

- Commercial: 0 °C to 70 °C
- Industrial: –25 °C to 85 °C
- Automotive: –40 °C to 85 °C
- Military: –55°C to 125°C

In some cases, part numbers reflect the temperature ratings. For example, an LM301A op amp is rated for the commercial temperature range; an LM201A op amp for the industrial range and an LM101A for the military range. It is usually acceptable, all other things being equal, to substitute ICs rated for a wider temperature range, but there are often other performance differences associated with the devices meeting wider temperature specifications that should be evaluated before making the substitution.

Table 22.27
Three-Terminal Voltage Regulators
Listed numerically by device

Device	Description	Package	Voltage	Current (A)
317	Adj Pos	TO-205	+1.2 to +37	0.5
317	Adj Pos	TO-204,TO-220	+1.2 to +37	1.5
317L	Low Current Adj Pos	TO-205,TO-92	+1.2 to +37	0.1
317M	Med Current Adj Pos	TO-220	+1.2 to +37	0.5
338	Adj Pos	TO-3	+1.2 to +32	5.0
350	High Current Adj Pos	TO-204,TO-220	+1.2 to +33	3.0
337	Adj Neg	TO-205	−1.2 to −37	0.5
337	Adj Neg	TO-204,TO-220	−1.2 to −37	1.5
337M	Med Current Adj Neg	TO-220	−1.2 to −37	0.5
309		TO-205	+5	0.2
309		TO-204	+5	1.0
323		TO-204,TO-220	+5	3.0
140-XX	Fixed Pos	TO-204,TO-220	Note 1	1.0
340-XX		TO-204,TO-220		1.0
78XX		TO-204,TO-220		1.0
78LXX		TO-205,TO-92		0.1
78MXX		TO-220		0.5

Device	Description	Package	Voltage	Current (A)
78TXX		TO-204		3.0
79XX	Fixed Neg	TO-204,TO-220	Note 1	1.0
79LXX		TO-205,TO-92		0.1
79MXX		TO-220		0.5

Note 1—XX indicates the regulated voltage; this value may be anywhere from 1.2 V to 35 V. A 7815 is a positive 15-V regulator, and a 7924 is a negative 24-V regulator.

The regulator package may be denoted by an additional suffix, according to the following:

Package	Suffix
TO-204 (TO-3)	K
TO-220	T
TO-205 (TO-39)	H, G
TO-92	P, Z

For example, a 7812K is a positive 12-V regulator in a TO-204 package. An LM340T-5 is a positive 5-V regulator in a TO-220 package. In addition, different manufacturers use different prefixes. An LM7805 is equivalent to a µA7805 or MC7805.

Common Voltage Regulators — Fixed Positive Voltage

Device	Output Voltage (V)	Output Current (A)	Load Regulation (mV)	Dropout Voltage (V)	Min. Input Voltage (V)	Max. Input Voltage (V)
Surface Mount SOT-89 Case						
78L05ACPK	5.0	0.1	60	1.7	7.0	20
78L06ACPK	6.2	0.1	80	1.7	8.5	20
78L08ACPK	8.0	0.1	80	1.7	10.5	23
78L09ACPK	9.0	0.1	90	1.7	11.5	24
78L12ACPK	12	0.1	100	1.7	14.5	27
78L15ACPK	15	0.1	150	1.7	17.5	30
TO-92 Case						
78L33ACZ	3.3	0.1	60	1.7	5.0	30
78L05ACZ	5.0	0.1	60	1.7	7.0	30
78L06ACZ	6.0	0.1	60	1.7	8.5	30
78L08ACZ	8.0	0.1	80	1.7	10.5	30
78L09ACZ	9.0	0.1	80	1.7	11.5	30
78L12ACZ	12	0.1	100	1.7	14.5	35
78L15ACZ	15	0.1	150	1.7	17.5	35
TO-220 Case						
78M05CV	5.0	0.5	100	2.0	7.0	35
7805ACV	5.0	1.0	100	2.0	7.0	35
7806ACV	6.0	1.0	100	2.0	8.0	35
7808ACV	8.0	1.0	100	2.0	10.0	35
7809ACV	9.0	1.0	100	2.0	11.0	35
7812ACV	12	1.0	100	2.0	14.0	35
7815CV	15	1.0	300	2.0	17.0	35

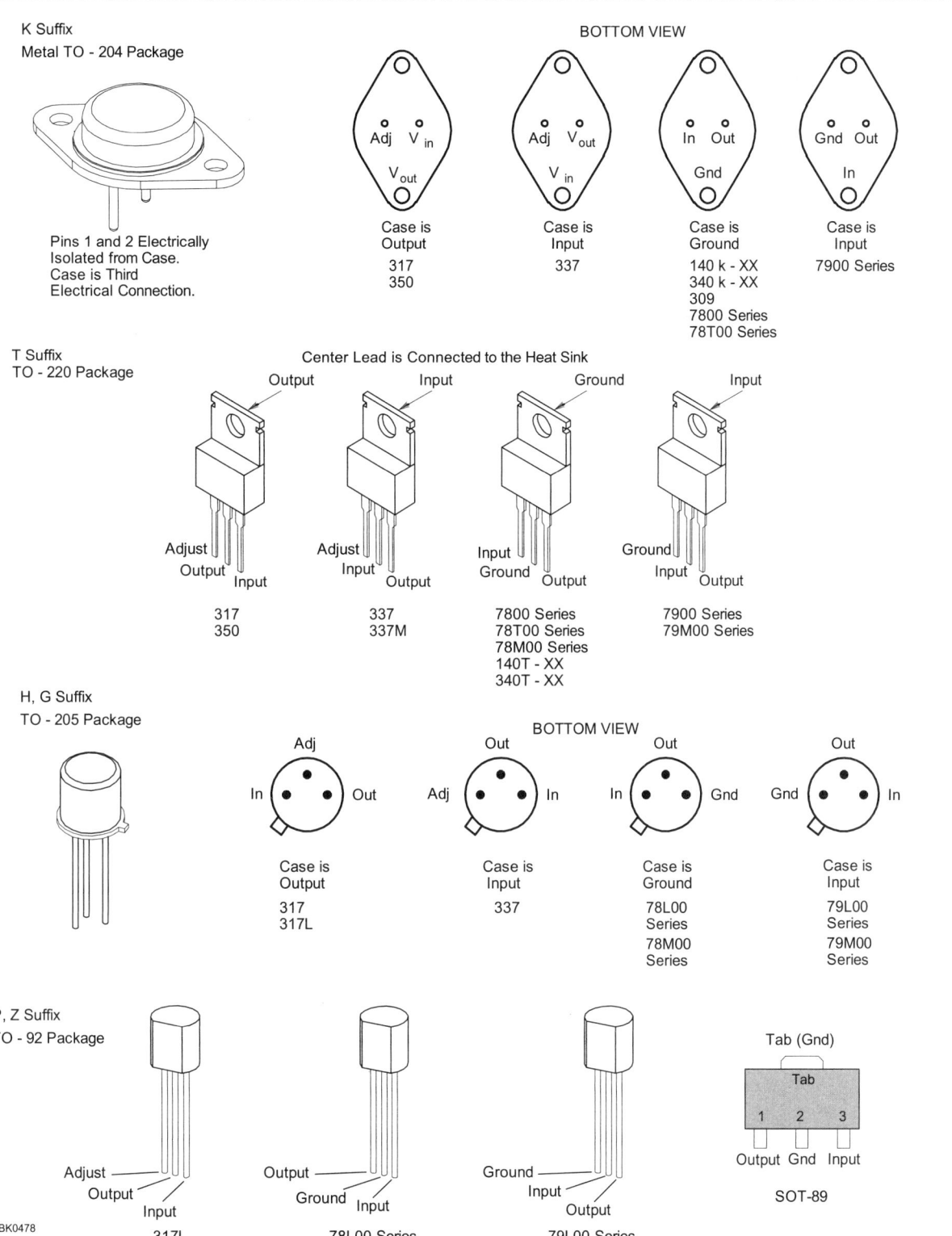

Component Data and References 22.21

Table 22.28
Monolithic 50-Ω Amplifiers (MMIC Gain Blocks)

Device	Case Style	Freq. Range (MHz)	Gain at 100 MHz (dB)	Gain at 1000 MHz (dB)	Output Power P1dB (dBm)	IP3 (dB)	NF (dB)	DC Conditions Vb @ Ib
Avago Technologies								
MSA-0386	B	dc-2400	12.5	11.9	+10.0	+23.0	6.0	5.0 V @ 35 mA
MSA-0486	B	dc-3200	16.4	15.9	+12.5	+25.5	6.5	5.3 V @ 50 mA
MSA-0505	A	dc-2300	7.8	7.0	+18.0	+29.0	6.5	8.4 V @ 80 mA
MSA-0611	C	dc-700	19.5	12.0	+2.0	+14.0	3.0	3.3 V @ 16 mA
MSA-0686	B	dc-800	20.0	16.0	+2.0	+14.5	3.0	3.5 V @ 16 mA
MSA-0786	B	dc-2000	13.5	12.6	+2.0	+14.5	3.0	3.5 V @ 16 mA
MSA-0886	B	dc-1000	32.5	22.4	+5.5	+19.0	5.5	4.0 V @ 22 mA
Mini-Circuits "ERA" Series								
ERA-1+	A, B	dc-8000	12.2	12.1	+11.7	+26.0	5.3	3.6 V @ 40 mA
ERA-2+	A, B	dc-6000	16.2	16.0	+12.8	+26.0	4.7	3.6 V @ 40 mA
ERA-3+	A, B	dc-3000	22.9	22.2	+12.1	+23.0	3.8	3.5 V @ 35 mA
ERA-4+	A, B	dc-4000	13.8	13.7	+17.0	+32.5	5.5	5.0 V @ 65 mA
ERA-5+	A, B	dc-4000	20.2	19.8	+18.4	+33.0	4.5	4.9 V @ 65 mA
ERA-6+	A, B	dc-4000	11.1	11.1	+18.5	+36.5	8.4	5.2 V @ 70 mA
Mini-Circuits "MAR" Series								
MAR-1SM+	A, B	dc-1000	18.5	15.5	+1.5	+14.0	5.5	5.0 V @ 17 mA
MAR-2SM+	A, B	dc-2000	12.5	12.0	+4.5	+17.0	6.5	5.0 V @ 25 mA
MAR-3SM+	A, B	dc-2000	12.5	12.0	+10.0	+23.0	6.0	5.0 V @ 35 mA
MAR-4SM+	A, B	dc-1000	8.3	8.0	+12.5	+25.5	7.0	5.3 V @ 50 mA
MAR-6SM+	A, B	dc-2000	20.0	16.0	+2.0	+14.5	3.0	3.5 V @ 16 mA
MAR-7SM+	A, B	dc-2000	13.5	12.5	+5.5	+19.0	5.0	4.0 V @ 22 mA
MAR-8SM+	A, B	dc-1000	32.5	22.5	+12.5	+27.0	3.3	7.8 V @ 36 mA
Mini-Circuits "VAM" Series								
VAM-3+	C	dc-2000	11.5	11.0	+9.0	+22.0	6.0	4.7 V @ 35 mA
VAM-6+	C	dc-2000	19.5	15.0	+2.0	+14.0	3.0	3.3 V @ 16 mA
VAM-7+	C	dc-2000	13.0	12.0	+5.5	+18.0	5.0	3.8 V @ 22 mA
Mini–Circuits "GALI" Series								
GALI-1+	D	dc-8000	12.7	12.5	+10.5	+27.0	4.5	3.4 V @ 40 mA
GALI-2+	D	dc-8000	16.2	15.8	+12.9	+27.0	4.8	3.5 V @ 40 mA
GALI-3+	D	dc-3000	22.4	21.1	+12.5	+25.0	3.5	3.3 V @ 35 mA
GALI-39+	D	dc-7000	20.8	21.1	+10.5	+22.9	2.4	3.5 V @ 35 mA
GALI-4+	D	dc-4000	14.4	14.1	+17.5	+34.0	4.0	4.6 V @ 65 mA
GALI-5+	D	dc-4000	20.6	19.4	+18.0	+35.0	3.5	4.4 V @ 65 mA
GALI-6+	D	dc-4000	12.2	12.2	+18.2	+35.5	4.5	5.0 V @ 70 mA
GALI-S66+	D	dc-3000	22.0	20.3	+2.8	+18.0	2.7	3.5 V @ 16 mA
Mini–Circuits "RAM" Series								
RAM–1+	B	dc-1000	19.0	15.5	+1.5	+14.0	5.5	5.0 V @ 17 mA
RAM–2+	B	dc-2000	12.5	11.8	+4.5	+17.0	6.5	5.0 V @ 25 mA
RAM–3+	B	dc-2000	12.5	12.0	+10.0	+23.0	6.0	5.0 V @ 35 mA
RAM–4+	B	dc-1000	8.5	8.0	+12.5	+25.5	6.5	5.3 V @ 50 mA
RAM–6+	B	dc-2000	20.0	16.0	+2.0	+14.5	2.8	3.5 V @ 16 mA
RAM–7+	B	dc-2000	13.5	12.5	+5.5	+19.0	4.5	4.0 V @ 22 mA
RAM–8+	B	dc-1000	32.5	23.0	+12.5	+27.0	3.0	7.8 V @ 36 mA

Mini-Circuits Labs — www.minicircuits.com

22.6.5 MMIC Amplifiers

Monolithic microwave integrated circuit (MMIC) amplifiers are single-supply 50-Ω wideband gain blocks offering high dynamic range for output powers to about +15 dBm. MMIC amplifiers are becoming increasingly popular in homebrew communications circuits. With bandwidths over 1 GHz, they are well suited for HF, VHF, UHF and lower microwave frequencies.

MMIC amplifiers produce power gains from 10 dB to 30 dB. They also have a high third-order intercept point (IP3), usually in the +20 to +30 dBm range, easing the concerns about amplifier compression for most applications. They are used for RF and IF amplifiers, local oscillator amplifiers, transmitter drivers, and other medium power applications in 50-Ω systems. MMICs are especially well suited for driving 50-Ω double-balanced mixers (DBM). **Figure 22.17** shows the typical circuit arrangement for most MMIC amplifiers.

MMICs are available in a variety of packages, mostly surface mount as shown in **Figure 22.18**, requiring very few external components. Vendor data sheets and application notes, found on the manufacturer's websites, should be used for the proper selection of the biasing resistor, coupling capacitors, and other design criteria. Some of the popular MMIC amplifiers are listed in **Table 22.28**.

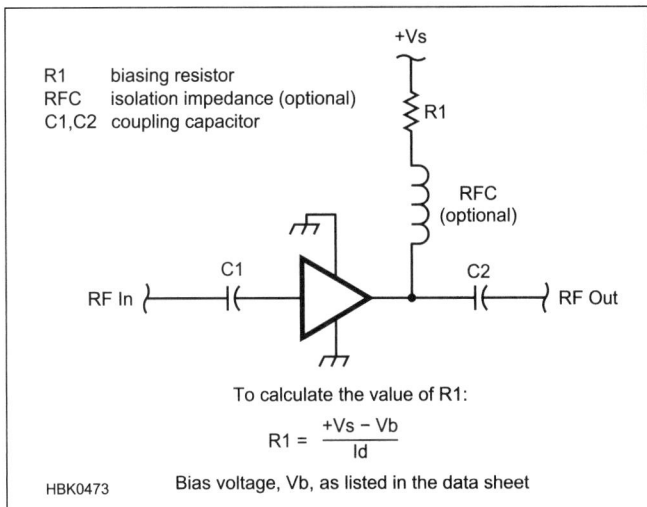

Figure 22.17 — MMIC application.

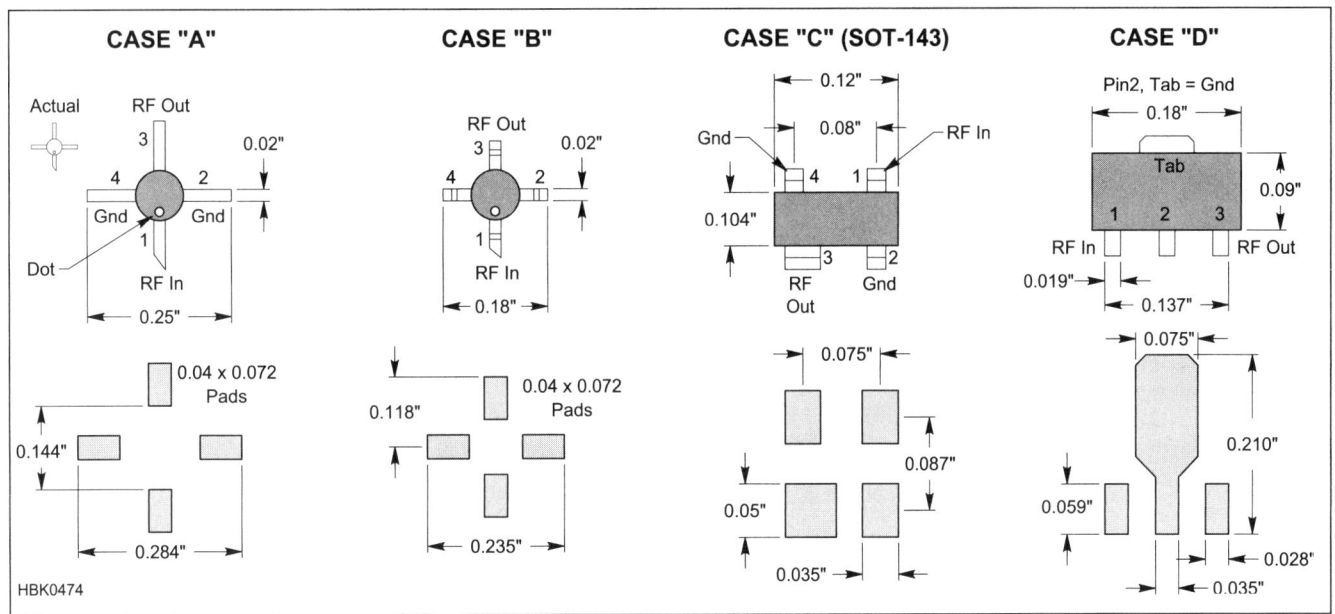

Figure 22.18 — MMIC package styles.

The main disadvantage of MMIC amplifiers is their relatively high current demands, usually in the 30 mA to 80 mA range per device, making them unsuitable for battery-powered portable equipment. On the other hand, the high current demand is what establishes their high gain and high IP3 characteristics with 50-Ω loads.

Another disadvantage is their wide gain-bandwidth. Their gain should be band-limited by input and output tuned circuits or filters to reduce the gain outside the desired ranges. For example, for an HF amplifier, 30 MHz low-pass filters can be used to reduce the gain outside the HF spectrum, or a band-pass filter used for the frequency band of interest.

Selecting the proper MMIC amplifier is fairly straightforward. First, select a device for the desired frequency bandwidth, gain, and output power. Ensure device current is compatible with the design application. Calculate the value for the bias resistor (R1 in Figure 22.17) based on the biasing voltage (V_b) listed in Table 22.28 and whatever value of supply voltage (V_s) is available.

With increasing availability and ease of use, there are many circuits where MMIC amplifiers can be used. There are many MMIC amplifiers that are relatively inexpensive for hobby use.

Component Data and References 22.23

Table 22.29
Small-Signal FETs

Device	Type	Max Diss (mW)	Max V_{DS} (V)	$V_{GS(off)}$ (V)	Min gfs (µS)	Input C (pF)	Max ID (mA)[1]	f_{max} (MHz)	Noise Figure (typ)	Case	Base	Applications
2N4416	N-JFET	300	30	−6	4500	4	−15	450	4 dB @ 400 MHz	TO-72	1	VHF/UHF amp, mix, osc
2N5484	N-JFET	310	25	−3	2500	5	30	200	4 dB @ 200 MHz	TO-92	2	VHF/UHF amp, mix, osc
2N5485	N-JFET	310	25	−4	3500	5	30	400	4 dB @ 400 MHz	TO-92	2	VHF/UHF amp, mix, osc
2N5486	N-JFET	360	25	−2	5500	5	15	400	4 dB @ 400 MHz	TO-92	2	VHF/UHF amp. mix, osc
3N200 NTE222 SK3065	N-dual-gate MOSFET	330	20	−6	10,000	4-8.5	50	500	4.5 dB @ 400 MHz	TO-72	3	VHF/UHF amp, mix, osc
3N202 NTE454 SK3991	N-dual-gate MOSFET	360	25	−5	8000	6	50	200	4.5 dB @ 200 MHz	TO-72	3	VHF amp, mixer
MPF102 NTE451 SK9164	N-JFET	310	25	−8	2000	4.5	20	200	4 dB @ 400 MHz	TO-92	2	HF/VHF amp, mix, osc
MPF106 2N5484	N-JFET	310	25	−6	2500	5	30	400	4 dB @ 200 MHz	TO-92	2	HF/VHF/UHF amp, mix, osc
40673 NTE222 SK3050	N-dual-gate MOSFET	330	20	−4	12,000	6	50	400	6 dB @ 200 MHz	TO-72	3	HF/VHF/UHF amp, mix, osc
U304	P-JFET	350	−30	+10	27	—	−50	—	—	TO-18	4	analog switch chopper
U310	N-JFET	500 300	30 30	−6	10,000	2.5	60	450	3.2 dB @ 450 MHz	TO-52	5	common-gate VHF/UHF amp,
U350	N-JFET Quad	1W	25	−6	9000	5	60	100	7 dB @ 100 MHz	TO-99	6	matched JFET doubly bal mix
U431	N-JFET Dual	300	25	−6	10,000	5	30	100	—	TO-99	7	matched JFET cascode amp and bal mix
2N5670	N-JFET	350	25	8	3000	7	20	400	2.5 dB @ 100 MHz	TO-92	2	VHF/UHF osc, mix, front-end amp
2N5668	N-JFET	350	25	4	1500	7	5	400	2.5 dB @ 100 MHz	TO-92	2	VHF/UHF osc, mix, front-end amp
2N5669	N-JFET	350	25	6	2000	7	10	400	2.5 dB @ 100 MHz	TO-92	2	VHF/UHF osc, mix, front-end amp
J308	N-JFET	350	25	6.5	8000	7.5	60	1000	1.5 dB @ 100 MHz	TO-92	2	VHF/UHF osc, mix, front-end amp
J309	N JFET	350	25	4	10,000	7.5	30	1000	1.5 dB @ 100 MHz	TO-92	2	VHF/UHF osc, mix, front-end amp
J310	N-JFET	350	25	6.5	8000	7.5	60	1000	1.5 dB @ 100 MHz	TO-92	2	VHF/UHF osc, mix, front-end amp
NE32684A	HJ-FET	165	2.0	−0.8	45,000	—	30	20 GHz	0.5 dB @ 12 GHz	84A		Low-noise amp

Notes:
[1] 25°C.
For package shape, size and pin-connection information, see manufacturers' data sheets.

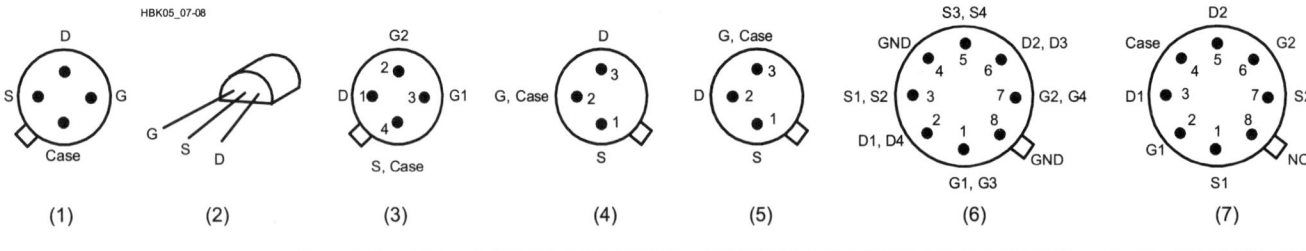

Table 22.30
Low-Noise Bipolar Transistors

Device	NF (dB)	F (MHz)	f_T (GHz)	I_C (mA)	Gain (dB)	F (MHz)	$V_{(BR)CEO}$ (V)	I_C (mA)	P_T (mW)	Case
MRF904	1.5	450	4	15	16	450	15	30	200	TO-206AF
MRF571	1.5	1000	8	50	12	1000	10	70	1000	Macro-X
MRF2369	1.5	1000	6	40	12	1000	15	70	750	Macro-X
MPS911	1.7	500	7	30	16.5	500	12	40	625	TO-226AA
MRF581A	1.8	500	5	75	15.5	500	15	200	2500	Macro-X
BFR91	1.9	500	5	30	16	500	12	35	180	Macro-T
BFR96	2	500	4.5	50	14.5	500	15	100	500	Macro-T
MPS571	2	500	6	50	14	500	10	80	625	TO-226AA
MRF581	2	500	5	75	15.5	500	18	200	2500	Macro-X
MRF901	2	1000	4.5	15	12	1000	15	30	375	Macro-X
MRF941	2.1	2000	8	15	12.5	2000	10	15	400	Macro-X
MRF951	2.1	2000	7.5	30	12.5	2000	10	100	1000	Macro-X
BFR90	2.4	500	5	14	18	500	15	30	180	Macro-T
MPS901	2.4	900	4.5	15	12	900	15	30	300	TO-226AA
MRF1001A	2.5	300	3	90	13.5	300	20	200	3000	TO-205AD
2N5031	2.5	450	1.6	5	14	450	10	20	200	TO-206AF
MRF4239A	2.5	500	5	90	14	500	12	400	3000	TO-205AD
BFW92A	2.7	500	4.5	10	16	500	15	35	180	Macro-T
MRF521*	2.8	1000	4.2	−50	11	1000	−10	−70	750	Macro-X
2N5109	3	200	1.5	50	11	216	20	400	2500	TO-205AD
2N4957*	3	450	1.6	−2	12	450	−30	−30	200	TO-206AF
MM4049*	3	500	5	−20	11.5	500	−10	−30	200	TO-206AF
2N5943	3.4	200	1.5	50	11.4	200	30	400	3500	TO-205AD
MRF586	4	500	1.5	90	9	500	17	200	2500	TO-205AD
2N5179	4.5	200	1.4	10	15	200	12	50	200	TO-206AF
2N2857	4.5	450	1.6	8	12.5	450	15	40	200	TO-206AF
2N6304	4.5	450	1.8	10	15	450	15	50	200	TO-206AF
MPS536*	4.5	500	5	−20	4.5	500	−10	−30	625	TO-226AA
MRF536*	4.5	1000	6	−20	10	1000	−10	−30	300	Macro-X

*denotes a PNP device

Complementary devices

NPN	PNP
2N2857	2N4957
MRF904	MM4049
MRF571	MRF521

For package shape, size and pin-connection information, see manufacturers' data sheets. Many retail suppliers and manufacturers offer data sheets on their websites.

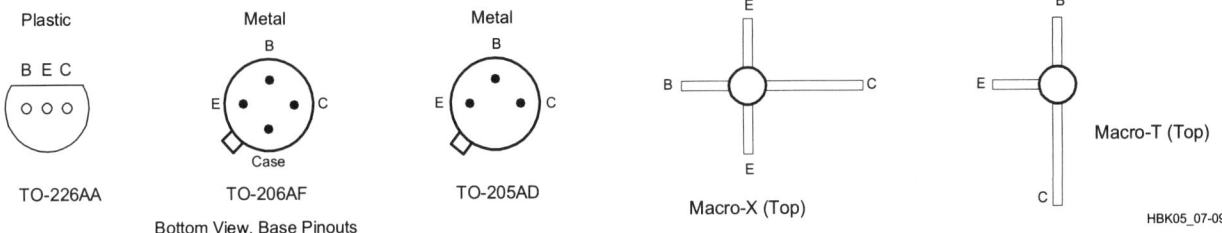

Table 22.31
General-Purpose Bipolar Transistors
Listed numerically by device

Device	Type	V_{CEO} Maximum Collector Emitter Voltage (V)	V_{CBO} Maximum Collector Base Voltage (V)	V_{EBO} Maximum Emitter Base Voltage (V)	I_C Maximum Collector Current (mA)	P_O Maximum Device Dissipation (W)	**Minimum DC Current Gain** $I_C = 0.1$ mA	**Minimum DC Current Gain** $I_C = 150$ mA	Current-Gain Bandwidth Product f_T (MHz)	Noise Figure NF Maximum (dB)	Base
2N918	NPN	15	30	3.0	50	0.2	20 (3 mA)	—	600	6.0	3
2N2102	NPN	65	120	7.0	1000	1.0	20	40	60	6.0	2
2N2218	NPN	30	60	5.0	800	0.8	20	40	250		2
2N2218A	NPN	40	75	6.0	800	0.8	20	40	250		2
2N2219	NPN	30	60	5.0	800	3.0	35	100	250		2
2N2219A	NPN	40	75	6.0	800	3.0	35	100	300	4.0	2
2N2222	NPN	30	60	5.0	800	1.2	35	100	250		2
2N2222A	NPN	40	75	6.0	800	1.2	35	100	200	4.0	2
2N2905	PNP	40	60	5.0	600	0.6	35	—	200		2
2N2905A	PNP	60	60	5.0	600	0.6	75	100	200		2
2N2907	PNP	40	60	5.0	600	0.4	35	—	200		2
2N2907A	PNP	60	60	5.0	600	0.4	75	100	200		2
2N3053	NPN	40	60	5.0	700	5.0	—	50	100		2
2N3053A	NPN	60	80	5.0	700	5.0	—	50	100		2
2N3563	NPN	15	30	2.0	50	0.6	20	—	800		1
2N3904	NPN	40	60	6.0	200	0.625	40	—	300	5.0	1
2N3906	PNP	40	40	5.0	200	0.625	60	—	250	4.0	1
2N4037	PNP	40	60	7.0	1000	5.0	—	50			2
2N4123	NPN	30	40	5.0	200	0.35	—	25 (50 mA)	250	6.0	1
2N4124	NPN	25	30	5.0	200	0.35	120 (2 mA)	60 (50 mA)	300	5.0	1
2N4125	PNP	30	30	4.0	200	0.625	50 (2 mA)	25 (50 mA)	200	5.0	1
2N4126	PNP	25	25	4.0	200	0.625	120 (2 mA)	60 (50 mA)	250	4.0	1
2N4401	NPN	40	60	6.0	600	0.625	20	100	250		1
2N4403	PNP	40	40	5.0	600	0.625	30	100	200		1
2N5320	NPN	75	100	7.0	2000	10.0	—	30 (1 A)			2
2N5415	PNP	200	200	4.0	1000	10.0	—	30 (50 mA)	15		2
MM4003	PNP	250	250	4.0	500	1.0	20 (10 mA)	—			2
MPSA55	PNP	60	60	4.0	500	0.625	—	50 (0.1 A)	50		1
MPS6531	NPN	40	60	5.0	600	0.625	60 (10 mA)	90 (0.1 A)			1
MPS6547	NPN	25	35	3.0	50	0.625	20 (2 mA)	—	600		1

Test conditions: $I_C = 20$ mA dc; $V_{CE} = 20$ V; f = 100 MHz

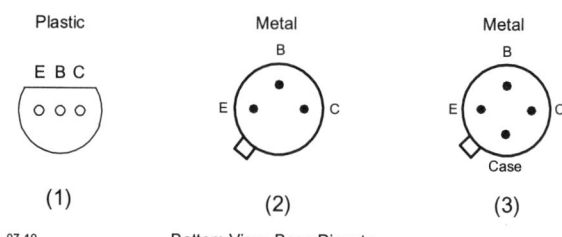

Bottom View, Base Pinouts

(1) Plastic — E B C

(2) Metal — B, E, C

(3) Metal — B, E, C, Case

Table 22.32
General Purpose Silicon Bipolar Power Transistors

TO-220 Case, Pin 1=Base, Pin 2, Case = Collector; Pin 3 = Emitter

TO-204 Case (TO-3), Pin 1=Base, Pin 2 = Emitter, Case = Collector;

NPN	PNP	I_C Max (A)	V_{CEO} Max (V)	h_{FE} Min	F_T (MHz)	Power Dissipation (W)
D44C8		4	60	100/220	50	30
	D45C8	4	60	40/120	50	30
TIP29		1	40	15/75	3	30
	TIP30	1	40	15/75	3	30
TIP29A		1	50	15/75	3	30
	TIP30A	1	60	15/75	3	30
TIP29B		1	80	15/75	3	30
TIP29C		1	100	15/75	3	30
	TIP30C	1	100	15/75	3	30
TIP47		1	250	30/150	10	40
TIP48		1	300	30/150	10	40
TIP49		1	350	30/150	10	40
TIP50		1	400	30/150	10	40
TIP110*		2	60	500	> 5	50
	TIP115*	2	60	500	> 5	50
TIP116		2	80	500	25	50
TIP31		3	40	25	3	40
	TIP32	3	40	25	3	40
TIP31A		3	60	25	3	40
	TIP32A	3	60	25	3	40
TIP31B		3	80	25	3	40
	TIP32B	3	80	25	3	40
TIP31C		3	100	25	3	40
	TIP32C	3	100	25	3	40
2N6124		4	45	25/100	2.5	40
2N6122		4	60	25/100	2.5	40
MJE1300		4	300	6/30	4	60
TIP120*		5	60	1000	> 5	65
	TIP125*	5	60	1000	> 10	65
	TIP42	6	40	15/75	3	65
TIP41A		6	60	15/75	3	65
TIP41B		6	80	15/75	3	65
2N6290		7	50	30/150	4	40
	2N6109	7	50	30/150	4	40
2N6292		7	70	30/150	4	40
	2N6107	7	70	30/150	4	40
MJE3055T		10	50	20/70	2	75
	MJE2955T	10	60	20/70	2	75
2N6486		15	40	20/150	5	75
2N6488		15	80	20/150	5	75
TIP140*		10	60	500	> 5	125
	TIP145*	10	60	600	> 10	125
2N3055A		15	60	20/70	0.8	115

NPN	PNP	I_C Max (A)	V_{CEO} Max (V)	h_{FE} Min	F_T (MHz)	Power Dissipation (W)
2N3055		15	60	20/70	2.5	115
	MJ2955	15	60	20/70	2.5	115
2N6545		8	400	7/35	6	125
2N5039		20	75	20/100	—	140
2N3771		30	40	15	0.2	150
2N3789		10	60	15	4	150
2N3715		10	60	30	4	150
	2N3791	10	60	30	4	150
	2N5875	10	60	20/100	4	150
	2N3790	10	80	15	4	150
2N3716		10	80	30	4	150
	2N3792	10	80	30	4	150
2N3773		16	140	15/60	4	150
2N6284		20	100	750/18K	—	160
	2N6287	20	100	750/18K	—	160
2N5881		15	60	20/100	4	160
2N5880		15	80	20/100	4	160
2N6249		15	200	10/50	2.5	175
2N6250		15	275	8/50	2.5	175
2N6546		15	300	6/30	6-28	175
2N6251		15	350	6/50	2.5	175
2N5630		16	120	20/80	1	200
2N5301		30	40	15/60	2	200
2N5303		20	80	15/60	2	200
2N5885		25	60	20/100	4	200
2N5302		30	60	15/60	2	200
	2N4399	30	60	15/60	4	200
2N5886		25	80	20/100	4	200
	2N5884	25	80	20/100	4	200
MJ802		30	100	25/100	2	200
	MJ4502	30	100	25/100	2	200
MJ15003		20	140	25/150	2	250
	MJI5004	20	140	25/150	2	250
MJ15024		25	250	15/60	4	250

▓ = Complimentary pairs
* = Darlington transistor

Useful URLs for finding transistor/IC data sheets:
Line of replacement transistors and ICs: www.nteinc.com
General-purpose replacements: www.mouser.com, www.digikey.com
NXP Semiconductors: www.nxp.com
Mitsubishi: www.mitsubishielectric.com/semiconductors/products
ON Semiconductor: www.onsemi.com
M/A-COM: www.macomtech.com
STMicroelectronics: www.st.com
Microsemi: www.microsemi.com

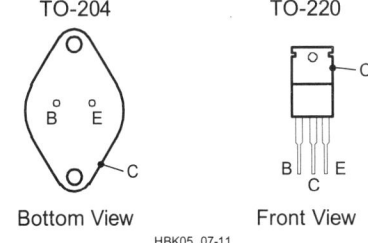

Component Data and References

Table 22.33
General Purpose JFETs and MOSFETs

Device	Type	VDSS min (V)	RDS(on) max (Ω)	ID max (A)	PD max (W)	Case†	Mfr
BS250P	P-channel	45	14	0.23	0.7	E-line	Z
IRFZ30	N-channel	50	0.050	30	75	TO-220	IR
IRFZ42	N-channel	50	0.035	50	150	TO-220	IR
2N7000	N-channel	60	5	0.20	0.4	E-line	Z
VN10LP	N-channel	60	7.5	0.27	0.625	E-line	Z
VN10KM	N-channel	60	5	0.3	1	TO-237	S
ZVN2106B	N-channel	60	2	1.2	5	TO-39	Z
IRF511	N-channel	60	0.6	2.5	20	TO-220AB	IR
IRF531	N-channel	60	0.180	14	75	TO-220AB	IR
IRF531	N-channel	80	0.160	14	79	TO-220	IR
ZVP3310A	P-channel	100	20	0.14	0.625	E-line	Z
ZVN2110B	N-channel	100	4	0.85	5	TO-39	Z
ZVP3310B	P-channel	100	20	0.3	5	TO-39	Z
IRF510	N-channel	100	0.6	2	20	TO-220AB	IR
IRF520	N-channel	100	0.27	5	40	TO-220AB	IR
IRF150	N-channel	100	0.055	40	150	TO-204AE	IR
IRFP150	N-channel	100	0.055	40	180	TO-247	IR
ZVP1320A	P-channel	200	80	0.02	0.625	E-line	Z
ZVN0120B	N-channel	200	16	0.42	5	TO-39	Z
ZVP1320B	P-channel	200	80	0.1	5	TO-39	Z
IRF620	N-channel	200	0.800	5	40	TO-220AB	IR
IRF220	N-channel	200	0.400	8	75	TO-220AB	IR
IRF640	N-channel	200	0.18	10	125	TO-220AB	IR

Manufacturers: IR = International Rectifier; M = Motorola; S = Siliconix; Z = Zetex.

†For package shape, size and pin-connection information, see manufacturers' data sheets. Many retail suppliers offer data sheets to buyers free of charge on request. Data books are available from many manufacturers and retailers.

Table 22.34
RF Power Transistors — By Part Number

Part Number	P_O (W)	Type	Gain (dB)	V_{DD} (V)	Package	f(MHz)	BV_{DSS}	P_D max (W)	Mfr
ARF1500	750	MOS	16	125	T1	40	500		MS
ARF1501	750	MOS	17	250	T1	40	1000		MS
ARF460AG	150	MOS	15	125	TO-247s	65	500		MS
ARF461AG	150	MOS	15	250	TO-247s	65	1000		MS
ARF463AG	100	MOS	15	125	TO-247s	100	500		MS
ARF465AG	150	MOS	15	300	TO-247s	60	1200		MS
ARF466AG	300	MOS	16	200	TO-247s	45	1000		MS
ARF466FL	300	MOS	16	200	T3	45	1000		MS
ARF473	300	MOS	14	165	M244	150	500		MS
ARF475FL	450	MOS	14	165	T3	150	500		MS
ARF476FL	450	MOS	14	165	T3	150	500		MS
ARF477FL	400	MOS	16	165	T3a	100	500		MS
ARF521	150	MOS	15	165	M174	150	500		MS
BLF1043	10	MOS	16.5	26	SOT538A	1000			NXP
BLF1046	45	MOS	14	26	SOT467C	1000			NXP
BLF145	30	MOS	20	28	SOT123A	30			NXP
BLF147	150	MOS	14	28	SOT121B	175			NXP
BLF174XR	600	LDMOS	28.5	50	SOT1214A	128			NXP
BLF175	30	MOS	20	50	SOT123A	108			NXP
BLF177	150	MOS	19	50	SOT121B	108			NXP
BLF202	2	MOS	13	12.5	SOT409A	175			NXP
BLF242	5	MOS	16	28	SOT123A	200			NXP
BLF244	15	MOS	17	28	SOT123A	175			NXP
BLF245	30	MOS	15.5	28	SOT123A	175			NXP
BLF245B	30	MOS	18	28	SOT279A	175			NXP
BLF246	80	MOS	18	28	SOT121B	175			NXP
BLF246B	60	MOS	19	28	SOT161A	175			NXP
BLF278	300	MOS	16	50	SOT262A1	225			NXP
BLF369	500	LDMOS	18	32	SOT800-2	500			NXP
BLF571	20	LDMOS	27.5	50	SOT467C	500			NXP

Table 22.34 continued

Part Number	P_O (W)	Type	Gain (dB)	V_{DD} (V)	Package	f(MHz)	BV_{DSS}	P_D max (W)	Mfr
BLF573	300	LDMOS	27.2	50	SOT502A	500			NXP
BLF573S	300	LDMOS	27.2	50	SOT502B	500			NXP
BLF574	600	LDMOS	26.5	50	SOT539A	500			NXP
BLF574XR	600	LDMOS	23	50	SOT1214A	500			NXP
BLF578	300	LDMOS	26	50	SOT539A	500			NXP
BLF642	35	LDMOS	19	32	SOT467C	1400			NXP
BLF645	100	LDMOS	18	32	SOT540A	1400			NXP
BLF871	100	LDMOS	21	40	SOT467C	1000			NXP
BLF871S	100	LDMOS	21	40	SOT467B	1000			NXP
BLF881	140	LDMOS	21	50	SOT467C	1000			NXP
BLF881S	140	LDMOS	21	50	SOT467B	1000			NXP
MRF141	150	MOS	21	28	M174	175			MA
MRF141G	300	MOS	21	28	M244	175			MA
MRF148A	30	MOS	18	50	M113	175			MA
MRF150	150	MOS	20	50	M174	150			MA
MRF151	150	MOS	21	50	M177	175			MA
MRF151G	300	MOS	20	50	M244	175			MA
MRF154	600	MOS	16	50	HOG	80			MA
MRFE6VP100H	100	LDMOS	27.2	50	Flange	0 to 2000			NXP
MRFE6VP5600H	600	LDMOS	24.6	50	Flange	1.8 to 600			NXP
MRFE6VP61K25H	1250	LDMOS	22.9	50	Flange	1.8 to 600			NXP
MRFE6VP6300H	300	LDMOS	25	50	Flange	1.8 to 600			NXP
MRFX1K89H	1800	LDMOS	25	65	NI-1230-4H	1.8 to 400	182		NXP
RD00HHS1	0.3	LDMOS	18.7	12.5	SOT-89	30	30	3.1	MT
RD00HVS1	0.5	LDMOS	20	12.5	SOT-89	175	30	3.1	MT
RD06HHF1	6	LDMOS	16	12.5	TO-220S	30	50	27.8	MT
RD06HVF1	6	LDMOS	16	12.5	TO-220S	175	50	27.8	MT
RD100HHF1	100	LDMOS	14	12.5	Flange large	30	50	176.5	MS
RD15HVF1	15	LDMOS	12	12.5	TO-220S	520	30	48	MT
RD16HHF1	16	LDMOS	16	12.5	TO-220S	30	50	56.8	MT
RD20HMF1	20	LDMOS	8.5	12.5	Flange small	900	30	71.4	MT
RD30HUF1	30	LDMOS	10	12.5	Flange small	520	30	75	MT
RD30HVF1	30	LDMOS	15	12.5	Flange small	175	30	75	MT
RD45HMF1	45	LDMOS	8	12.5	Flange large	900	30	125	MT
RD60HUF1	60	LDMOS	10	12.5	Flange large	520	30	150	MT
RD70HHF1	70	LDMOS	14	12.5	Flange large	30	50	150	MS
RD70HVF1	70	LDMOS	12	12.5	Flange large	175	30	150	MT
SD1274-01	30	BJT	10	13.6	M113	160			ST
SD1275-01	40	BJT	9	13.6	M113	160			ST
SD1726	150	BJT	14	50	M174	30			ST
SD1728	250	BJT	14.5	50	M177	30			ST
SD2902	15	BJT	12.5	28	M113	400			ST
SD2904	30	BJT	9.5	28	M113	400			ST
SD2918	30	MOS	18	50	M113	30			ST
SD2931-10	150	MOS	14	50	M174	175			ST
SD2932	300	MOS	15	50	M244	175			ST
SD2933	300	MOS	20	50	M177	30			ST
SD2941-10	175	MOS	15	50	M174	175			ST
SD2942	350	MOS	15	50	M244	175			ST
SD2943	350	MOS	22	50	M177	30			ST
SD3931-10	175	MOS	20	100	M174	150			ST
SD3932	350	MOS	24	100	M244	150			ST
SD3933	350	MOS	25	100	M177	30			ST
SD4931	150	MOS	14.8	50	M174	175			ST
SD4933	300	MOS	24	50	M177	30			ST
VRF141	150	MOS	13	28	M174	175	80		MS
VRF141G	300	MOS	14	28	M244	175	80		MS
VRF148A	30	MOS	16	50	M113	175	170		MS
VRF150	150	MOS	11	50	M174	150	170		MS
VRF151	150	MOS	14	50	M174	175	170		MS
VRF151E	150	MOS	14	50	M174	175	170		MS
VRF151G	300	MOS	16	50	M244	175	170		MS
VRF152	150	MOS	14	50	M174	175	170		MS
VRF154FL	600	MOS	17	50	T2	80	170		MS
VRF157FL	600	MOS	21	50	T2	80	170		MS
VRF2933	300	MOS	22	50	M177	100	170		MS

Manufacturer codes:
MA – M/A-COM: www.macomtech.com
MS - Microsemi: www.microsemi.com
MT – Mitsubishi: www.mitsubishielectric.com/semiconductors/products
NXP – NXP Semiconductors: www.nxp.com
ST – STMicroelectronics: www.st.com

Table 22.35
RF Power Transistors — By Power Output

Part Number	P_O (W)	Type	Gain (dB)	V_{DD} (V)	Package	f(MHz)	BV_{DSS}	P_D max (W)	Mfr
RD00HHS1	0.3	LDMOS	18.7	12.5	SOT-89	30	30	3.1	MT
RD00HVS1	0.5	LDMOS	20	12.5	SOT-89	175	30	3.1	MT
BLF202	2	MOS	13	12.5	SOT409A	175			NXP
BLF242	5	MOS	16	28	SOT123A	200			NXP
RD06HHF1	6	LDMOS	16	12.5	TO-220S	30	50	27.8	MT
RD06HVF1	6	LDMOS	16	12.5	TO-220S	175	50	27.8	MT
BLF1043	10	MOS	16.5	26	SOT538A	1000			NXP
BLF244	15	MOS	17	28	SOT123A	175			NXP
SD2902	15	BJT	12.5	28	M113	400			ST
RD15HVF1	15	LDMOS	12	12.5	TO-220S	520	30	48	MT
RD16HHF1	16	LDMOS	16	12.5	TO-220S	30	50	56.8	MT
BLF571	20	LDMOS	27.5	50	SOT467C	500			NXP
RD20HMF1	20	LDMOS	8.5	12.5	Flange small	900	30	71.4	MT
BLF145	30	MOS	20	28	SOT123A	30			NXP
SD2918	30	MOS	18	50	M113	30			ST
BLF175	30	MOS	20	50	SOT123A	108			NXP
SD1274-01	30	BJT	10	13.6	M113	160			ST
BLF245	30	MOS	15.5	28	SOT123A	175			NXP
BLF245B	30	MOS	18	28	SOT279A	175			NXP
MRF148A	30	MOS	18	50	M113	175			MA
RD30HVF1	30	LDMOS	15	12.5	Flange small	175	30	75	MT
VRF148A	30	MOS	16	50	M113	175	170		MS
SD2904	30	BJT	9.5	28	M113	400			ST
RD30HUF1	30	LDMOS	10	12.5	Flange small	520	30	75	MT
BLF642	35	LDMOS	19	32	SOT467C	1400			NXP
SD1275-01	40	BJT	9	13.6	M113	160			ST
RD45HMF1	45	LDMOS	8	12.5	Flange large	900	30	125	MT
BLF1046	45	MOS	14	26	SOT467C	1000			NXP
BLF246B	60	MOS	19	28	SOT161A	175			NXP
RD60HUF1	60	LDMOS	10	12.5	Flange large	520	30	150	MT
RD70HHF1	70	LDMOS	14	12.5	Flange large	30	50	150	MS
RD70HVF1	70	LDMOS	12	12.5	Flange large	175	30	150	MT
BLF246	80	MOS	18	28	SOT121B	175			NXP
RD100HHF1	100	LDMOS	14	12.5	Flange large	30	50	176.5	MS
ARF463AG	100	MOS	15	125	TO-247	100	500		MS
BLF871	100	LDMOS	21	40	SOT467C	1000			NXP
BLF871S	100	LDMOS	21	40	SOT467B	1000			NXP
BLF645	100	LDMOS	18	32	SOT540A	1400			NXP
MRFE6VP100H	100	LDMOS	27.2	50	Flange	0 to 2000			NXP
BLF881	140	LDMOS	21	50	SOT467C	1000			NXP
BLF881S	140	LDMOS	21	50	SOT467B	1000			NXP
SD1726	150	BJT	14	50	M174	30			ST
ARF465AG	150	MOS	15	300	TO-247s	60	1200		MS
ARF460AG	150	MOS	15	125	TO-247s	65	500		MS
ARF461AG	150	MOS	15	250	TO-247s	65	1000		MS
BLF177	150	MOS	19	50	SOT121B	108			NXP
ARF521	150	MOS	15	165	M174	150	500		MS
MRF150	150	MOS	20	50	M174	150			MA
VRF150	150	MOS	11	50	M174	150	170		MS
BLF147	150	MOS	14	28	SOT121B	175			NXP
MRF141	150	MOS	21	28	M174	175			MA
MRF151	150	MOS	21	50	M177	175			MA
SD2931-10	150	MOS	14	50	M174	175			ST
SD4931	150	MOS	14.8	50	M174	175			ST
VRF141	150	MOS	13	28	M174	175	80		MS
VRF151	150	MOS	14	50	M174	175	170		MS
VRF151E	150	MOS	14	50	M174	175	170		MS
VRF152	150	MOS	14	50	M174	175	170		MS
SD3931-10	175	MOS	20	100	M174	150			ST
SD2941-10	175	MOS	15	50	M174	175			ST
SD1728	250	BJT	14.5	50	M177	30			ST
SD2933	300	MOS	20	50	M177	30			ST
SD4933	300	MOS	24	50	M177	30			ST
ARF466AG	300	MOS	16	200	TO-247s	45	1000		MS
ARF466FL	300	MOS	16	200	T3	45	1000		MS
VRF2933	300	MOS	22	50	M177	100	170		MS
ARF473	300	MOS	14	165	M244	150	500		MS
MRF141G	300	MOS	21	28	M244	175			MA
MRF151G	300	MOS	20	50	M244	175			MA
SD2932	300	MOS	15	50	M244	175			ST
VRF141G	300	MOS	14	28	M244	175	80		MS
VRF151G	300	MOS	16	50	M244	175	170		MS
BLF278	300	MOS	16	50	SOT262A1	225			NXP
BLF573	300	LDMOS	27.2	50	SOT502A	500			NXP
BLF573S	300	LDMOS	27.2	50	SOT502B	500			NXP
BLF578	300	LDMOS	26	50	SOT539A	500			NXP
MRFE6VP6300H	300	LDMOS	25	50	Flange	1.8 to 600			NXP
SD2943	350	MOS	22	50	M177	30			ST
SD3933	350	MOS	25	100	M177	30			ST
SD3932	350	MOS	24	100	M244	150			ST

SD2942	350	MOS	15	50	M244	175			ST
ARF477FL	400	MOS	16	165	T3a	100	500		MS
ARF475FL	450	MOS	14	165	T3	150	500		MS
ARF476FL	450	MOS	14	165	T3	150	500		MS
BLF369	500	LDMOS	18	32	SOT800-2	500			NXP
MRF154	600	MOS	16	50	HOG	80			MA
VRF154FL	600	MOS	17	50	T2	80	170		MS
VRF157FL	600	MOS	21	50	T2	80	170		MS
BLF174XR	600	LDMOS	28.5	50	SOT1214A	128			NXP
BLF574	600	LDMOS	26.5	50	SOT539A	500			NXP
BLF574XR	600	LDMOS	23	50	SOT1214A	500			NXP
MRFE6VP5600H	600	LDMOS	24.6	50	Flange	1.8 to 600			NXP
ARF1500	750	MOS	16	125	T1	40	500		MS
ARF1501	750	MOS	17	250	T1	40	1000		MS
MRFE6VP61K25H	1250	LDMOS	22.9	50	Flange	1.8 to 600			NXP
MRFX1K89H	1800	LDMOS	25	65	NI-1230-4H	1.8-400	182		NXP

Manufacturer codes:
MA — M/A-COM: www.macomtech.com
MS — Microsemi: www.microsemi.com
MT — Mitsubishi: www.mitsubishielectric.com/semiconductors/php/eSearch.php

NXP — NXP Semiconductors: www.nxp.com
ST — STMicroelectronics: www.st.com

Table 22.36
RF Power Amplifier Modules
Listed by frequency

Device	Supply (V)	Frequency Range (MHz)	Output Power (W)	Power Gain (dB)	Package[†]	Mfr/ Notes
M57735	17	50-54	14	21	H3C	MI; SSB mobile – Discontinued*
M57719N	17	142-163	14	18.4	H2	MI; FM mobile – Discontinued*
S-AV17	16	144-148	60	21.7	5-53L	T, FM mobile
S-AV7	16	144-148	28	21.4	5-53H	T, FM mobile
MHW607-1	7.5	136-150	7	38.4	301K-02/3	NXP; class C
BGY35	12.5	132-156	18	20.8	SOT132B	NXP – Discontinued*
M67712	17	220-225	25	20	H3B	MI; SSB mobile – Discontinued*
M57774	17	220-225	25	20	H2	MI; FM mobile – Discontinued*
MHW720-1	12.5	400-440	20	21	700-04/1	NXP; class C
MHW720-2	12.5	440-470	20	21	700-04/1	NXP; class C
M57789	17	890-915	12	33.8	H3B	MI – Discontinued*
MHW912	12.5	880-915	12	40.8	301R-01/1	NXP; class AB
MHW820-3	12.5	870-950	18	17.1	301G-03/1	NXP; class C
HMC487LP5/E	7	9-12 GHz	2	20	25 mm^2 SMT	H

Manufacturer codes: H = Hittite; MI = Mitsubishi; NXP = NXP Semiconductors; T = Toshiba.
[†]For package shape, size and pin-connection information, see manufacturers' data sheets. See Tables of RF Power Transistors for manufacturers and URL for data sheets.
*Discontinued – no longer manufactured but may be found in older equipment and as surplus.

Table 22.37
Digital Logic Families

	Propagation Delay for C_L = 50 pF (ns)		Max Clock Frequency (MHz)	Power Dissipation (C_L = 0) @ 1 MHz (mW/gate)	Output Current @ 0.5 V max (mA)	Input Current (Max mA)	Threshold Voltage (V)	Supply Voltage (V)		
Type	Typ	Max						Min	Typ	Max
CMOS										
74AC	3	5.1	125	0.5	24	0	V+/2	2	5 or 3.3	6
74ACT	3	5.1	125	0.5	24	0	1.4	4.5	5	5.5
74HC	9	18	30	0.5	8	0	V+/2	2	5	6
74HCT	9	18	30	0.5	8	0	1.4	4.5	5	5.5
4000B/74C (10 V)	30	60	5	1.2	1.3	0	V+/2	3	5 - 15	18
4000B/74C (5V)	50	90	2	3.3	0.5	0	V+/2	3	5 - 15	18
TTL										
74AS	2	4.5	105	8	20	0.5	1.5	4.5	5	5.5
74F	3.5	5	100	5.4	20	0.6	1.6	4.75	5	5.25
74ALS	4	11	34	1.3	8	0.1	1.4	4.5	5	5.5
74LS	10	15	25	2	8	0.4	1.1	4.75	5	5.25
ECL										
ECL III	1.0	1.5	500	60	—	—	−1.3	−5.19	−5.2	−5.21
ECL 100K	0.75	1.0	350	40	—	—	−1.32	−4.2	−4.5	−5.2
ECL100KH	1.0	1.5	250	25	—	—	−1.29	−4.9	−5.2	−5.5
ECL 10K	2.0	2.9	125	25	—	—	−1.3	−5.19	−5.2	−5.21
GaAs										
10G	0.3	0.32	2700	125	—	—	−1.3	−3.3	−3.4	−3.5
10G	0.3	0.32	2700	125	—	—	−1.3	−5.1	−5.2	−5.5

Source: Horowitz (W1HFA) and Hill, *The Art of Electronics—2nd edition*, page 570. © Cambridge University Press 1980, 1989. Reprinted with the permission of Cambridge University Press.

Table 22.38
Operational Amplifiers (Op Amps)

Listed by device number

Device	Type	Freq Comp	Max Supply* (V)	Min Input Resistance (MΩ)	Max Offset Voltage (mV)	Min dc Open-Loop Gain (dB)	Min Output Current (mA)	Min Small-Signal Bandwidth (MHz)	Min Slew Rate (V/µs)	Notes
101A	Bipolar	ext	44	1.5	3.0	79	15	1.0	0.5	General purpose
108	Bipolar	ext	40	30	2.0	100	5	1.0		
124	Bipolar	int	32		5.0	100	5	1.0		Quad op amp, low power
148	Bipolar	int	44	0.8	5.0	90	10	1.0	0.5	Quad 741
158	Bipolar	int	32		5.0	100	5	1.0		Dual op amp, low power
301	Bipolar	ext	36	0.5	7.5	88	5	1.0	10	Bandwidth extendable with external components
324	Bipolar	int	32		7.0	100	10	1.0		Quad op amp, single supply
347	BiFET	ext	36	106	5.0	100	30	4	13	Quad, high speed
351	BiFET	ext	36	106	5.0	100	20	4	13	
353	BiFET	ext	36	106	5.0	100	15	4	13	
355	BiFET	ext	44	106	10.0	100	25	2.5	5	
355B	BiFET	ext	44	106	5.0	100	25	2.5	5	
356A	BiFET	ext	36	106	2.0	100	25	4.5	12	
356B	BiFET	ext	44	106	5.0	100	25	5.0	12	
357	BiFET	ext	36	106	10.0	100	25	20.0	50	
357B	BiFET	ext	36	106	5.0	100	25	20.0	30	
358	Bipolar	int	32		7.0	100	10	1.0		Dual op amp, single supply
411	BiFET	ext	36	106	2.0	100	20	4.0	15	Low offset, low drift
709	Bipolar	ext	36	0.05	7.5	84	5	0.3	0.15	
741	Bipolar	int	36	0.3	6.0	88	5	0.4	0.2	
741S	Bipolar	int	36	0.3	6.0	86	5	1.0	3	Improved 741 for AF
1436	Bipolar	int	68	10	5.0	100	17	1.0	2.0	High-voltage
1437	Bipolar	ext	36	0.050	7.5	90		1.0	0.25	Matched, dual 1709
1439	Bipolar	ext	36	0.100	7.5	100		1.0	34	
1456	Bipolar	int	44	3.0	10.0	100	9.0	1.0	2.5	
1458	Bipolar	int	36	0.3	6.0	100	20.0	0.5	3.0	Dual 1741
1458S	Bipolar	int	36	0.3	6.0	86	5.0	0.5	3.0	Improved 1458 for AF
1709	Bipolar	ext	36	0.040	6.0	80	10.0	1.0		
1741	Bipolar	int	36	0.3	5.0	100	20.0	1.0	0.5	
1747	Bipolar	int	44	0.3	6.0	100	25.0	1.0	0.5	Dual 1741
1748	Bipolar	ext	44	0.3	6.0	100	25.0	1.0	0.8	Non-compensated 1741
1776	Bipolar	int	36	50	5.0	110	5.0		0.35	Micro power, programmable
3140	BiFET	int	36	1.5×10^6	2.0	86	1	3.7	9	Strobable output
3403	Bipolar	int	36	0.3	10.0	80		1.0	0.6	Quad, low power
3405	Bipolar	ext	36		10.0	86	10	1.0	0.6	Dual op amp and dual comparator
3458	Bipolar	int	36	0.3	10.0	86	10	1.0	0.6	Dual, low power

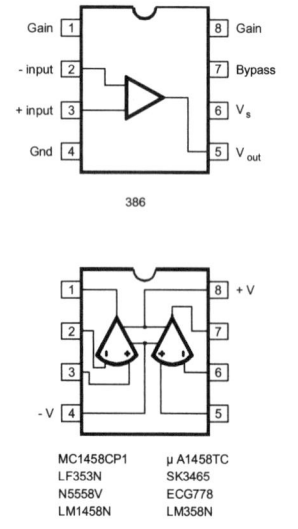

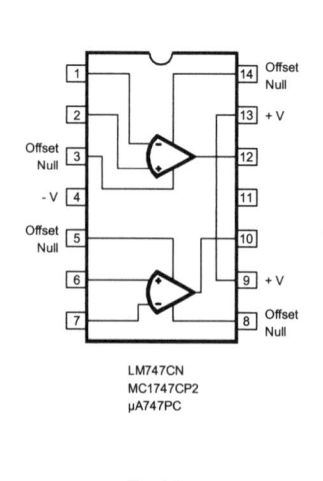

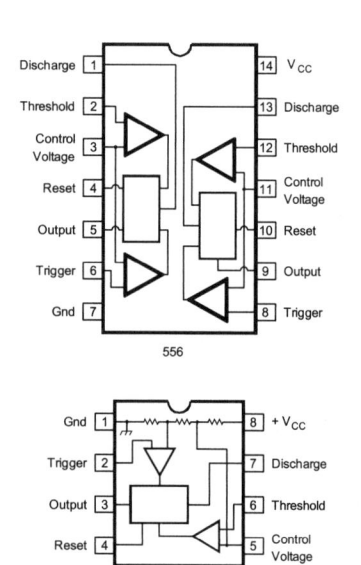

Device	Type	Freq Comp	Max Supply* (V)	Min Input Resistance (MΩ)	Max Offset Voltage (mV)	Min dc Open-Loop Gain (dB)	Min Output Current (mA)	Min Small-Signal Bandwidth (MHz)	Min Slew Rate (V/μs)	Notes
3476	Bipolar	int	36	5.0	6.0	92	12		0.8	
3900	Bipolar	int	32	1.0		65	0.5	4.0	0.5	Quad, Norton single supply
4558	Bipolar	int	44	0.3	5.0	88	10	2.5	1.0	Dual, wideband
4741	Bipolar	int	44	0.3	5.0	94	20	1.0	0.5	Quad 1741
5534	Bipolar	int	44	0.030	5.0	100	38	10.0	13	Low noise, can swing 20V P-P across 600
5556	Bipolar	int	36	1.0	12.0	88	5.0	0.5	1	Equivalent to 1456
5558	Bipolar	int	36	0.15	10.0	84	4.0	0.5	0.3	Dual, equivalent to 1458
34001	BiFET	int	44	106	2.0	94		4.0	13	JFET input
AD745	BiFET	int	±18	104	0.5	63	20	20	12.5	Ultra-low noise, high speed
LT1001	Precision op amp, low offset voltage (15 μV max), low drift (0.6 μV/°C max), low noise (0.3 μV p-p)									
LT1007	Extremely low noise (0.06 μV p-p), very high gain (20 x 10^6 into 2 kΩ load)									
LT1360	High speed, very high slew rate (800 V/μs), 50 MHz gain bandwidth, ±2.5 V to ±15 V supply range									
NE5514	Bipolar	int	±16	100	1		10	3	0.6	
NE5532	Bipolar	int	±20	0.03	4	47	10	10	9	Low noise
OP-27A	Bipolar	ext	44	1.5	0.025	115	5.0	1.7		Ultra-low noise, high speed
OP-37A	Bipolar	ext	44	1.5	0.025	115	45.0	11.0		
TL-071	BiFET	int	36	10^6	6.0	91	4.0	13.0		Low noise
TL-081	BiFET	int	36	10^6	6.0	88	4.0	8.0		
TL-082	BiFET	int	36	10^6	15.0	99	4.0	8.0		Low noise
TL-084	BiFET	int	36	10^6	15.0	88	4.0	8.0		Quad, high-performance AF
TLC27M2	CMOS	int	18	10^6	10	44	0.6	0.6		Low noise
TLC27M4	CMOS	int	18	10^6	10	44	0.6	0.6		Low noise

*From –V to +V terminals

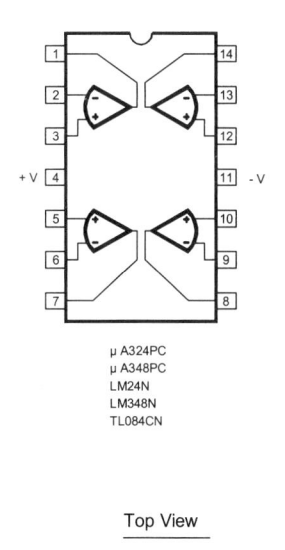

μA324PC
μA348PC
LM24N
LM348N
TL084CN

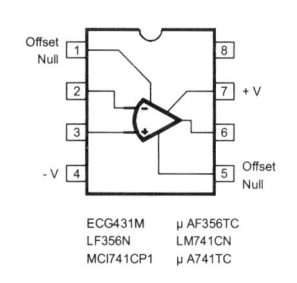

Top View

ECG431M   μAF356TC
LF356N   LM741CN
MCI741CP1 μA741TC

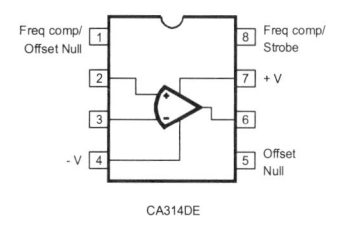

CA314DE

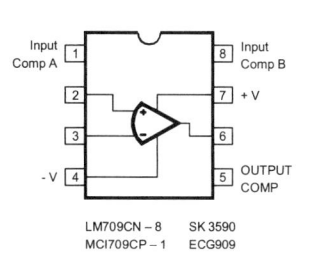

LM709CN – 8   SK 3590
MCI709CP – 1 ECG909

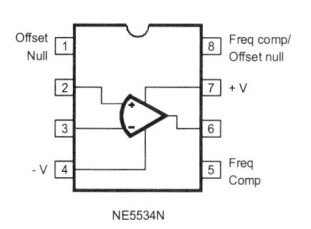

NE5534N

Component Data and References 22.33

22.7 Tubes, Wire, Materials, Attenuators, Miscellaneous

Table 22.39
Triode Transmitting Tubes

The full 1988 *Handbook* table of power tube specifications and base diagrams can be viewed in pdf format on the *ARRLWeb* at www.arrl.org/hf-tube-amplifiers.

Type	Power Diss.(W)	Plate (V)	Plate (mA)	Grid dc (mA)	Freq (MHz)	Ampl Factor	Fil (V)	Fil (A)	C_{IN} (pF)	C_{GP} (pF)	C_{OUT} (pF)	Base Diagram	Service Class[1]	Plate (V)	Grid (V)	Plate (mA)	Grid dc (mA)	Input (W)	P-P (kΩ)	Output (W)
5675	5	165	30	8	3000	20	6.3	0.135	2.3	1.3	0.09	Figure 21	GG0	120	−8	25	4	¾	—	0.05
2C40	6.5	500	25	—	500	36	6.3	0.75	2.1	1.3	0.05	Figure 11	CTO	250	−5	20	0.3	¾	—	0.075
5893	8.0	400	40	13	1000	27	6.0	0.33	2.5	1.75	0.07	Figure 21	CT	350	−33	35	13	2.4	—	6.5
													CP	300	−45	30	12	2.0	—	6.5
2C43	12	500	40	—	1250	48	6.3	0.9	2.9	1.7	0.05	Figure 11	CTO	470	—	38[7]	—	¾	—	9[2]
811-A	65	1000	175	50	60	160	6.3	4.0	5.9	5.6	0.7	3G	CT	1500	−70	173	40	7.1	—	200
													CP	1250	−120	140	45	10.0	—	135
													B/CG	1250	0	21/175	28	12	—	165
													AB_1	1250	0	27/175	13	3.0	—	155
812-A	65	1500	175	35	60	29	6.3	4.0	5.4	5.5	0.77	3G	CT	1500	−120	173	30	6.5	—	190
													CP	1250	−115	140	35	7.6	—	130
													B^2	1500	−48	28/310	270[4]	5.0	13.2	340
3CX100A5[6]	100	1000	125[5]	50	2500	100	6.0	1.05	7.0	2.15	0.035	—	AGG	800	−20	80	30	6	—	27
	70	600	100[5]										CP	600	−15	75	40	6	—	18
2C39	100	1000	60	40	500	100	6.3	1.1	6.5	1.95	0.03	—	G1C	600	−35	60	40	5.0	—	20
													CTO	900	−40	90	30	¾	—	40
													CP	600	−150	100[5]	50	¾	—	¾
AX9900, 5866	135	2500	200	40	150	25	6.3	5.4	5.8	5.5	0.1	Figure 3	CT	2500	−200	200	40	16	—	390
													CP	2000	−225	127	40	16	—	204
													B^2	2500	−90	80/330	350[4]	14[3]	15.68	560
572B	160	2750	275	—	—	170	6.3	4.0	—	—	—	3G	CT	1650	−70	165	32	6	—	205
T160L		2400											B/GG^2	2400	−2.0	90/500	—	100	—	600
8873	200	2200	250	—	500	160	6.3	3.2	19.5	7.0	0.03	Figure 87	AB_2	2000	—	22/500	98[3]	27[3]	—	505
8875	300	2200	250	—	500	160	6.3	3.2	19.5	7.0	0.03	—	AB_2	2000	—	22/500	98[3]	27[3]	—	505
833A	350	3300	500	100	30	35	10	10	12.3	6.3	8.5	Figure 41	CTO	2250	−125	445	85	23	—	780
													CTO	3000	−160	335	70	20	—	800
													CP	2500	−300	335	75	30	—	635
	450[6]	4000[6]	500	100	20[6]	35	10	10	12.3	6.3	8.5	Figure 41	CP	3000	−240	335	70	26	—	800
													B^2	3000	−70	100/750	400[4]	20[4]	9.5	1650
8874	400	2200	350	—	500	160	6.3	3.2	19.5	7.0	0.03	—	AB_2	2000	—	22/500	98[3]	27[3]	—	505
3-400Z	400	3000	400	—	110	200	5	14.5	7.4	4.1	0.07	Figure 3	B/GG	3000	0	100/333	120	32	—	655
3-500Z	500	4000	400	—	110	160	5	14.5	7.4	4.1	0.07	Figure 3	B/GG	3000	—	115	30	5	750
3-600Z	600	4000	425	—	110	165	5	15.0	7.8	4.6	0.08	Figure 3	B/GG	3000	—	370	115	33	—	810
													B/GG	3500	—	400	118	35	—	950
3CX800A7	800	2250	600	60	350	200	13.5	1.5	26	—	6.1	Figure 87	AB_2GG^7	2200	−8.2	500	36	16	—	750
3-1000Z	1000	3000	800	—	110	200	7.5	21.3	17	6.9	0.12	Figure 3	B/GG	3000	0	180/670	300	65	—	1360
3CX1200A7	1200	5000	800	—	110	200	7.5	21.0	20	12	0.2	Figure 3	AB_2GG	3600	−10	700	230	85	—	1500
8877	1500	4000	1000	—	250	200	5.0	10	42	10	0.1	—	AB_2	2500	−8.2	1000	—	57	—	1520

22.34 Chapter 22

Table 22-40
Tetrode Transmitting Tubes
Also see www.arrl.org/hf-tube-amplifiers.

[1]Service Class Abbreviations:
AB$_2$GD=AB$_2$ linear with 50-Ω passive grid circuit.
B=Class-B push-pull
CP=Class-C plate-modulated phone
CT=Class-C telegraph

GG=Grounded-grid (grid and screen connected together)
[2]Maximum signal value
[3]Peak grid-grid volts
[4]Forced-air cooling required.

[5]Two tubes triode-connected, G2 to G1 through 20kΩ to G2.
[6]Typical operation at 175 MHz.
[7]±1.5 V.
[8]Values are for two tubes.
[9]Single tone.

[10]24-Ω cathode resistance.
[11]Base same as 4CX250B. Socket is Russian SK2A.
[12]Socket is Russian SK1A.
[13]Socket is Russian SK3A.

Type	Max. Plate Diss. (W)	Max. Plate Volts (V)	Max. Screen Diss. (W)	Max. Screen Volts (V)	Max. Freq. (MHz)	Filament Volts (V)	Amps (A)	C$_{IN}$ (pF)	C$_{GP}$ (pF)	C$_{OUT}$ (pF)	Base	Serv. Class[1]	Plate (V)	Screen (V)	Grid (V)	Plate (mA)	Screen (mA)	Grid (mA)	P$_{IN}$ (W)	P-P (kΩ)	P$_{OUT}$ (W)
6146/	25	750	3	250	60	6.3	1.25	13	0.24	8.5	7CK	CT	500	170	−66	135	9	2.5	0.2	—	48
6146A												CT	700	160	−62	120	11	3.1	0.2	—	70
8032	25	750	3	250	60	12.6	0.585	13	0.24	8.5	7CK	CT[6]	400	190	−54	150	10.4	2.2	3.0	—	35
6883												CP	400	150	−87	112	7.8	3.4	0.4	—	32
												CP	600	150	−87	112	7.8	3.4	0.4	—	52
6159B/	25	750	3	250	60	26.5	0.3	13	0.24	8.5	7CK	AB$_2$[8]	600	190	−48	28/270	1.2/20	22	0.3	5	113
												AB$_2$[8]	750	165	−46	22/240	0.3/20	2.6[2]	0.4	7.4	131
												AB$_1$[8]	750	195	−50	23/220	1/26	100[3]	0	8	120
807, 807W	30	750	3.5	300	60	6.3	0.9	12	0.2	7	5AW	CT	750	250	−45	100	6	3.5	0.22	—	50
5933												CP	600	275	−90	100	6.5	4	0.4	—	42.5
												AB$_1$	750	300	−35	15/70	3/8	75[3]	0	—	72
1625	30	750	3.5	300	60	12.6	0.45	12	0.2	7	5AZ	B[5]	750	—	0	15/240	—	555[3]	5.3[2]	6.65	120
6146B	35	750	3	250	60	6.3	1.125	13	0.22	8.5	7CK	CT	750	200	−77	160	10	2.7	0.3	—	85
8298A												CP	600	175	−92	140	9.5	3.4	0.5	—	62
												AB$_1$	750	200	−48	24/125	6.3	—	—	3.5	61
813	125	2500	20	800	30	10.0	5.0	16.3	0.25	14.0	5BA	CTO	1250	300	−75	180	35	12	1.7	—	170
												CTO	2250	400	−155	220	40	15	4	—	375
												AB1	2500	750	−95	25/145	27[2]	0	0	—	245
												AB$_2$[8]	2000	750	−90	40/315	1.5/58	230[3]	0.1[2]	16	455
												AB$_2$[8]	2500	750	−95	35/260	1.2/55	235[3]	0.35[2]	17	650
4CX250B	250	2000	12	400	175	6.0	2.9	18.5	0.04	4.7	—	CTO	2000	250	−90	250	25	27	2.8	—	410
												CP	1500	250	−100	200	25	17	2.1	—	250
												AB$_1$[8]	2000	350	−50	500	30	100	—	8.26	650
4-400A	400[4]	4000	35	600	110	5.0	14.5	12.5	0.12	4.7	5BK	CT/CP	4000	300	−170	270	22.5	10	10	—	720
												GG	2500	0	0	80/270[9]	55[9]	100[9]	39[9]	4.0	435
												AB1	2500	750	−130	95/317	0/14	0	0	—	425
4CX400A	400	2500	8	400	500	6.3	3.2	24	0.08	7	See[11]	AB$_2$GD2200	325	−30	100/270	22	2	9	—	405
												AB$_2$GD2500	400	−35	100/400	18	1	13	—	610
4CX800A	800	2500	15	350	150	12.6	3.6	51	0.9	11	See[12]	AB$_2$GD2200	350	−56	160/550	24	1	32	—	750
4-1000A	1000	6000	75	1000	—	7.5	21	27.2	0.24	7.6	—	CT	3000	500	−150	700	146	38	11	—	1430
8166												CP	3000	500	−200	600	145	36	12	—	1390
												AB$_2$	4000	500	−60	300/1200	0/95	—	11	7	3000
												GG	3000	0	0	100/700[9]	105[9]	170[9]	130[9]	2.5	1475
4CX1000A	1000	3000	12	400	110	6.0	9.0	81.5	0.01	11.8	—	AB$_1$[8]	2000	325	−55	500/2000	−4/60	—	—	2.5	2160
												AB$_1$[8]	2500	325	−55	500/2000	−4/60	—	—	3.1	2920
												AB$_1$[8]	3000	325	−55	500/1800	−4/60	—	—	3.85	3360
4CX1500B	1500	3000	12	400	110	6.0	10.0	81.5	0.02	11.8	—	AB$_1$	2750	225	−34	300/755	−14/60	0.95	1.5	1.9	1100
4CX1600B	1600	3300	20	350	250	12.6	4.4	86	0.15	12	See[13]	AB$_2$GD2400	350	−53	500/1100	20	2	28	—	1600
												AB$_2$GD2400	350	−70	200/870	48	2	83[10]	—	1500
												AB$_2$GD3200	240	−57	200/740	21	1	33	—	1600

Table 22.41
EIA Vacuum-Tube Base Diagrams

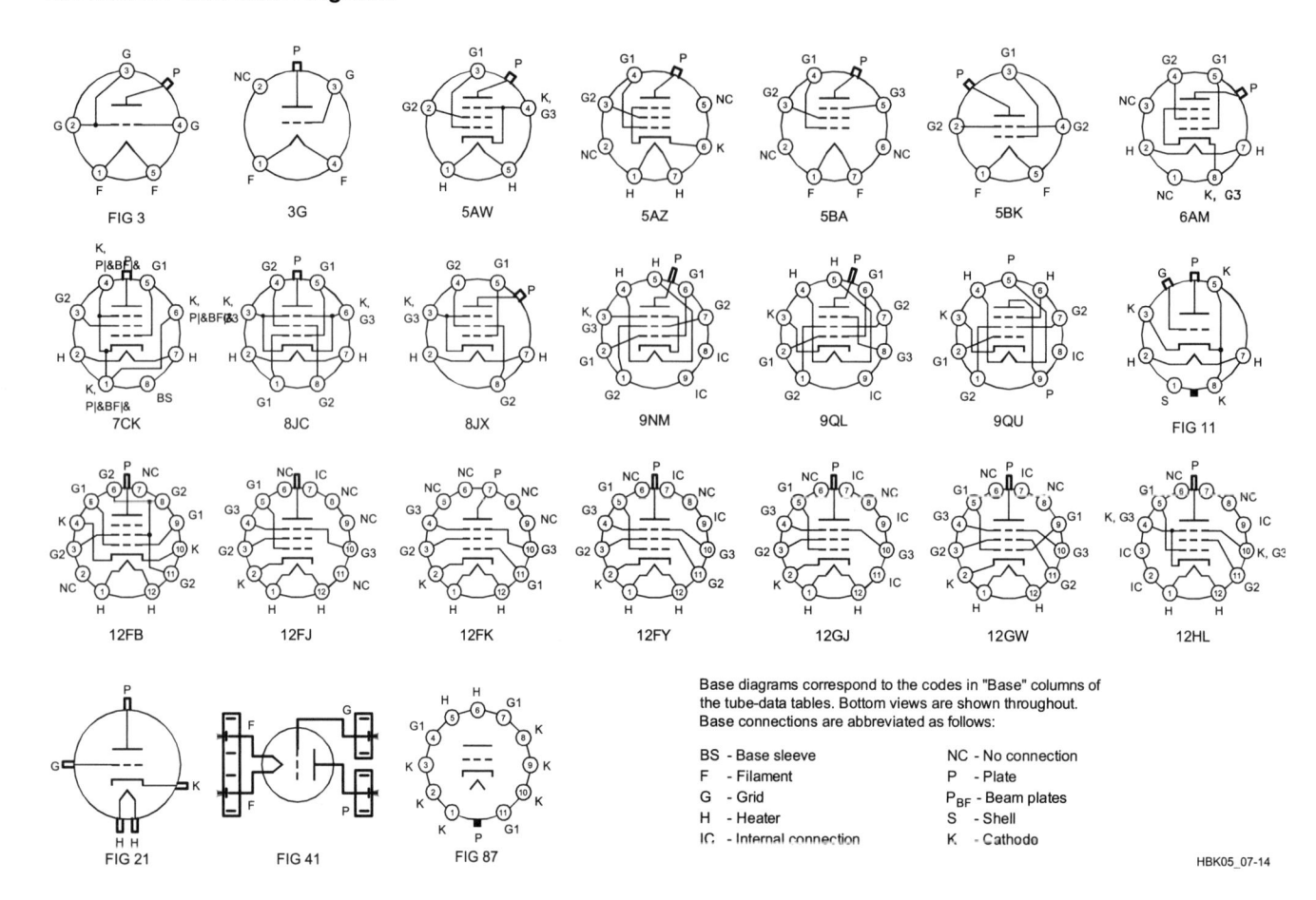

Base diagrams correspond to the codes in "Base" columns of the tube-data tables. Bottom views are shown throughout. Base connections are abbreviated as follows:

- BS – Base sleeve
- F – Filament
- G – Grid
- H – Heater
- IC – Internal connection
- NC – No connection
- P – Plate
- P_{BF} – Beam plates
- S – Shell
- K – Cathode

Alphabetical subscripts (D = diode, P = pentode, T = triode and HX = hexode) indicate structures in multistructure tubes. Subscript CT indicates filament or heater center tap.

Generally, when pin 1 of a metal-envelope tube (except all triodes) is shown connected to the envelope, pin 1 of a glass-envelope counterpart (suffix G or GT) is connected to an internal shield.

Table 22.42
Metal-Oxide Varistor (MOV) Transient Suppressors
Listed by voltage

Type No.	ECG/NTE†† no.	V acRMS	Maximum Applied Voltage V acPeak	Maximum Energy (Joules)	Maximum Peak Current (A)	Maximum Power (W)	Maximum Varistor Voltage (V)
V180ZA1	1V115	115	163	1.5	500	0.2	285
V180ZA10	2V115	115	163	10.0	2000	0.45	290
V130PA10A		130	184	10.0	4000	8.0	350
V130PA20A		130	184	20.0	4000	15.0	350
V130LA1	1V130	130	184	1.0	400	0.24	360
V130LA2	1V130	130	184	2.0	400	0.24	360
V130LA10A	2V130	130	184	10.0	2000	0.5	340
V130LA20A	524V13	130	184	20.0	4000	0.85	340
V150PA10A		150	212	10.0	4000	8.0	410
V150PA20A		150	212	20.0	4000	15.0	410
V150LA1	1V150	150	212	1.0	400	0.24	420
V150LA2	1V150	150	212	2.0	400	0.24	420
V150LA10A	524V15	150	212	10.0	2000	0.5	390
V150LA20A	524V15	150	212	20.0	4000	0.85	390
V250PA10A		250	354	10.0	4000	0.85	670
V250PA20A		250	354	20.0	4000	7.0	670
V250PA40A		250	354	40.0	4000	13.0	670
V250LA2	1V250	250	354	2.0	400	0.28	690
V250LA4	1V250	250	354	4.0	400	0.28	690
V250LA15A	2V250	250	354	15.0	2000	0.6	640
V250LA20A	2V250	250	354	20.0	2000	0.6	640
V250LA40A	524V25	250	354	40.0	4000	0.9	640

††ECG and NTE numbers for these parts are identical, except for the prefix. Add the "ECG" or "NTE" prefix to the numbers shown for the complete part number.

Table 22.43
Crystal Holders

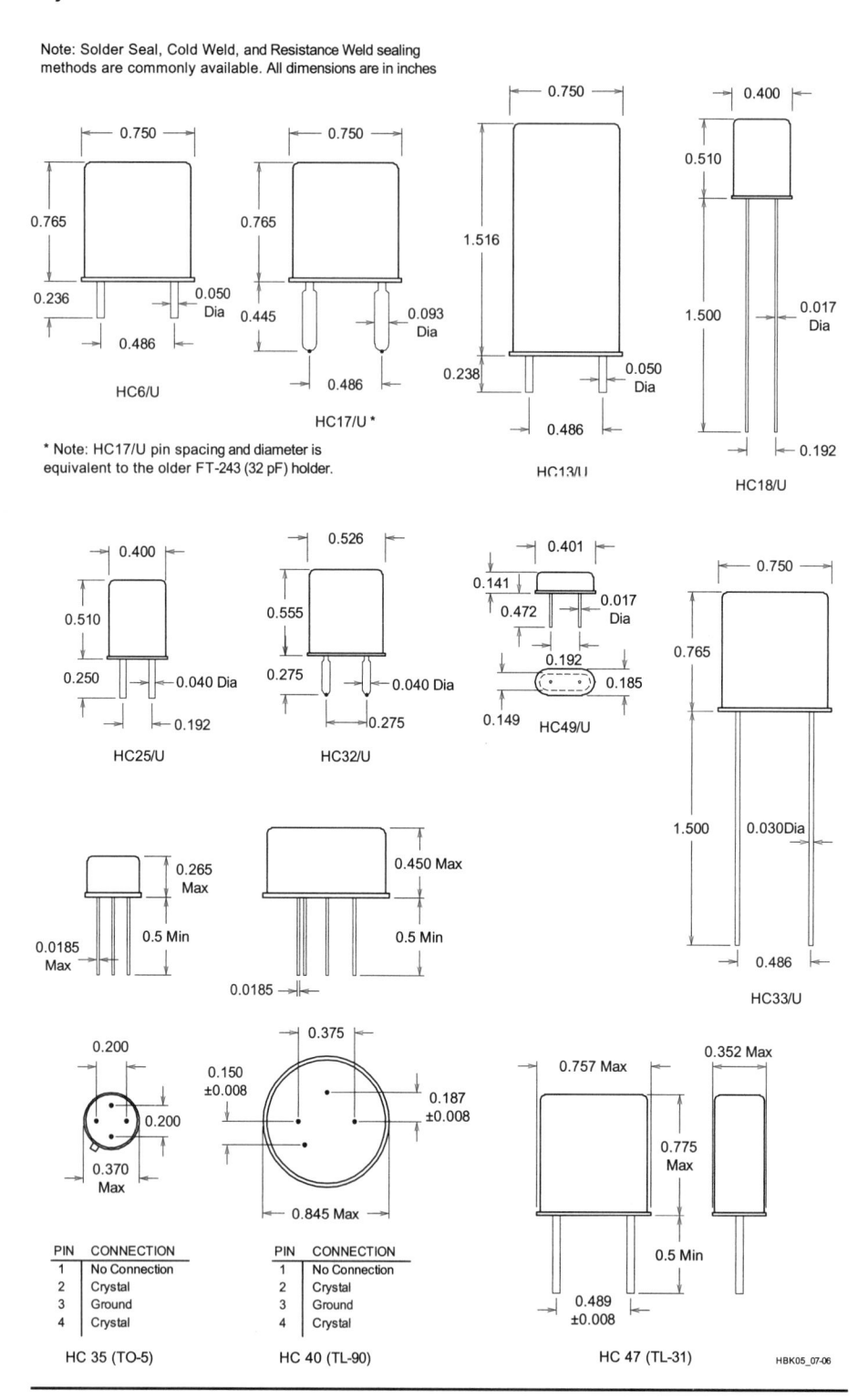

Note: Solder Seal, Cold Weld, and Resistance Weld sealing methods are commonly available. All dimensions are in inches

HC6/U: 0.750 wide, 0.765 tall, 0.236, 0.050 Dia, 0.486

HC17/U*: 0.750 wide, 0.765 tall, 0.445, 0.093 Dia, 0.486

* Note: HC17/U pin spacing and diameter is equivalent to the older FT-243 (32 pF) holder.

HC13/U: 0.750 wide, 1.516 tall, 0.238, 0.050 Dia, 0.486

HC18/U: 0.400 wide, 0.510 tall, 1.500, 0.017 Dia, 0.192

HC25/U: 0.400 wide, 0.510 tall, 0.250, 0.040 Dia, 0.192

HC32/U: 0.526 wide, 0.555 tall, 0.275, 0.040 Dia, 0.275

HC49/U: 0.401 wide, 0.141, 0.472, 0.017 Dia, 0.192, 0.185, 0.149

HC33/U: 0.750 wide, 0.765 tall, 1.500, 0.030 Dia, 0.486

0.265 Max, 0.0185 Max, 0.5 Min

0.450 Max, 0.5 Min, 0.0185

HC 35 (TO-5): 0.200, 0.200, 0.370 Max

PIN	CONNECTION
1	No Connection
2	Crystal
3	Ground
4	Crystal

HC 40 (TL-90): 0.375, 0.150 ±0.008, 0.187 ±0.008, 0.845 Max

PIN	CONNECTION
1	No Connection
2	Crystal
3	Ground
4	Crystal

HC 47 (TL-31): 0.757 Max, 0.352 Max, 0.775 Max, 0.5 Min, 0.489 ±0.008

HBK05_07-06

Table 22.44
Copper Wire Specifications
Bare and Enamel-Coated Wire

One mil = 0.001 inch

Wire Size (AWG)	Diam (Mils)	Area (CM[1])	Enamel Wire Coating Turns / Linear inch[2] Single	Heavy	Triple	Feet per Pound Bare	Ohms per 1000 ft 25° C	Current Carrying Capacity Continuous Duty[3] at 700 CM per Amp[4]	Open air	Conduit or bundles	Nearest British SWG No.
1	289.3	83694.49				3.948	0.1239	119.564			1
2	257.6	66357.76				4.978	0.1563	94.797			2
3	229.4	52624.36				6.277	0.1971	75.178			4
4	204.3	41738.49				7.918	0.2485	59.626			5
5	181.9	33087.61				9.98	0.3134	47.268			6
6	162.0	26244.00				12.59	0.3952	37.491			7
7	144.3	20822.49				15.87	0.4981	29.746			8
8	128.5	16512.25				20.01	0.6281	23.589			9
9	114.4	13087.36				25.24	0.7925	18.696			11
10	101.9	10383.61				31.82	0.9987	14.834			12
11	90.7	8226.49				40.16	1.2610	11.752			13
12	80.8	6528.64				50.61	1.5880	9.327			13
13	72.0	5184.00				63.73	2.0010	7.406			15
14	64.1	4108.81	15.2	14.8	14.5	80.39	2.5240	5.870	32	17	15
15	57.1	3260.41	17.0	16.6	16.2	101.32	3.1810	4.658			16
16	50.8	2580.64	19.1	18.6	18.1	128	4.0180	3.687	22	13	17
17	45.3	2052.09	21.4	20.7	20.2	161	5.0540	2.932			18
18	40.3	1624.09	23.9	23.2	22.5	203.5	6.3860	2.320	16	10	19
19	35.9	1288.81	26.8	25.9	25.1	256.4	8.0460	1.841			20
20	32.0	1024.00	29.9	28.9	27.9	322.7	10.1280	1.463	11	7.5	21
21	28.5	812.25	33.6	32.4	31.3	406.7	12.7700	1.160			22
22	25.3	640.09	37.6	36.2	34.7	516.3	16.2000	0.914		5	22
23	22.6	510.76	42.0	40.3	38.6	646.8	20.3000	0.730			24
24	20.1	404.01	46.9	45.0	42.9	817.7	25.6700	0.577			24
25	17.9	320.41	52.6	50.3	47.8	1031	32.3700	0.458			26
26	15.9	252.81	58.8	56.2	53.2	1307	41.0200	0.361			27
27	14.2	201.64	65.8	62.5	59.2	1639	51.4400	0.288			28
28	12.6	158.76	73.5	69.4	65.8	2081	65.3100	0.227			29
29	11.3	127.69	82.0	76.9	72.5	2587	81.2100	0.182			31
30	10.0	100.00	91.7	86.2	80.6	3306	103.7100	0.143			33
31	8.9	79.21	103.1	95.2		4170	130.9000	0.113			34
32	8.0	64.00	113.6	105.3		5163	162.0000	0.091			35
33	7.1	50.41	128.2	117.6		6553	205.7000	0.072			36
34	6.3	39.69	142.9	133.3		8326	261.3000	0.057			37
35	5.6	31.36	161.3	149.3		10537	330.7000	0.045			38
36	5.0	25.00	178.6	166.7		13212	414.8000	0.036			39
37	4.5	20.25	200.0	181.8		16319	512.1000	0.029			40
38	4.0	16.00	222.2	204.1		20644	648.2000	0.023			
39	3.5	12.25	256.4	232.6		26969	846.6000	0.018			
40	3.1	9.61	285.7	263.2		34364	1079.2000	0.014			
41	2.8	7.84	322.6	294.1		42123	1323.0000	0.011			
42	2.5	6.25	357.1	333.3		52854	1659.0000	0.009			
43	2.2	4.84	400.0	370.4		68259	2143.0000	0.007			
44	2.0	4.00	454.5	400.0		82645	2593.0000	0.006			
45	1.8	3.10	526.3	465.1		106600	3348.0000	0.004			
46	1.6	2.46	588.2	512.8		134000	4207.0000	0.004			

Teflon Coated, Stranded Wire
(As supplied by Belden Wire and Cable)

Turns per Linear inch[2]
UL Style No.

Size	Strands[5]	1180	1213	1371
16	19×29	11.2		
18	19×30	12.7		
20	7×28	14.7	17.2	
20	19×32	14.7	17.2	
22	19×34	16.7	20.0	23.8
22	7×30	16.7	20.0	23.8
24	19×36	18.5	22.7	27.8
24	7×32		22.7	27.8
26	7×34		25.6	32.3
28	7×36		28.6	37.0
30	7×38		31.3	41.7
32	7×40			47.6

Notes
[1] A circular mil (CM) is a unit of area equal to that of a one-mil-diameter circle ($\pi/4$ square mils). The CM area of a wire is the square of the mil diameter.
[2] Figures given are approximate only; insulation thickness varies with manufacturer.
[3] Maximum wire temperature of 212°F (100°C) with a maximum ambient temperature of 135°F (57°C) as specified by the manufacturer. The *National Electrical Code* or local building codes may differ.
[4] 700 CM per ampere is a satisfactory design figure for small transformers, but values from 500 to 1000 CM are commonly used. The *National Electrical Code* or local building codes may differ.
[5] Stranded wire construction is given as "count" × "strand size" (AWG).

Table 22.45
Standard vs American Wire Gauge

SWG	Diam (in.)	Nearest AWG
12	0.104	10
14	0.08	12
16	0.064	14
18	0.048	16
20	0.036	19
22	0.028	21
24	0.022	23
26	0.018	25
28	0.0148	27
30	0.0124	28
32	0.0108	29
34	0.0092	31
36	0.0076	32
38	0.006	34
40	0.0048	36
42	0.004	38
44	0.0032	40
46	0.0024	—

Table 22.46
Antenna Wire Strength

American Wire Gauge	Recommended Tension[1] (pounds) Copper-clad steel[2]	Hard-drawn copper	Weight (pounds per 1000 feet) Copper-clad steel[2]	Hard-drawn copper
4	495	214	115.8	126
6	310	130	72.9	79.5
8	195	84	45.5	50
10	120	52	28.8	31.4
12	75	32	18.1	19.8
14	50	20	11.4	12.4
16	31	13	7.1	7.8
18	19	8	4.5	4.9
20	12	5	2.8	3.1

[1]Approximately one-tenth the breaking load. Might be increased 50% if end supports are firm and there is no danger of ice loading.
[2]"Copperweld," 40% copper.

Table 22.47
Guy Wire Lengths to Avoid

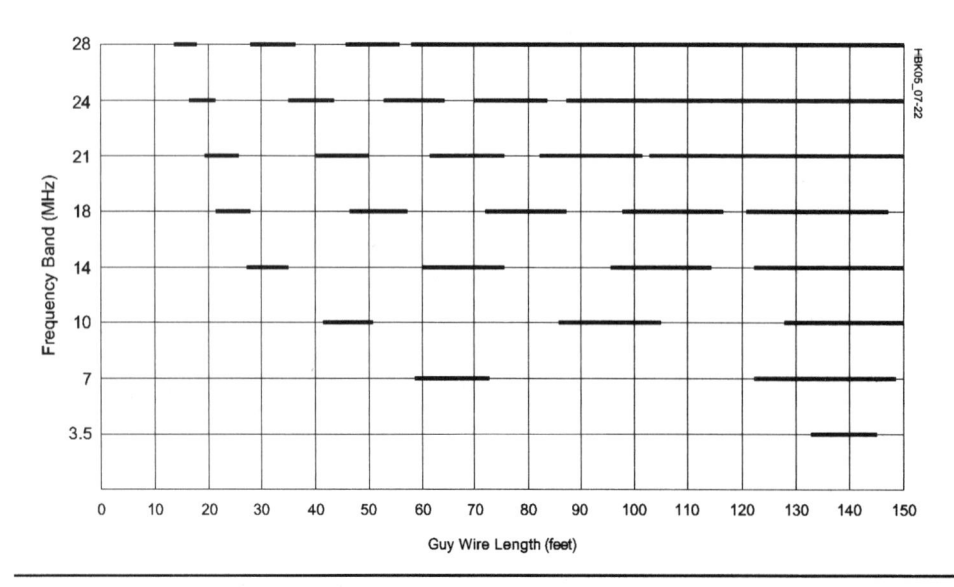

The black bars indicate ungrounded guy wire lengths to avoid for the eight HF amateur bands. This chart is based on resonance within 10% of any frequency in the band. Grounded wires will exhibit resonance at odd multiples of a quarter wavelength. *(Jerry Hall, K1TD)*

Table 22.48
Aluminum Alloy Specifications

Common Alloy Numbers

Type	Characteristic
2024	Good formability, high strength
5052	Excellent surface finish, excellent corrosion resistance, normally not heat treatable for high strength
6061	Good machinability, good weldability, can be brittle at high tempers
7075	Good formability, high strength

General Uses

Type	Uses
2024-T3	Chassis boxes, antennas, anything that will be bent or flexed repeatedly
7075-T3	
6061-T6	Mounting plates, welded assemblies or machined parts

Common Tempers

Type	Characteristics
T0	Special soft condition
T3	Hard
T6	Very hard, possibly brittle
TXXX	Three digit tempers—usually specialized high-strength heat treatments, similar to T6

Table 22.49
Impedance of Two-Conductor Twisted Pair Lines

Twists per Inch

Wire Size	2.5	5	7.5	10	12.5
#20	43	39	35		
#22	46	41	39	37	32
#24	60	45	44	43	41
#26	65	57	54	48	47
#28	74	53	51	49	47
#30			49	46	47

Measured in ohms at 14.0 MHz.

This illustrates the impedance of various two-conductor lines as a function of the wire size and number of twists per inch.

Table 22.50
Attenuation per Foot of Two-Conductor Twisted Pair Lines

Twists per Inch

Wire Size	2.5	5	7.5	10	12.5
#20	0.11	0.11	0.12		
#22	0.11	0.12	0.12	0.12	0.12
#24	0.11	0.12	0.12	0.13	0.13
#26	0.11	0.13	0.13	0.13	0.13
#28	0.11	0.13	0.13	0.16	0.16
#30			0.25	0.27	0.27

Measured in decibels at 14.0 MHz.

Attenuation in dB per foot for the same lines as shown above.

Table 22.51
Large Machine-Wound Coil Specifications

Coil Dia, Inches	Turns Per Inch	Inductance in μH Per Inch
1¼	4	2.75
	6	6.3
	8	11.2
	10	17.5
	16	42.5
1½	4	3.9
	6	8.8
	8	15.6
	10	24.5
	16	63
1¾	4	5.2
	6	11.8
	8	21
	10	33
	16	85
2	4	6.6
	6	15
	8	26.5
	10	42
	16	108
2½	4	10.2
	6	23
	8	41
	10	64
3	4	14
	6	31.5
	8	56
	10	89

Table 22.53
Small Machine-Wound Coil Specifications

Coil Dia, Inches	Turns Per Inch	Inductance in μH Per Inch
½ (A)	4	0.18
	6	0.40
	8	0.72
	10	1.12
	16	2.8
	32	12
⅝ (A)	4	0.28
	6	0.62
	8	1.1
	10	1.7
	16	4.4
	32	18
¾ (B)	4	0.6
	6	1.35
	8	2.4
	10	3.8
	16	9.9
	32	40
1 (B)	4	1.0
	6	2.3
	8	4.2
	10	6.6
	16	16.9
	32	68

Table 22.52
Inductance Factor for Large Machine-Wound Coils

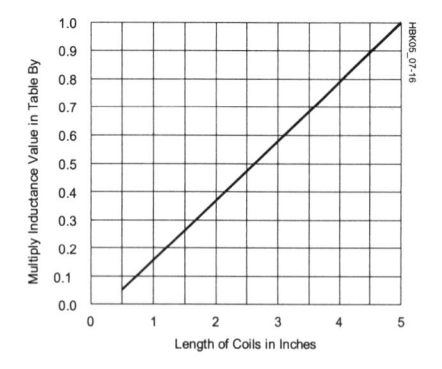

Factor to be applied to the inductance of large coils for coil lengths up to 5 inches.

Table 22.54
Inductance Factor for Small Machine-Wound Coils

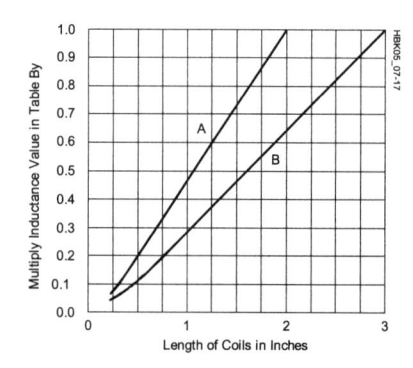

Factor to be applied to the inductance of small coils as a function of coil length. Use curve A for coils marked A, and curve B for coils marked B.

Table 22.55
Measured Inductance for #12 AWG Wire Windings

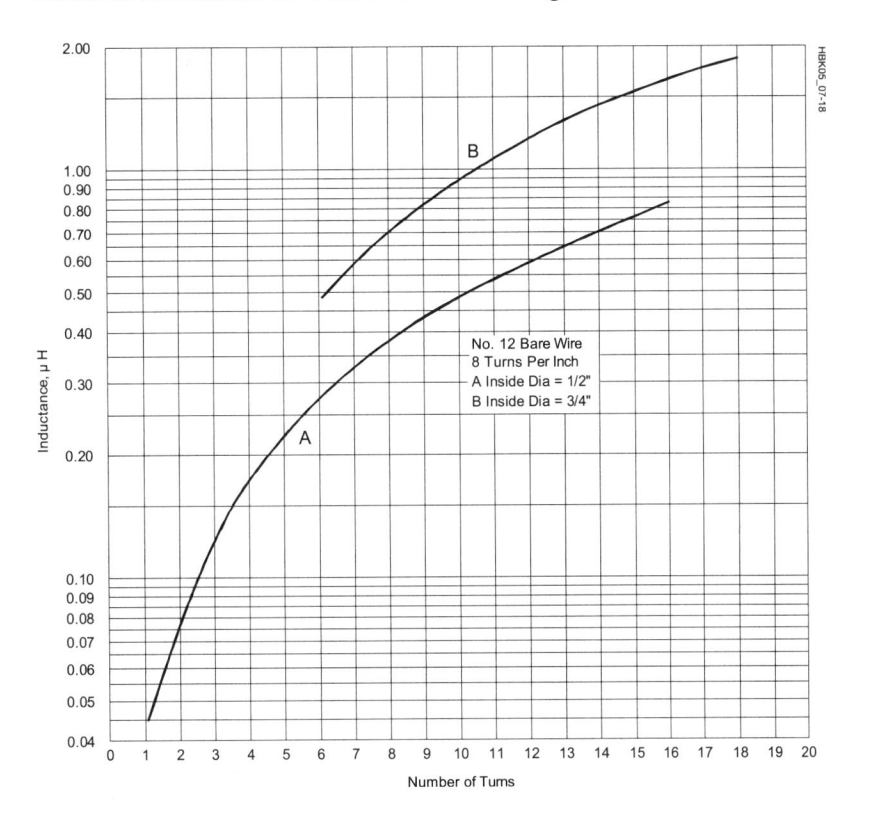

No. 12 Bare Wire
8 Turns Per Inch
A Inside Dia = 1/2"
B Inside Dia = 3/4"

Values are for inductors with half-inch leads and wound with eight turns per inch.

Table 22.56
Relationship Between Noise Figure and Noise Temperature

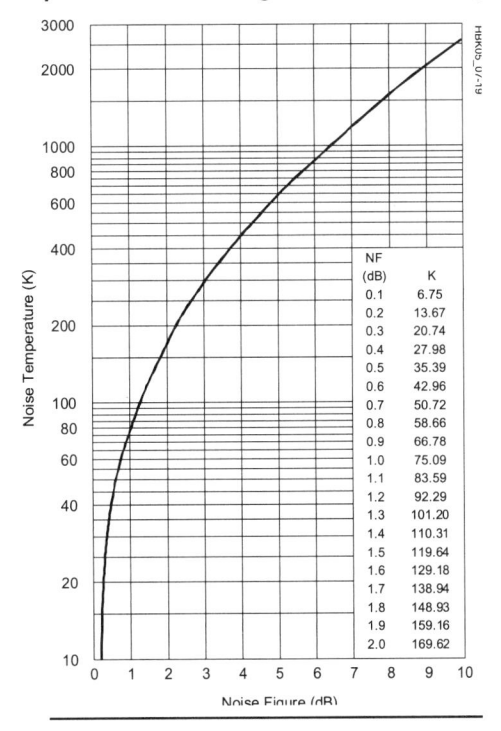

NF (dB)	K
0.1	6.75
0.2	13.67
0.3	20.74
0.4	27.98
0.5	35.39
0.6	42.96
0.7	50.72
0.8	58.66
0.9	66.78
1.0	75.09
1.1	83.59
1.2	92.29
1.3	101.20
1.4	110.31
1.5	119.64
1.6	129.18
1.7	138.94
1.8	148.93
1.9	159.16
2.0	169.62

Table 22.57
Pi-Network Resistive Attenuators (50 Ω)

dB Atten.	R1 (Ohms)	R2 (Ohms)
1.0	870	5.77
2.0	436	11.6
3.0	292	17.6
4.0	221	23.8
5.0	178	30.4
6.0	150	37.4
7.0	131	44.8
8.0	116	52.8
9.0	105	61.6
10.0	96.2	71.2
11.0	89.2	81.7
12.0	83.5	93.2
13.0	78.8	106
14.0	74.9	120
15.0	71.6	136
16.0	68.8	154
17.0	66.4	173
18.0	64.4	195
19.0	62.6	220
20.0	61.1	248
21.0	59.8	278
22.0	58.6	313
23.0	57.6	352
24.0	56.7	395
25.0	56.0	443
30.0	53.2	790
35.0	51.8	1405
40.0	51.0	2500
45.0	50.5	4446
50.0	50.3	7906
55.0	50.2	14,058
60.0	50.1	25,000

An RF Step Attenuator project is shown in the Test Equipment and Measurements chapter of this *Handbook*, and a Low Power Step Attenuator PC board is available from FAR Circuits at **www.farcircuits.net/test2.htm**.

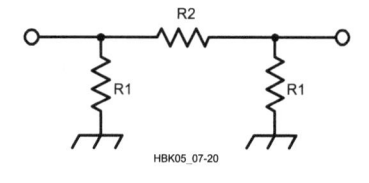

Table 22.58
T-Network Resistive Attenuators (50 Ω)

dB Atten.	R1 (Ohms)	R2 (Ohms)
1.0	2.88	433
2.0	5.73	215
3.0	8.55	142
4.0	11.3	105
5.0	14.0	82.2
6.0	16.6	66.9
7.0	19.1	55.8
8.0	21.5	47.3
9.0	23.8	40.6
10.0	26.0	35.1
11.0	28.0	30.6
12.0	30.0	26.8
13.0	31.7	23.5
14.0	33.3	20.8
15.0	35.0	18.4
16.0	36.3	16.2
17.0	37.6	14.4
18.0	38.8	12.8
19.0	40.0	11.4
20.0	41.0	10.0
21.0	41.8	9.0
22.0	42.6	8.0
23.0	43.4	7.1
24.0	44.0	6.3
25.0	44.7	5.6
30.0	47.0	3.2
35.0	48.2	1.8
40.0	49.0	1.0
45.0	49.4	0.56
50.0	49.7	0.32
55.0	49.8	0.18
60.0	49.9	0.10

22.8 Computer Connectors

Most connections between computers and their peripherals are made with some form of multi-conductor cable. Examples include shielded, unshielded and ribbon cable. **Table 22.59** shows a variety of computer connectors and pin outs, including some used for internal connections, such as power supplies and disk drives.

Table 22.59
Computer Connector Pinouts

Parallel Port (DB 25 pin) Female

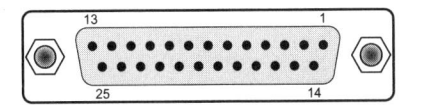

Pin	Signal	Pin	Signal
1	Strobe	10	Acknowledge
2	Data 0	11	Busy
3	Data 1	12	Paper Empty
4	Data 2	13	Select
5	Data 3	14	Auto Feed
6	Data 4	15	Error
7	Data 5	16	Initialize
8	Data 6	17	Select In
9	Data 7	18-25	GND

Serial Port (DB 9 pin) Male

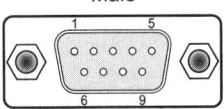

Pin	Signal
1	DCD (Data Carrier Detect)
2	RxD (Receive Data)
3	TxD (Transmit Data)
4	DTR (Data Terminal Ready)
5	GND (Signal Ground)
6	DSR (Data Set Ready)
7	RTS (Request To Send)
8	CTS (Clear To Send)
9	RI (Ring Indicator)

Serial Port (DB 25 pin) Male

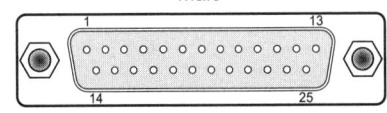

Pin	Signal	Pin	Signal
1	N/C (not connected)	20	DTR (Data Terminal Ready)
2	TxD (Transmit Data)	21	N/C
3	RxD (Receive Data)	22	RI (Ring Indicator)
4	RTS (Request To Send)	23	N/C
5	CTS (Clear To Send)	24	N/C
6	DSR (Data Set Ready)	25	N/C
7	GND (Signal Ground)		
8	DCD (Data Carrier Detect)		
9-19	N/C		

Plug (end views)

USB Type A, **USB Type B**

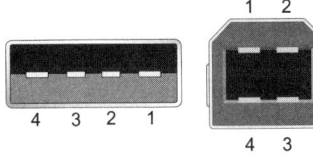

Pin	Signal
1	VBUS (+5 V)
2	D− (Data −)
3	D+ (Data +)
4	GND (Ground)

Pin	Signal
1	VBUS (+5 V)
2	D− (Data −)
3	D+ (Data +)
4	ID (host = GND; slave = N/C)
5	GND (Signal Ground)

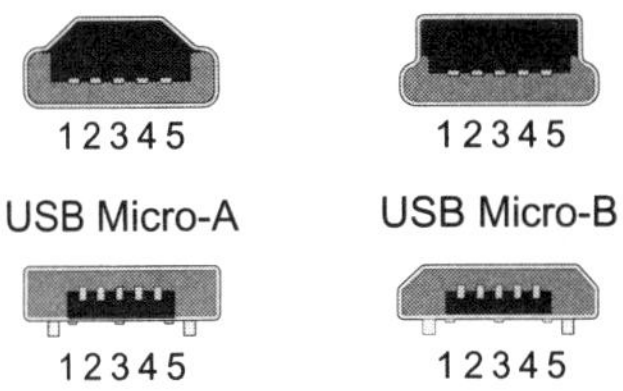

USB Mini-A, **USB Mini-B**, **USB Micro-A**, **USB Micro-B**

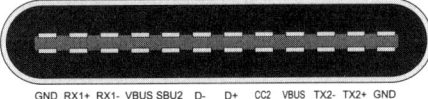

USB Type-C approximate size 0.33 x 0.10 in. (8.4 x 2.6 mm)

USB Type-C plug (end view)

A12 A11 A10 A9 A8 A7 A6 A5 A4 A3 A2 A1
GND RX2+ RX2− VBUS SBU1 D− D+ CC1 VBUS TX1− TX1+ GND

GND TX2+ TX2− VBUS VCONN SBU2 VBUS RX1− RX1+ GND
B1 B2 B3 B4 B5 B6 B7 B8 B9 B10 B11 B12

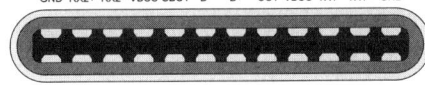

USB Type-C receptacle (end view)

A1 A2 A3 A4 A5 A6 A7 A8 A9 A10 A11 A12
GND TX1+ TX1− VBUS CC1 D+ D− SBU1 VBUS RX2− RX2+ GND

GND RX1+ RX1− VBUS SBU2 D− D+ CC2 VBUS TX2− TX2+ GND
B12 B11 B10 B9 B8 B7 B6 B5 B4 B3 B2 B1

Type-C plug and receptacle pinouts

Pin	Name	Description	Pin	Name	Description
A1	GND	Ground return	B12	GND	Ground return
A2	SSTXp1	SuperSpeed differential pair #1, TX, positive	B11	SSRXp1	SuperSpeed differential pair #2, RX, positive
A3	SSTXn1	SuperSpeed differential pair #1, TX, negative	B10	SSRXn1	SuperSpeed differential pair #2, RX, negative
A4	VBUS	Bus power	B9	VBUS	Bus power
A5	CC1	Configuration channel	B8	SBU2	Sideband use (SBU)
A6	D+	Non-SuperSpeed differential pair, position 1, positive	B7	D−	Non-SuperSpeed differential pair, position 2, negative*
A7	D−	Non-SuperSpeed differential pair, position 1, negative	B6	D+	Non-SuperSpeed differential pair, position 2, positive*
A8	SBU1	Sideband use (SBU)	B5	CC2	Configuration channel
A9	VBUS	Bus power	B4	VBUS	Bus power
A10	SSRXn2	SuperSpeed differential pair #4, RX, negative	B3	SSTXn2	SuperSpeed differential pair #3, TX, negative
A11	SSRXp2	SuperSpeed differential pair #4, RX, positive	B2	SSTXp2	SuperSpeed differential pair #3, TX, positive
A12	GND	Ground return	B1	GND	Ground return

*There is only a single Non-SuperSpeed differential pair in the cable. This pin is not connected in the plug/cable.

Ethernet Connector (RJ45-8 pin) Female

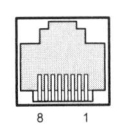

Pin	Signal
1	Output Transmit Data (+)
2	Output Transmit Data (−)
3	Input Receive Data (+)
4	N/C (not connected)
5	N/C
6	Input Receive Data (−)
7	N/C
8	N/C

Disk Drive, CD and Other Device Power Connector Viewed from Connector End

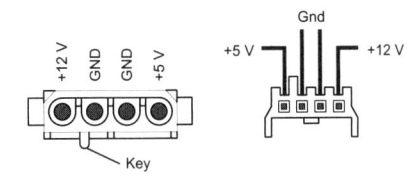

PC-ATX Type Power Connector Viewed from Connector End

Note: All figures not drawn to same scale.

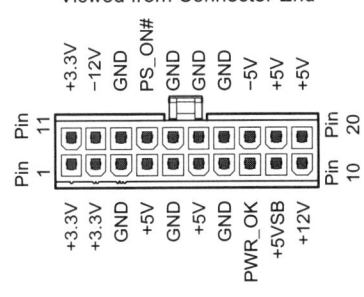

HBK0870

22.9 RF Connectors and Transmission Lines

There are many different types of transmission lines and RF connectors for coaxial cable, but the three most common for amateur use are the UHF, Type N and BNC families. The type of connector used for a specific job depends on the size of the cable, the frequency of operation and the power levels involved. **Table 22.60** shows the characteristics of many popular transmission lines, while **Table 22.61** details coax connectors.

22.9.1 UHF Connectors

The so-called UHF connector (the series name is not related to frequency) is found on most HF and some VHF equipment. It is the only connector many hams will ever see on coaxial cable. PL-259 is another name for the UHF male, and the female is also known as the SO-239. These connectors are rated for full legal amateur power at HF. They are poor for UHF work because they do not present a constant impedance, so the UHF label is a misnomer. PL-259 connectors are designed to fit RG-8 and RG-11 size cable (0.405-inch OD). Adapters are available for use with smaller RG-58, RG-59 and RG-8X size cable. UHF connectors are not weatherproof.

Figure 22.19 shows how to install the solder type of PL-259 on RG-8 cable. Proper preparation of the cable end is the key to success. Follow these simple steps. Measure back about ¾-inch from the cable end and slightly score the outer jacket around its circumference. With a sharp knife, cut through the outer jacket, through the braid and through the dielectric — almost to the center conductor. Be careful not to score the center conductor. Cutting through all outer layers at once keeps the braid from separating. (Using a coax stripping tool with preset blade depth makes this and subsequent trimming steps much easier.)

Pull the severed outer jacket, braid and dielectric off the end of the cable as one piece. Inspect the area around the cut, looking for any strands of braid hanging loose and snip them off. There won't be any if your knife was sharp enough. Next, score the outer jacket about 5⁄16-inch back from the first cut. Cut through the jacket lightly; do not score the braid. This step takes practice. If you score the braid, start again. Remove the outer jacket.

Tin the exposed braid and center conductor, but apply the solder sparingly and avoid melting the dielectric. Slide the coupling ring onto the cable. Screw the connector body onto the cable. If you prepared the cable to the right dimensions, the center conductor will protrude through the center pin, the braid will show through the solder holes, and the body will actually thread onto the outer cable jacket. A very small amount of lubricant on the cable jacket will help the threading process.

Solder the braid through the solder holes. Solder through all four holes; poor connection

Figure 22.20 — Installing PL-259 plugs on RG-58 or RG-59 cable requires the use of UG-175 or UG-176 adapters, respectively. The adapter screws into the plug body using the threads of the connector that grip the jacket on larger cables. (*Courtesy Amphenol Electronic Components*)

83-1SP (PL-259) Plug with adapters (UG-176/U OR UG-175/U)

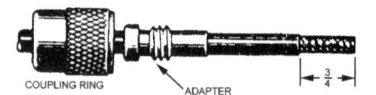

1. Cut end of cable even. Remove vinyl jacket 3/4" - don't nick braid. Slide coupling ring and adapter on cable.

2. Fan braid slightly and fold back over cable.

3. Position adapter to dimension shown. Press braid down over body of adapter and trim to 3/8". Bare 5/8" of conductor. Tin exposed center conductor.

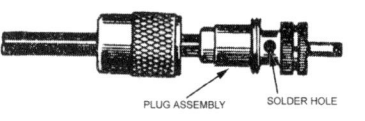

4. Screw the plug assembly on adapter. Solder braid to shell through solder holes. Solder conductor to contact sleeve.

5. Screw coupling ring on plug assembly.

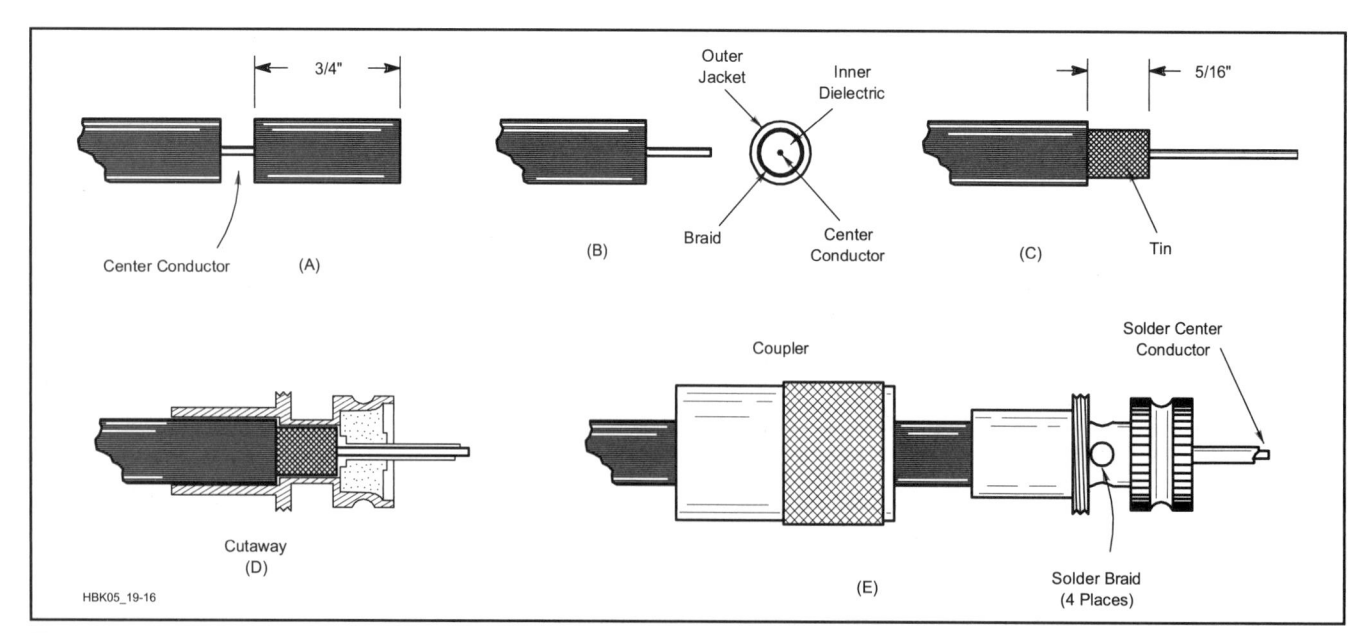

Figure 22.19 — The PL-259, or UHF, connector is almost universal for amateur HF work and is popular for equipment operating in the VHF range. Steps A through E are described in detail in the text.

to the braid is the most common form of PL-259 failure. A good connection between connector and braid is just as important as that between the center conductor and connector. Use a large soldering iron for this job. With practice, you'll learn how much heat to use. If you use too little heat, the solder will bead up, not really flowing onto the connector body. If you use too much heat, the dielectric will melt, letting the braid and center conductor touch. Most PL-259s are nickel plated, but silver-plated connectors are much easier to solder and only slightly more expensive.

Solder the center conductor to the center pin. The solder should flow on the inside, not the outside, of the center pin. If you wait until the connector body cools off from soldering the braid, you'll have less trouble with the dielectric melting. Trim the center conductor to be even with the end of the center pin. Use a small file to round the end, removing any solder that built up on the outer surface of the center pin. Use a sharp knife, very fine sandpaper or steel wool to remove any solder flux from the outer surface of the center pin. Screw the coupling ring onto the body, and you're finished.

Figure 22.20 shows how to install a PL-259 connector on RG-58 or RG-59 cable. An adapter is used for the smaller cable with standard RG-8 size PL-259s. (UG-175 for RG-58 and UG-176 for RG-59.) Prepare the cable as shown. Once the braid is prepared, screw the adapter into the PL-259 shell and finish the job as you would a PL-259 on RG-8 cable.

Figure 22.21 shows the instructions and dimensions for crimp-on UHF connectors that fit all common sizes of coaxial cable. While amateurs have been reluctant to adopt crimp-on connectors, the availability of good quality connectors and inexpensive crimping tools make crimp technology a good choice, even for connectors used outside. Soldering the center conductor to the connector tip is optional.

UHF connectors are not waterproof and must be waterproofed whether soldered or crimped as shown in the section of the **Safety** chapter on Antenna and Tower Safety.

22.9.2 BNC, N and F Connectors

The BNC connectors illustrated in **Figure 22.22** are popular for low power levels at VHF and UHF. They accept RG-58 and RG-59 cable, and are available for cable mounting in both male and female versions. Several different styles are available, so be sure to use the dimensions for the type you have. Follow the installation instructions carefully. If you prepare the cable to the wrong dimensions, the center pin will not seat properly with connectors of the opposite gender. Sharp scissors are a big help for trimming the braid evenly. Crimp-on BNC connectors are also available, with a large number of

(Text continues on page 22.51)

UHF Connectors
Braid Crimp - Solder Center Contact

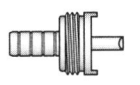

Ferrule   Coupling Nut   Body assembly

Amphenol	Cable RG-/U	Cable Attachment		Hex Crimp Data			Stripping Dims, inches (mm)		
		Outer	Inner	Cavity for Outer Ferrule	Die Set Tool 227-994	CTL Series Tool No.	a	b	c
83-58SP	58, 141	Crimp	Solder	0.213(5.4)	227-1221-11	CTL-1	1.14 (29.0)	0.780 (19.9)	0.250 (6.4)
83-58SP-1002	400	Crimp	Solder	0.213(5.4)	227-1221-11	CTL-1	1.14 (29.0)	0.780 (19.9)	0.250 (6.4)
83-59DCP-RFX	59	Crimp	Solder	0255(6.5)	227-1221-13	CTL-1	1.22 (30.9)	0.890* (22.6)	0.543 (13.8)
83-58SCP-RFX	58	Crimp	Solder	0.213(5.4)	227-1221-11	CTL-1	1.22 (30.9)	0.890* (22.6)	0.543 (13.8)
83-59SP	59	Crimp	Solder	0.255(6.5)	227-1221-13	CTL-1	1.22 (30.9)	0.890* (22.6)	0.543 (13.8)
83-8SP-RFX	8	Crimp	Solder	0.429(10.9)	227-1221-25	CTL-3	1.22 (30.9)	0.890* (22.6)	0.543 (13.8)

See www.AmphenolRF.com for assembly instructions for all other connectore types. These dimensions only apply to Amphenol connectors and may not be correct for other manufacturers.
* Manufacturer's assembly dimensions incorrectly show 0.574 inches.

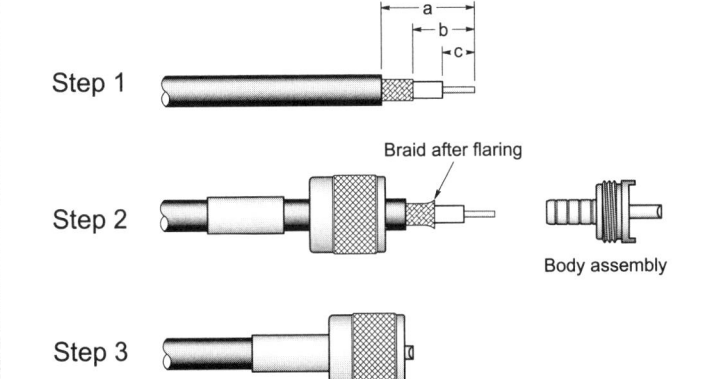

Step 1
Step 2 — Braid after flaring — Body assembly
Step 3
HBK0475

Step 1 Cut end of cable even. Strip cable to dimensions shown in table. All cuts are to be sharp and square. Do not nick braid, dielectric or center conductor. Tin center conductor avoiding excessive heat.

Step 2 Slide coupling nut and ferrule over cable jacket. Flair braid slightly as shown. Install cable into body assembly, so inner ferrule portion slides under braid, until braid butts shoulder. Slide outer ferrule over braid until it butts shoulder. Crimp ferrule with tool and die set indicated in table.

Step 3 Soft solder center conductor to contact. Avoid heating contact excessively to prevent damaging insulator. Slide/screw coupling nut over body.

Figure 22.21 — Crimp-on UHF connectors are available for all sizes of popular coaxial cable and save considerable time over soldered connectors. The performance and reliability of these connectors is equivalent to soldered connectors, if crimped properly. (*Courtesy Amphenol Electronic Components*)

Table 22.60
Nominal Characteristics of Commonly Used Transmission Lines

RG or Type	Part Number	Nom. Z_0 Ω	VF %	Cap. pF/ft	Cent. Cond. AWG	Diel. Type	Shield Type	Jacket Matl	OD inches	Max V (RMS)	1 MHz	10	100	1000
RG-6	Belden 1694A	75	82	16.2	#18 Solid BC	FPE	FC	P1	0.275	300	0.3	.7	1.8	5.9
RG-6	Belden 8215	75	66	20.5	#21 Solid CCS	PE	D	PE	0.332	2700	0.4	0.8	2.7	9.8
RG-8	Belden 7810A	50	86	23.0	#10 Solid BC	FPE	FC	PE	0.405	300	0.1	0.4	1.2	4.0
RG-8	TMS LMR400	50	85	23.9	#10 Solid CCA	FPE	FC	PE	0.405	600	0.1	0.4	1.3	4.1
RG-8	Belden 9913	50	84	24.6	#10 Solid BC	ASPE	FC	P1	0.405	300	0.1	0.4	1.3	4.5
RG-8	CXP1318FX	50	84	24.0	#10 Flex BC	FPE	FC	P2N	0.405	600	0.1	0.4	1.3	4.5
RG-8	Belden 9913F	50	83	24.6	#11 Flex BC	FPE	FC	P1	0.405	300	0.2	0.6	1.5	4.8
RG-8	Belden 9914	50	82	24.8	#10 Solid BC	FPE	FC	P1	0.405	300	0.2	0.5	1.5	4.8
RG-8	TMS LMR400UF	50	85	23.9	#10 Flex BC	FPE	FC	PE	0.405	600	0.1	0.4	1.4	4.9
RG-8	DRF-BF	50	84	24.5	#9.5 Flex BC	FPE	FC	PE	0.405	600	0.1	0.5	1.6	5.2
RG-8	WM CQ106	50	84	24.5	#9.5 Flex BC	FPE	FC	P2N	0.405	600	0.2	0.6	1.8	5.3
RG-8	CXP008	50	78	26.0	#13 Flex BC	FPE	S	P1	0.405	600	0.1	0.5	1.8	7.1
RG-8	Belden 8237	52	66	29.5	#13 Flex BC	PE	S	P1	0.405	3700	0.2	0.6	1.9	7.4
RG-8X	Belden 7808A	50	86	23.5	#15 Solid BC	FPE	FC	PE	0.240	300	0.2	0.7	2.3	7.4
RG-8X	TMS LMR240	50	84	24.2	#15 Solid BC	FPE	FC	PE	0.242	300	0.2	0.8	2.5	8.0
RG-8X	WM CQ118	50	82	25.0	#16 Flex BC	FPE	FC	P2N	0.242	300	0.3	0.9	2.8	8.4
RG-8X	TMS LMR240UF	50	84	24.2	#15 Flex BC	FPE	FC	PE	0.242	300	0.2	0.8	2.8	9.6
RG-8X	Belden 9258	50	82	24.8	#16 Flex BC	FPE	S	P1	0.242	300	0.3	0.9	3.2	11.2
RG-8X	CXP08XB	50	80	25.3	#16 Flex BC	FPE	S	P1	0.242	300	0.3	1.0	3.1	14.0
RG-9	Belden 8242	51	66	30.0	#13 Flex SPC	PE	SCBC	P2N	0.420	5000	0.2	0.6	2.1	8.2
RG-11	Belden 8213	75	84	16.1	#14 Solid BC	FPE	S	PE	0.405	300	0.1	0.4	1.3	5.2
RG-11	Belden 8238	75	66	20.5	#10 Flex TC	PE	S	P1	0.405	300	0.2	0.7	2.0	7.1
RG-58	Belden 7807A	50	85	23.7	#18 Solid BC	FPE	FC	PE	0.195	300	0.3	1.0	3.0	9.7
RG-58	TMS LMR200	50	83	24.5	#17 Solid BC	FPE	FC	PE	0.195	300	0.3	1.0	3.2	10.5
RG-58	WM CQ124	52	66	28.5	#20 Solid BC	PE	S	PE	0.195	1400	0.4	1.3	4.3	14.3
RG-58	Belden 8240	52	66	29.9	#20 Solid BC	PE	S	P1	0.193	1400	0.3	1.1	3.8	14.5
RG-58A	Belden 8219	53	73	26.5	#20 Flex TC	FPE	S	P1	0.195	300	0.4	1.3	4.5	18.1
RG-58C	Belden 8262	50	66	30.8	#20 Flex TC	PE	S	P2N	0.195	1400	0.4	1.4	4.9	21.5
RG-58A	Belden 8259	50	66	30.8	#20 Flex TC	PE	S	P1	0.192	1400	0.5	1.5	5.4	22.8
RG-59	Belden 1426A	75	83	16.3	#20 Solid BC	FPE	S	P1	0.242	300	0.3	0.9	2.6	8.5
RG-59	CXP 0815	75	82	16.2	#20 Solid BC	FPE	S	P1	0.232	300	0.5	0.9	2.2	9.1
RG-59	Belden 8212	75	78	17.3	#20 Solid CCS	FPE	S	P1	0.242	300	0.2	1.0	3.0	10.9
RG-59	Belden 8241	75	66	20.4	#23 Solid CCS	PE	S	P1	0.242	1700	0.6	1.1	3.4	12.0
RG-62A	Belden 9269	93	84	13.5	#22 Solid CCS	ASPE	S	P1	0.240	750	0.3	0.9	2.7	8.7
RG-62B	Belden 8255	93	84	13.5	#24 Flex CCS	ASPE	S	P2N	0.242	750	0.3	0.9	2.9	11.0
RG-63B	Belden 9857	125	84	9.7	#22 Solid CCS	ASPE	S	P2N	0.405	750	0.2	0.5	1.5	5.8
RG-83	WM165	35	66	44.0	#10 Solid BC	PF	S	P2	0.405	2000	0.23	0.0	2.0	9.8
RG-142	CXP 183242	50	69.5	29.4	#19 Solid SCCS	TFE	D	FEP	0.195	1900	0.3	1.1	3.8	12.8
RG-142B	Belden 83242	50	69.5	29.0	#19 Solid SCCS	TFE	D	TFE	0.195	1400	0.3	1.1	3.9	13.5
RG-174	Belden 7805R	50	73.5	26.2	#25 Solid BC	FPE	FC	P1	0.110	300	0.6	2.0	6.5	21.3
RG-174	Belden 8216	50	66	30.8	#26 Flex CCS	PE	S	P1	0.110	1100	0.8	2.5	8.6	33.7
RG-213	Belden 8267	50	66	30.8	#13 Flex BC	PE	S	P2N	0.405	3700	0.2	0.6	2.1	8.0
RG-213	CXP213	50	66	30.8	#13 Flex BC	PE	S	P2N	0.405	600	0.2	0.6	2.0	8.2
RG-214	Belden 8268	50	66	30.8	#13 Flex SPC	PE	D	P2N	0.425	3700	0.2	0.7	2.2	8.0
RG-216	Belden 9850	75	66	20.5	#18 Flex TC	PE	D	P2N	0.425	3700	0.2	0.7	2.0	7.1
RG-217	WM CQ217F	50	66	30.8	#10 Flex BC	PE	D	PE	0.545	7000	0.1	0.4	1.4	5.2
RG-217	M17/78-RG217	50	66	30.8	#10 Solid BC	PE	D	P2N	0.545	7000	0.1	0.4	1.4	5.2
RG-218	M17/79-RG218	50	66	29.5	#4.5 Solid BC	PE	S	P2N	0.870	11000	0.1	0.2	0.8	3.4
RG-223	Belden 9273	50	66	30.8	#19 Solid SPC	PE	D	P2N	0.212	1400	0.4	1.2	4.1	14.5
RG-303	Belden 84303	50	69.5	29.0	#18 Solid SCCS	TFE	S	TFE	0.170	1400	0.3	1.1	3.9	13.5
RG-316	CXP TJ1316	50	69.5	29.4	#26 Flex BC	TFE	S	FEP	0.098	1200	1.2	2.7	8.0	26.1
RG-316	Belden 84316	50	69.5	29.0	#26 Flex SCCS	TFE	S	FEP	0.096	900	0.8	2.5	8.3	26.0
RG-393	M17/127-RG393	50	69.5	29.4	#12 Flex SPC	TFE	D	FEP	0.390	5000	0.2	0.5	1.7	6.1
RG-400	M17/128-RG400	50	69.5	29.4	#20 Flex SPC	TFE	D	FEP	0.195	1400	0.4	1.3	4.3	15.0
LMR500	TMS LMR500UF	50	85	23.9	#7 Flex BC	FPE	FC	PE	0.500	2500	0.1	0.4	1.2	4.0
LMR500	TMS LMR500	50	85	23.9	#7 Solid CCA	FPE	FC	PE	0.500	2500	0.1	0.3	0.9	3.3
LMR600	TMS LMR600	50	86	23.4	#5.5 Solid CCA	FPE	FC	PE	0.590	4000	0.1	0.2	0.8	2.7
LMR600	TMS LMR600UF	50	86	23.4	#5.5 Flex BC	FPE	FC	PE	0.590	4000	0.1	0.2	0.8	2.7
LMR1200	TMS LMR1200	50	88	23.1	#0 Copper Tube	FPE	FC	PE	1.200	4500	0.04	0.1	0.4	1.3
Hardline														
1/2"	CATV Hardline	50	81	25.0	#5.5 BC	FPE	SM	none	0.500	2500	0.05	0.2	0.8	3.2
1/2"	CATV Hardline	75	81	16.7	#11.5 BC	FPE	SM	none	0.500	2500	0.1	0.2	0.8	3.2
7/8"	CATV Hardline	50	81	25.0	#1 BC	FPE	SM	none	0.875	4000	0.03	0.1	0.6	2.9
7/8"	CATV Hardline	75	81	16.7	#5.5 BC	FPE	SM	none	0.875	4000	0.03	0.1	0.6	2.9
LDF4-50A	Heliax – ½"	50	88	25.9	#5 Solid BC	FPE	CC	PE	0.630	1400	0.02	0.2	0.6	2.4
LDF5-50A	Heliax – ⅞"	50	88	25.9	0.355" BC	FPE	CC	PE	1.090	2100	0.03	0.10	0.4	1.3
LDF6-50A	Heliax – 1¼"	50	88	25.9	0.516" BC	FPE	CC	PE	1.550	3200	0.02	0.08	0.3	1.1
Parallel Lines														
TV Twinlead (Belden 9085)		300	80	4.5	#22 Flex CCS	PE	none	P1	0.400	**	0.1	0.3	1.4	5.9
Twinlead (Belden 8225)		300	80	4.4	#20 Flex BC	PE	none	P1	0.400	8000	0.1	0.2	1.1	4.8
Generic Window Line		450	91	2.5	#18 Solid CCS	PE	none	P1	1.000	10000	0.02	0.08	0.3	1.1
WM CQ 554		440	91	2.7	#14 Solid CCS	PE	none	P1	1.000	10000	0.04	0.01	0.6	3.0
WM CQ 552		440	91	2.5	#16 Flex CCS	PE	none	P1	1.000	10000	0.05	0.2	0.6	2.6
WM CQ 553		450	91	2.5	#18 Solid CCS	PE	none	P1	1.000	10000	0.06	0.2	0.7	2.9
WM CQ 551		450	91	2.5	#18 Solid CCS	PE	none	P1	1.000	10000	0.05	0.02	0.6	2.8
Open-Wire Line		600	0.95-99***	1.7	#12 BC	none	none	none	**	12000	0.02	0.06	0.2	—

Approximate Power Handling Capability (1:1 SWR, 40°C Ambient):

	1.8 MHz	7	14	30	50	150	220	450	1 GHz
RG-58 Style	1350	700	500	350	250	150	120	100	50
RG-59 Style	2300	1100	800	550	400	250	200	130	90
RG-8X Style	1830	840	560	360	270	145	115	80	50
RG-8/213 Style	5900	3000	2000	1500	1000	600	500	350	250
RG-217 Style	20000	9200	6100	3900	2900	1500	1200	800	500
LDF4-50A	38000	18000	13000	8200	6200	3400	2800	1900	1200
LDF5-50A	67000	32000	22000	14000	11000	5900	4800	3200	2100
LMR500	18000	9200	6500	4400	3400	1900	1600	1100	700
LMR1200	52000	26000	19000	13000	10000	5500	4500	3000	2000

Legend:

**	Not Available or varies	N	Non-Contaminating
***	Varies with spacer material and spacing	P1	PVC, Class 1
ASPE	Air Spaced Polyethylene	P2	PVC, Class 2
BC	Bare Copper	PE	Polyethylene
CC	Corrugated Copper	S	Single Braided Shield
CCA	Copper Cover Aluminum	SC	Silver Coated Braid
CCS	Copper Covered Steel	SCCS	Silver Plated Copper Coated Steel
CXP	Cable X-Perts, Inc.	SM	Smooth Aluminum
D	Double Copper Braids	SPC	Silver Plated Copper
DRF	Davis RF	TC	Tinned Copper
FC	Foil + Tinned Copper Braid	TFE	Teflon®
FEP	Teflon ® Type IX	TMS	Times Microwave Systems
Flex	Flexible Stranded Wire	UF	Ultra Flex
FPE	Foamed Polyethylene	WM	Wireman
Heliax	Andrew Corp Heliax		

Figure 22.22 (below) — BNC connectors are common on VHF and UHF equipment at low power levels. (*Courtesy Amphenol Electronic Components*)

BNC CONNECTORS

Standard Clamp

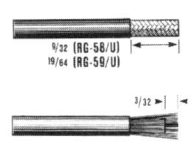

1. Cut cable even. Strip jacket. Fray braid and strip dielectric. **Don't nick braid or center conductor.** Tin center conductor.

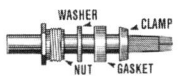

2. Taper braid. Slide nut, washer, gasket and clamp over braid. Clamp inner shoulder should fit squarely against end of jacket.

3. With clamp in place, comb out braid, fold back smooth as shown. Trim center conductor.

4. Solder contact on conductor through solder hole. Contact should butt against dielectric. Remove excess solder from outside of contact. Avoid excess heat to prevent swollen dielectric which would interfere with connector body.

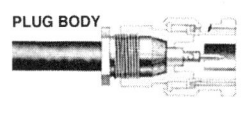

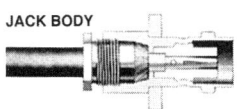

5. Push assembly into body. Screw nut into body with wrench until tight. **Don't rotate body on cable to tighten.**

Improved Clamp

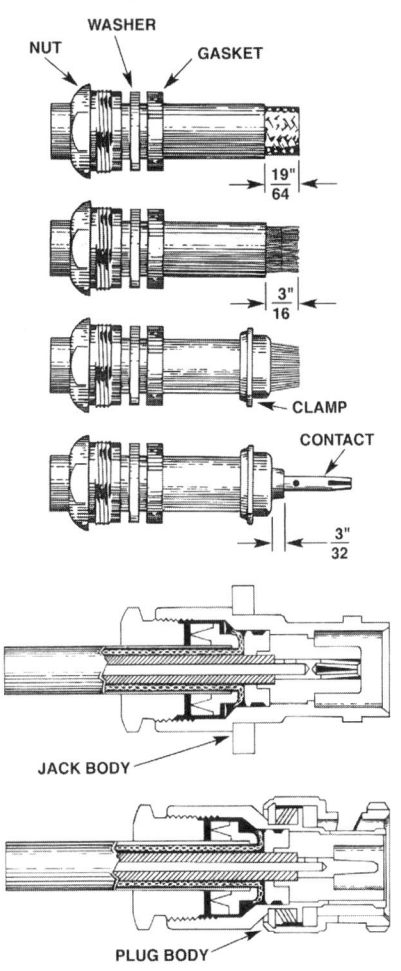

Follow 1, 2, 3 and 4 in BNC connectors (standard clamp) except as noted. Strip cable as shown. Slide gasket on cable *with groove facing clamp.* Slide clamp *with sharp edge facing gasket.* Clamp *should* cut gasket to seal properly.

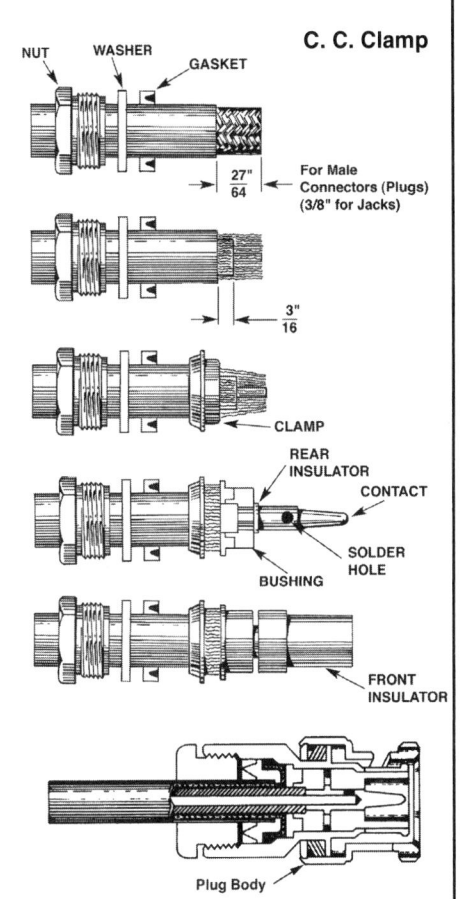

C. C. Clamp

1. Follow steps 1, 2, and 3 as outlined for the standard-clamp BNC connector.

2. Slide on bushing, rear insulator and contact. The parts must butt securely against each other, as shown.

3. Solder the center conductor to the contact. Remove flux and excess solder.

4. Slide the front insulator over the contact, making sure it butts against the contact shoulder.

5. Insert the prepared cable end into the connector body and tighten the nut. Make sure the sharp edge of the clamp seats properly in the gasket.

Component Data and References 22.49

Table 22.61
Coaxial Cable Connectors

UHF Connectors

Military No.	Style	Cable RG- or Description
PL-259	Str (m)	8, 9, 11, 13, 63, 87, 149, 213, 214, 216, 225
UG-111	Str (m)	59, 62, 71, 140, 210
SO-239	Pnl (f)	Std, mica/phenolic insulation
UG-266	Blkhd (f)	Rear mount, pressurized, copolymer of styrene ins.

Adapters

PL-258	Str (f/f)	Polystyrene ins.
UG-224,363	Blkhd (f/f)	Polystyrene ins.
UG-646	Ang (f/m)	Polystyrene ins.
M-359A	Ang (m/f)	Polystyrene ins.
M-358	T (f/m/f)	Polystyrene ins.

Reducers

UG-175	55, 58, 141, 142 (except 55A)
UG-176	59, 62, 71, 140, 210

Family Characteristics:

All are nonweatherproof and have a nonconstant impedance. Frequency range: 0-500 MHz. Maximum voltage rating: 500 V (peak).

N Connectors

Military No.	Style	Cable RG-	Notes
UG-21	Str (m)	8, 9, 213, 214	50 Ω
UG-94A	Str (m)	11, 13, 149, 216	70 Ω
UG-536	Str (m)	58, 141, 142	50 Ω
UG-603	Str (m)	59, 62, 71, 140, 210	50 Ω
UG-23, B-E	Str (f)	8, 9, 87, 213, 214, 225	50 Ω
UG-602	Str (f)	59, 62, 71, 140, 210	—
UG-228B, D, E	Pnl (f)	8, 9, 87, 213, 214, 225	—
UG-1052	Pnl (f)	58, 141, 142	50 Ω
UG-593	Pnl (f)	59, 62, 71, 140, 210	50 Ω
UG-160A, B, D	Blkhd (f)	8, 9, 87, 213, 214, 225	50 Ω
UG-556	Blkhd (f)	58, 141, 142	50 Ω
UG-58, A	Pnl (f)		50 Ω
UG-997A	Ang (f)		50 Ω

Panel mount (f) with clearance above panel

M39012/04-	Blkhd (f)	Front mount hermetically sealed
UG-680	Blkhd (f)	Front mount pressurized

N Adapters

Military No.	Style	Notes
UG-29,A,B	Str (f/f)	50 Ω, TFE ins.
UG-57A.B	Str (m/m)	50 Ω, TFE ins.
UG-27A,B	Ang (f/m)	Mitre body
UG-212A	Ang (f/m)	Mitre body
UG-107A	T (f/m/f)	—
UG-28A	T (f/f/f)	—
UG-107B	T (f/m/f)	—

Family Characteristics:

N connectors with gaskets are weatherproof. RF leakage: –90 dB min @ 3 GHz. Temperature limits: TFE: –67° to 390°F (–55° to 199°C). Insertion loss 0.15 dB max @ 10 GHz. Copolymer of styrene: –67° to 185°F (–55° to 85°C). Frequency range: 0-11 GHz. Maximum voltage rating: 1500 V P-P. Dielectric withstanding voltage 2500 V RMS. SWR (MIL-C-39012 cable connectors) 1.3 max 0-11 GHz.

BNC Connectors

Military No.	Style	Cable RG-	Notes
UG-88C	Str (m)	55, 58, 141, 142, 223, 400	

Military No.	Style	Cable RG-	Notes
UG-959	Str (m)	8, 9	
UG-260,A	Str (m)	59, 62, 71, 140, 210	Rexolite ins.
UG-262	Pnl (f)	59, 62, 71, 140, 210	Rexolite ins.
UG-262A	Pnl (f)	59, 62, 71, 140, 210	nwx, Rexolite ins.
UG-291	Pnl (f)	55, 58, 141, 142, 223, 400	
UG-291A	Pnl (f)	55, 58, 141, 142, 223, 400	nwx
UG-624	Blkhd (f)	59, 62, 71, 140, 210	Front mount Rexolite ins.
UG-1094A	Blkhd		Standard
UG-625B	Receptacle		
UG-625			

BNC Adapters

Military No.	Style	Notes
UG-491,A	Str (m/m)	
UG-491B	Str (m/m)	Berylium, outer contact
UG-914	Str (f/f)	
UG-306	Ang (f/m)	
UG-306A,B	Ang (f/m)	Berylium outer contact
UG-414,A	Pnl (f/f)	# 3-56 tapped flange holes
UG-306	Ang (f/m)	
UG-306A,B	Ang (f/m)	Berylium outer contact
UG-274	T (f/m/f)	
UG-274A,B	T (f/m/f)	Berylium outer contact

Family Characteristics:

Z = 50 Ω. Frequency range: 0-4 GHz w/low reflection; usable to 11 GHz. Voltage rating: 500 V P-P. Dielectric withstanding voltage 500 V RMS. SWR: 1.3 max 0-4 GHz. RF leakage –55 dB min @ 3 GHz. Insertion loss: 0.2 dB max @ 3 GHz. Temperature limits: TFE: –67° to 390°F (–55° to 199°C); Rexolite insulators:
–67° to 185°F (–55° to 85°C). "Nwx" = not weatherproof.

HN Connectors

Military No.	Style	Cable RG-	Notes
UG-59A	Str (m)	8, 9, 213, 214	
UG-1214	Str (f)	8, 9, 87, 213, 214, 225	Captivated contact
UG-60A	Str (f)	8, 9, 213, 214	Copolymer of styrene ins.
UG-1215	Pnl (f)	8, 9, 87, 213, 214, 225	Captivated contact
UG-560	Pnl (f)		
UG-496	Pnl (f)		
UG-212C	Ang (f/m)		Berylium outer contact

Family Characteristics:

Connector Styles: Str = straight; Pnl = panel; Ang = Angle; Blkhd = bulkhead. Z = 50 Ω. Frequency range = 0-4 GHz. Maximum voltage rating = 1500 V P-P. Dielectric withstanding voltage = 5000 V RMS SWR = 1.3. All HN series are weatherproof. Temperature limits: TFE: –67° to 390°F (–55° to 199°C); copolymer of styrene: –67° to 185°F (–55° to 85°C).

Cross-Family Adapters

Families	Description	Military No.
HN to BNC	HN-m/BNC-f	UG-309
N to BNC	N-m/BNC-f	UG-201,A
	N-f/BNC-m	UG-349,A
	N-m/BNC-m	UG-1034
N to UHF	N-m/UHF-f	UG-146
	N-f/UHF-m	UG-83,B
	N-m/UHF-m	UG-318
UHF to BNC	UHF-m/BNC-f	UG-273
	UHF-f/BNC-m	UG-255

Type N assembly instructions

HBK05_19-19

CLAMP TYPES

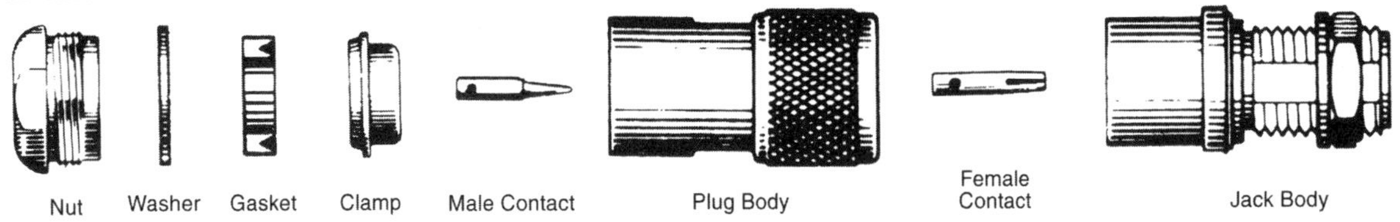

Nut Washer Gasket Clamp Male Contact Plug Body Female Contact Jack Body

Step 1

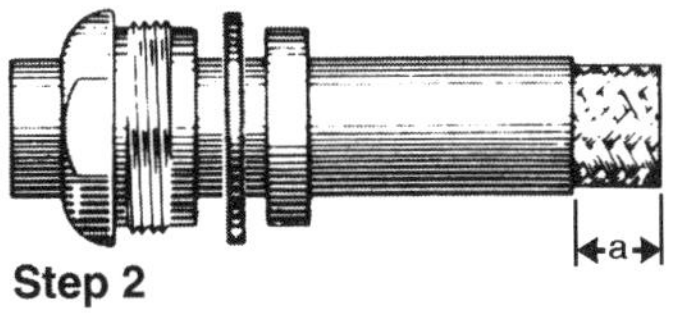

Step 2

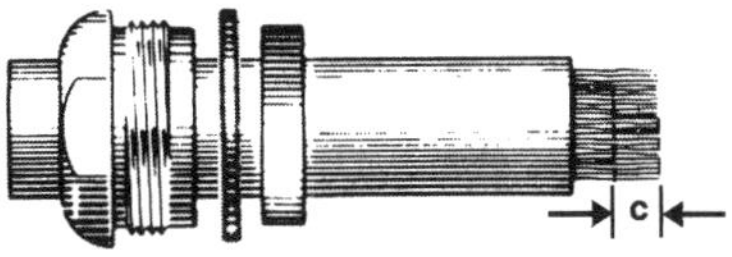

Step 3

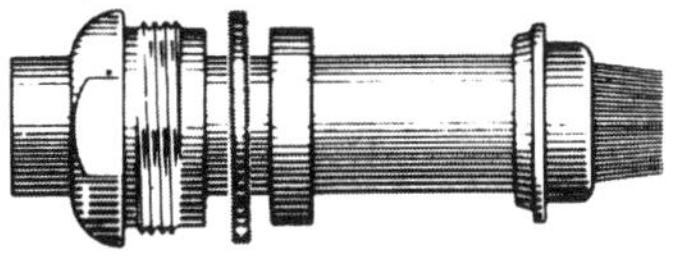

Step 4

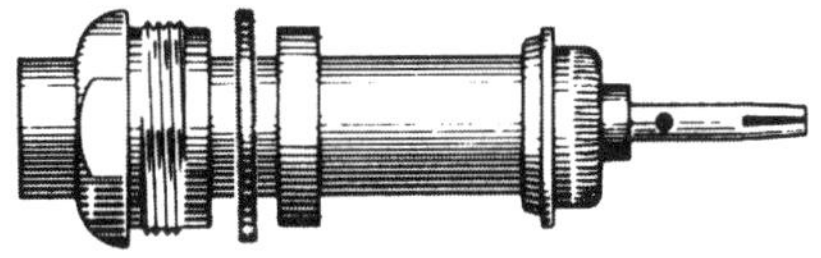

Step 5

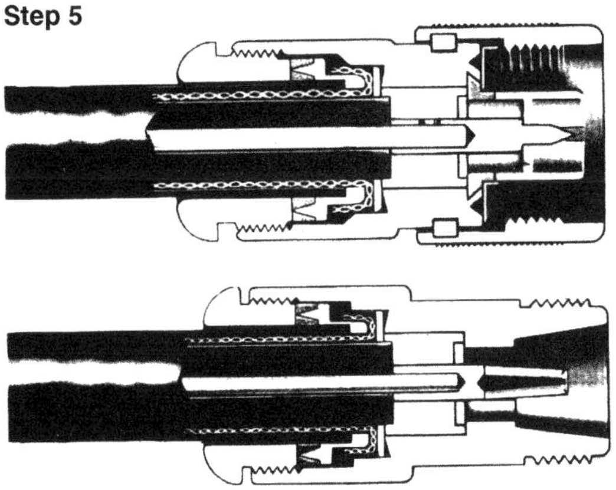

Amphenol Number	Connector Type	Cable RG-/U	Strip Dims., inches (mm) a	c
82-61	N Plug	8, 9, 144, 165, 213, 214, 216, 225	0.359(9.1)	0.234(6.0)
82-62	N Panel Jack		0.312(7.9)	0.187(4.7)
82-63	N Jack	8, 9, 87A, 144, 165, 213, 214, 216, 225	0.281(7.1)	0.156(4.0)
82-67	N Bulkhead Jack			
82-202	N Plug	8, 9, 144, 165, 213, 214, 216, 225	0.359(9.1)	0.234(6.0)
82-202-RFX	N Plug	8, 213, 214	0.315(8.0)	0.177(4.5)
82-202-1006	N Plug	Belden 9913	0.359(9.1)	0.234(6.0)
82-835	N Angle Plug	8, 9, 87A, 144, 165, 213, 214, 216, 225	0.281(7.1)	0.156(4.0)
18750	N Angle Plug		0.484(12.3)	0.234(5.9)
34025	N Plug	58, 141, 142	0.390(9.9)	0.203(5.2)
34525	N Plug	59, 62, 71, 140, 210	0.410(10.4)	0.230(5.8)
35025	N Jack	58, 141, 142	0.375(9.5)	0.187(4.7)
36500	N Jack	59, 62, 71, 140, 210	0.484(12.3)	0.200(5.1)

See www.AmphenolRF.com for assembly instructions for all other connector types. These dimensions only apply to Amphenol connectors and may not be correct for other manufacturers.

Step 1 Place nut, washer, and gasket, with "V" groove toward clamp, over cable and cut off jacket to dimension a.

Step 2 Comb out braid and fold out. Cut off cable dielectric to dim. c as shown.

Step 3 Pull braid wires forward and taper toward center conductor. Place clamp over braid and push back against cable jacket.

Step 4 Fold back braid wires as shown, trim braid to proper length and form over clamp as shown. Solder contact to center conductor.

Step 5 Insert cable and parts into connector body. Make sure sharp edge of clamp seats properly in gasket. Tighten nut.

Figure 22.23 — Type N connectors are a must for high-power VHF and UHF operation. (*Courtesy Amphenol Electronic Components*)

(Continued from page 22.47)

variations, including a twist-on version. A guide to installing these connectors is available with the downloadable supplemental content.

The Type N connector, illustrated in **Figure 22.23**, is a must for high-power VHF and UHF operation. N connectors are available in male and female versions for cable mounting and are designed for RG-8 size cable. Unlike UHF connectors, they are designed to maintain a constant impedance at cable joints. Like BNC connectors, it is important to prepare the cable to the right dimensions. The center pin must be positioned correctly to mate with the center pin of connectors of the opposite gender. Use the right dimensions for the connector style you have. Crimp-on N connectors are also available, again with a large number of variations. A guide to installing these connectors is available with the downloadable supplemental content.

Type F connectors, used primarily on cable

Component Data and References 22.51

TV connections, are also popular for receive-only antennas and can be used with RG-59 or the increasingly popular RG-6 cable available at low cost. Crimp-on connectors are the only option for these connectors and **Figure 22.24** shows a general guide for installing them. The exact dimensions vary between connector styles and manufacturers — information on crimping is generally provided with the connectors. There are two styles of crimp; ferrule and compression. The ferrule crimp method is similar to that for UHF, BNC, and N connectors in which a metal ring is compressed around the exposed coax shield. The compression crimp forces a bushing into the back of the connector, clamping the shield against the connector body. In all cases, the exposed center conductor of the cable — a solid wire — must end flush with the end of the connector. A center conductor that is too short may not make a good connection.

22.9.3 Connector Identifier and Range Chart

The following pages of figures provide dimensions and side views to help identify the different types of connectors used for RF through microwave frequencies. Dimensions are provided in both imperial and metric units as appropriate. For mm-wave and microwave connectors, calipers or a micrometer may be required to provide an accurate measurement capable of distinguishing between similar connectors. These specifications are intended for connector identification only and should not be the sole dimensions used when laying out a circuit board or drilling a mounting hole.

These figures and chart were provided by Pasternack (**www.pasternack.com**), a major distributor of coaxial connectors, cable, tools, and other RF materials and supplies.

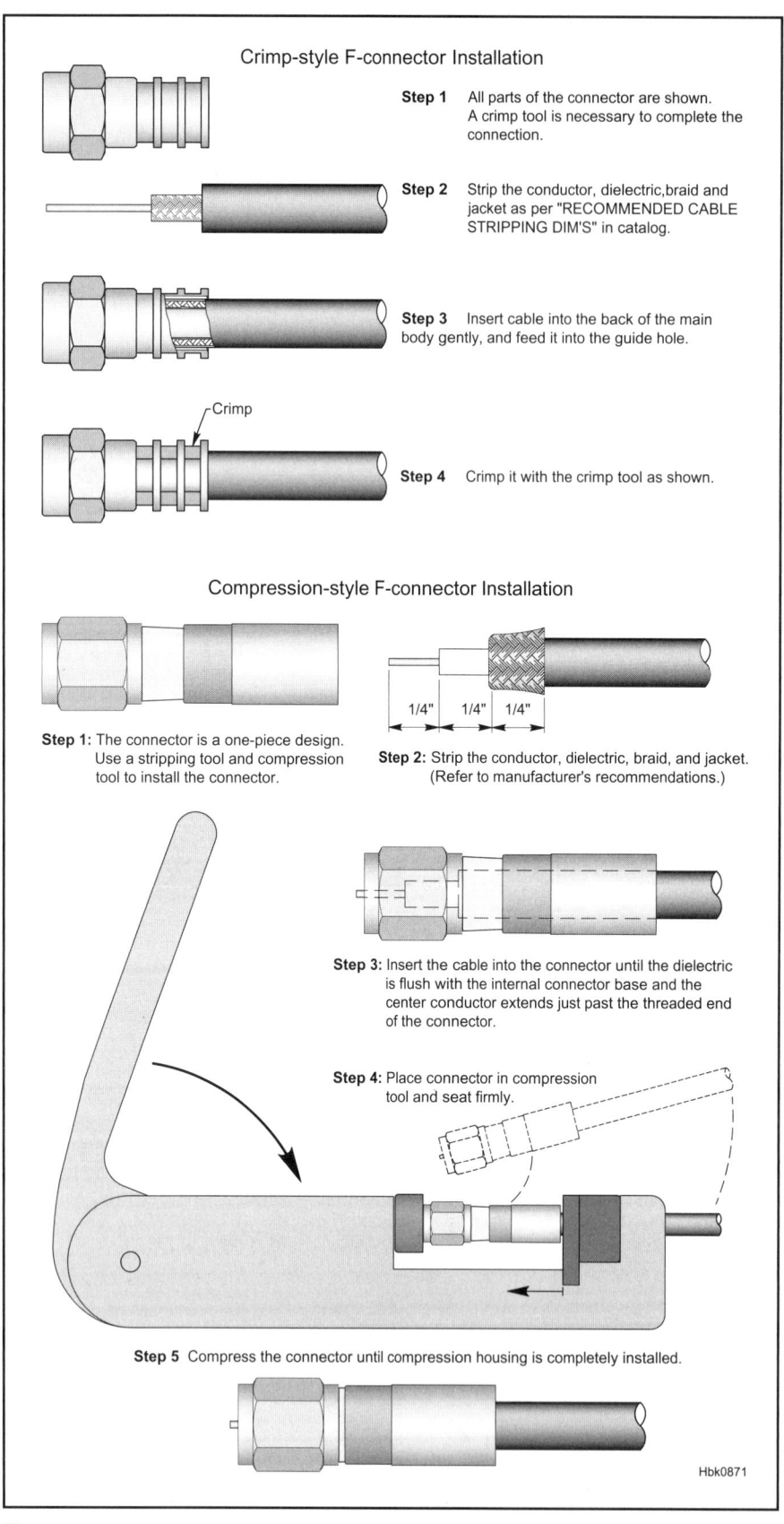

Figure 22.24 — Type F connectors, commonly used for cable TV connections, can be used for receive-only antennas with inexpensive RG-59 and RG-6 cable. The older crimp-style connectors have largely been replaced by the more reliable and weather-resistant compression-style connectors. Follow the manufacturer's instruction for the cable and connector selected. [Courtesy Amphenol Electronic Components and Technetix, Inc.]

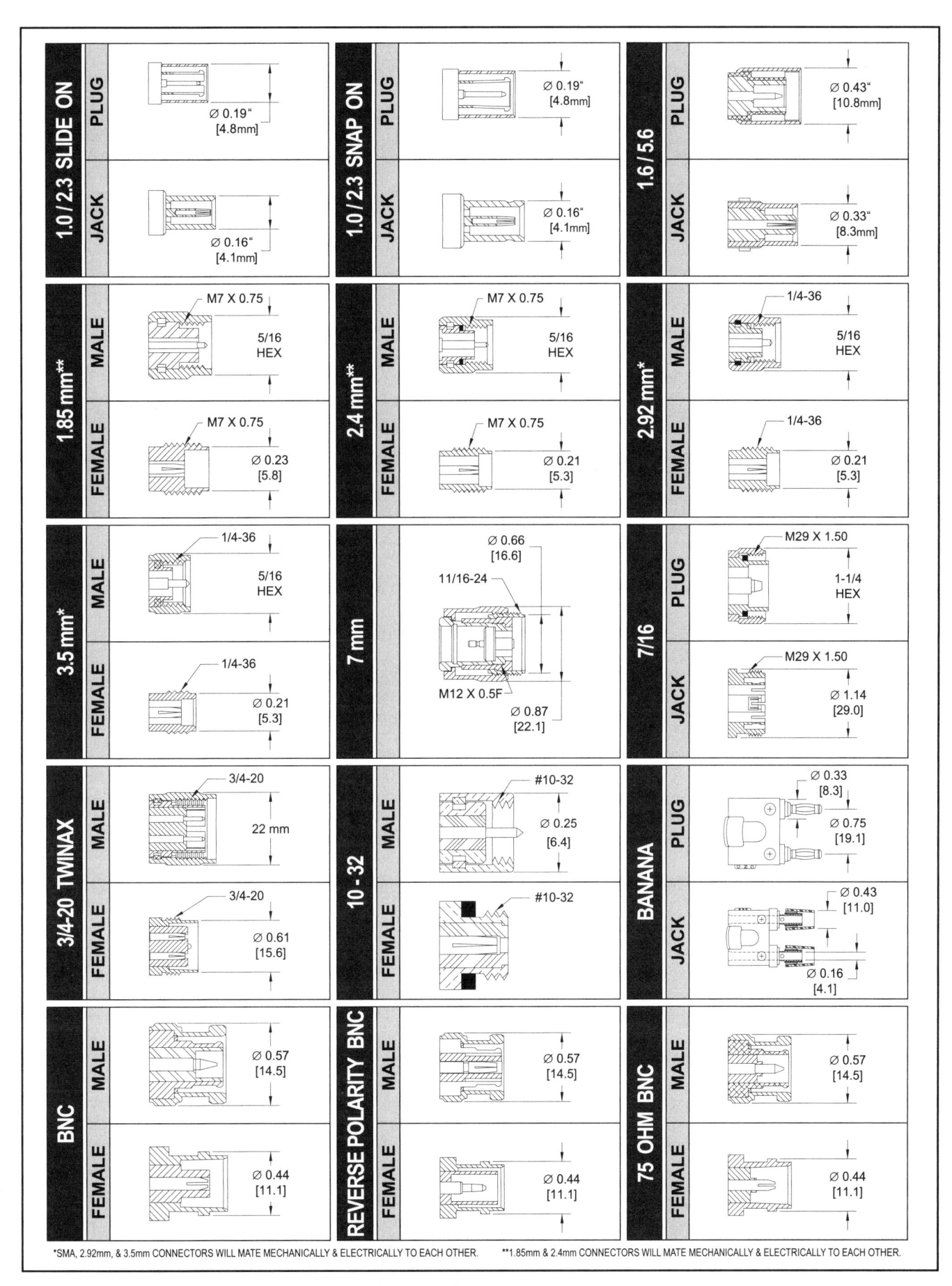

Figure 22.25A — Connector side views, set 1 of 4. [Courtesy of Pasternak]

*SMA, 2.92mm, & 3.5mm CONNECTORS WILL MATE MECHANICALLY & ELECTRICALLY TO EACH OTHER.   **1.85mm & 2.4mm CONNECTORS WILL MATE MECHANICALLY & ELECTRICALLY TO EACH OTHER.

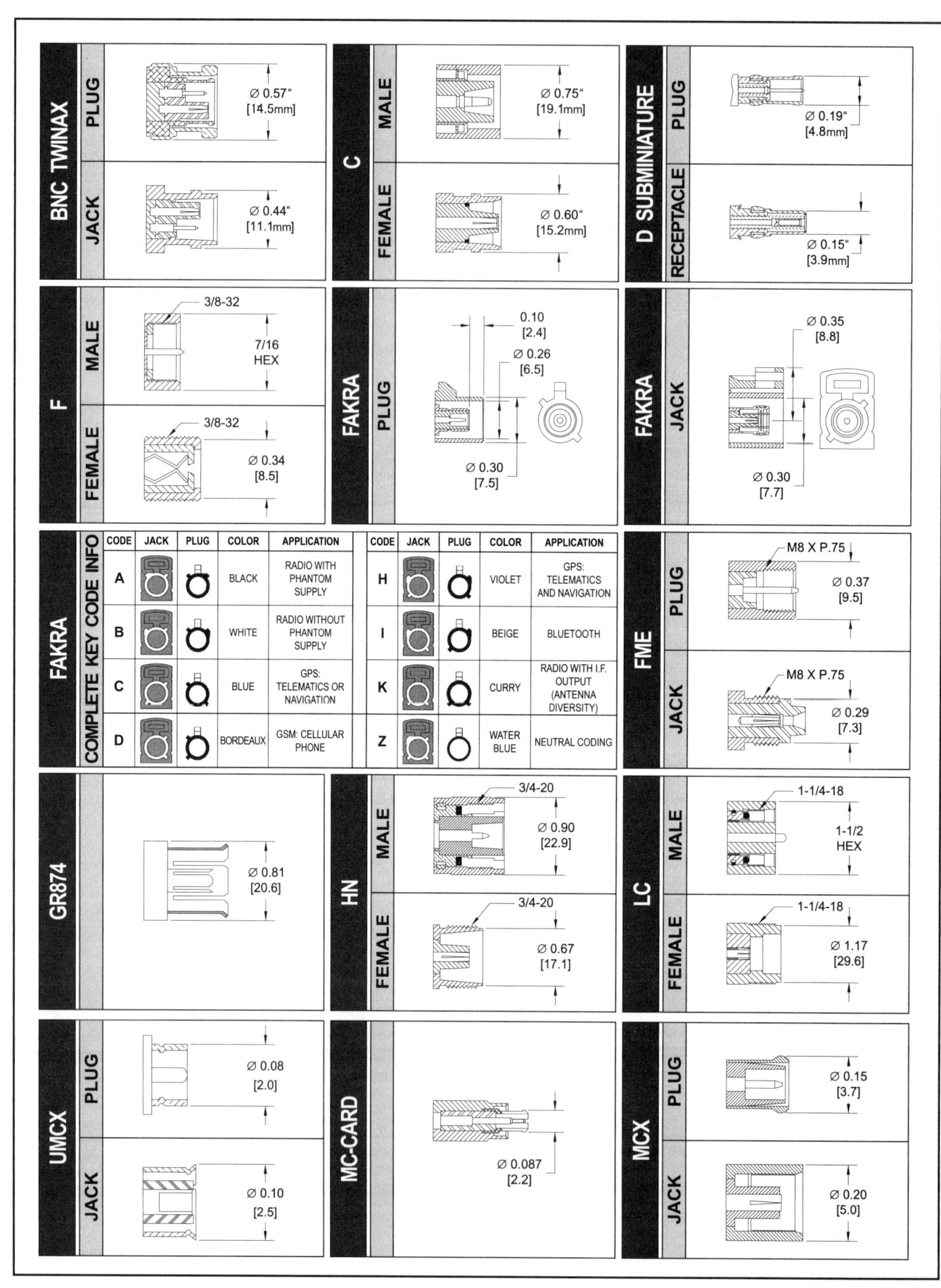

Figure 22.25B — Connector side views, set 2 of 4. [Courtesy of Pasternak]

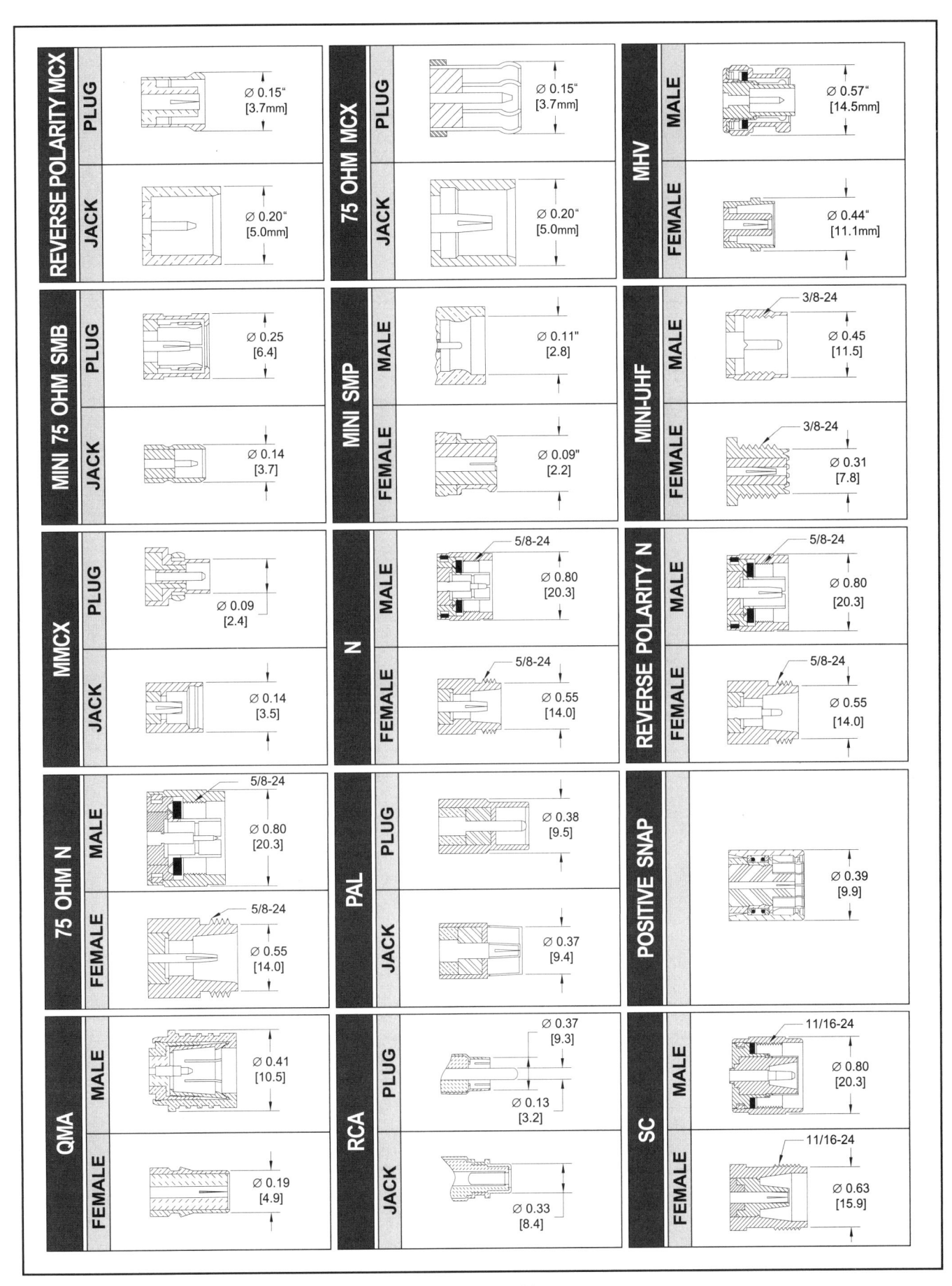

Figure 22.25C — Connector side views, set 3 of 4. [Courtesy of Pasternak]

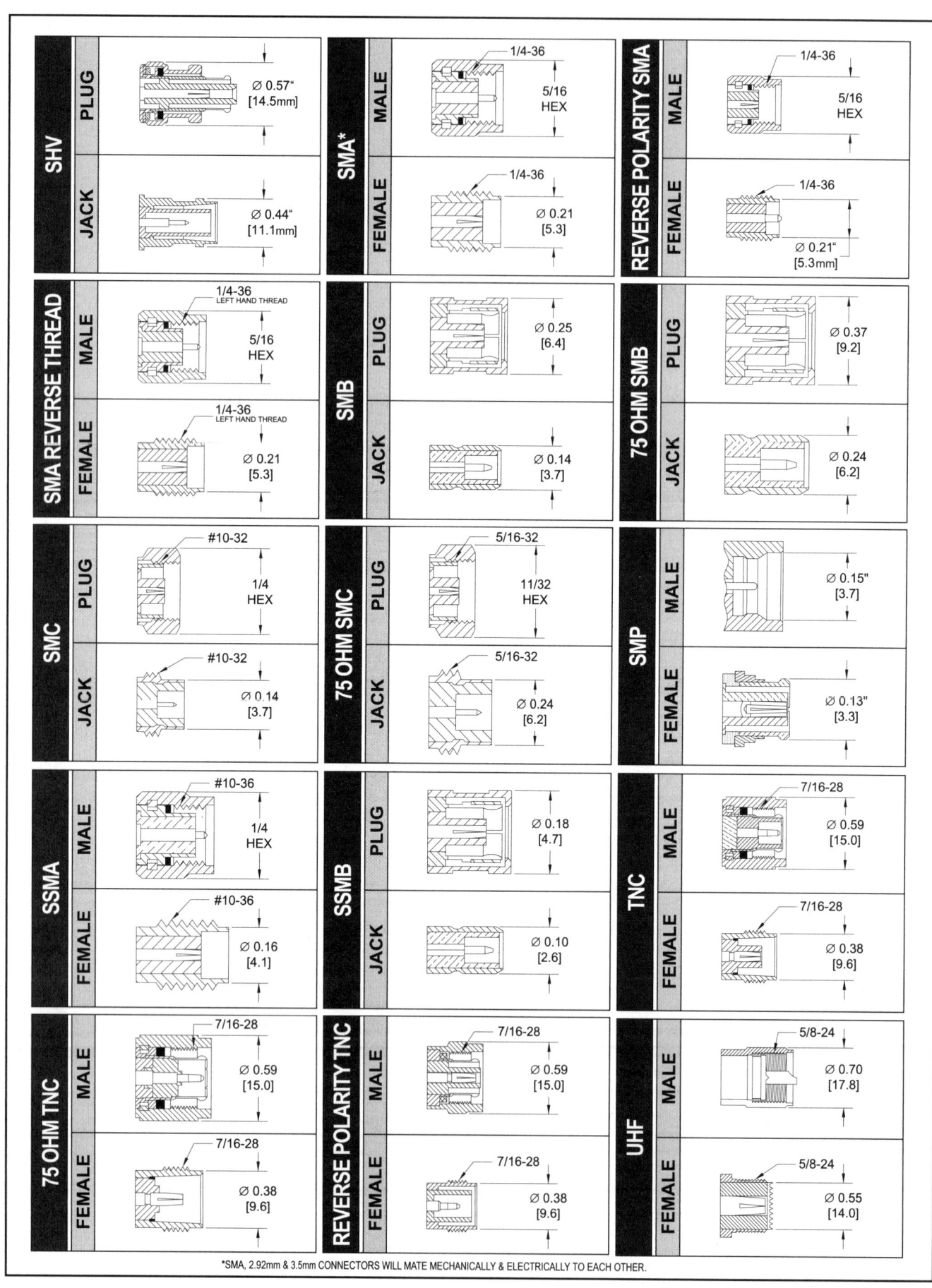

Figure 22.25D — Connector side views, set 4 of 4. [Courtesy of Pasternak]

22.56   Chapter 22

Figure 22.26 — Recommended frequency ranges by connector type. [Courtesy of Pasternak]

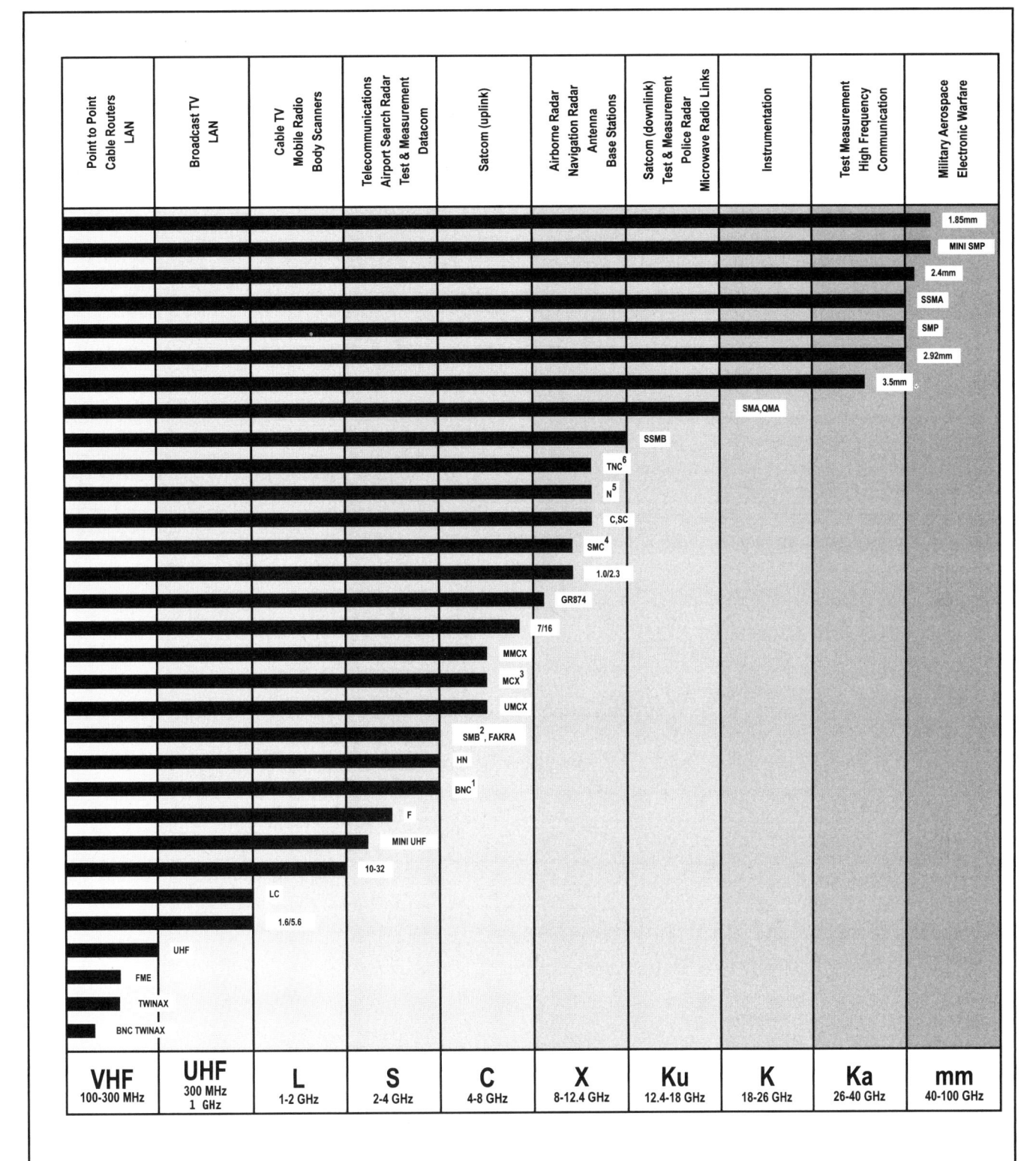

Notes:

1: BNC-75 Ohm connectors operate up to 1 GHz
2: SMB-75 Ohm & Mini SMB-75 Ohm connectors operate up to 4 GHz
3: MCX-75 Ohm connectors operate up to 6 GHz
4: SMC-75 Ohm connectors operate up to 10 GHz
5: N-75 Ohm connectors operate up to 1.5 GHz
6: TNC-75 Ohm connectors operate up to 1 GHz

Avoiding Poor-Quality Connectors

*[This guidance is provided by Hal Kennedy, N4GG, and is repeated in the **Station Construction** chapter. Many easily-avoided station problems are caused by poor-quality or poorly attached connectors or adapters — Ed.]*

PL-259s have four parts: the outer sleeve called the "knurled nut," the connector body, the insulator/dielectric and the center pin. All four components can be compromised to the point of making a bargain connector useless.

Problems frequently encountered:

• **Finish:** Bargain connectors sometimes have a finish you can't solder to! They may have a chrome-like appearance, but the plating may not take solder well and has to be filed down for a good connection.

• **Threading:** The internal threads at the rear of the body are there to accept a UG-style insert that narrows the connector barrel to accept smaller diameter coax such as RG-8X or RG-58. The threads may be metric! UG inserts also sometimes appear in the US market with metric threads. Either way, the insert will not screw into the body.

• **Dielectric:** Good connectors use quality phenolic or Teflon insulation between the center pin and the body. Bargain connectors might use anything, including materials such as polystyrene, which will melt when the center pin is soldered.

• **Center pin diameter:** This is one of the most common and insidious problems in mystery PL-259s. The center pin outer diameter (OD) is almost always slightly smaller than it should be and it's hard to notice. The center pin connection between a PL-259 and an SO-239 or barrel connector depends on the male side pin OD being correct and the matching fingers on the female side being the correct diameter and made of the proper spring material.

• **Center socket spring tension:** If the SO-239 socket metal relaxes over time and/or temperature, an intermittent connection will be created that can be very hard to track down.

• **Mating indentions:** The indentations on the end of the SO-239 that mate to a PL-259 (the annulus flange) may only have four indentations to match up with the short prongs on the body of the male connector. A quality SO-239 or barrel connector has indentations all the way around. If the PL-259 and SO-239 don't seat completely, an intermittent connection is likely to develop.

• **Tee and right-angle (elbow) UHF adapters:** The center conductor has to make a right-angle turn inside the shell. In poor-quality adapters the right-angle connection is done with a spring contact — these do not hold up. Quality tee and right-angle adapters are reliable because the internal conductors are tapped and threaded — the conductors are screwed together within the body at the right angle junction.

How can we tell the good connectors? If the price is too good to be true — well, it is. PL-259s with good silver plating have a dull appearance. Good connectors have a part number and manufacturer's name stamped into them. You can look up the connector's specifications if it's marked. An example is the connectors made by Amphenol — all of which have parts numbers such as 83-1SP (PL-259) or 83-1R (SO-239) stamped into or onto the connector body.

22.10 Reference Tables

Table 22.62
International System of Units (SI) — Metric Units

Prefix	Symbol	Multiplication Factor		
exe	E	10^{18}	=	1,000,000 000,000,000,000
peta	P	10^{15}	=	1,000 000,000,000,000
tera	T	10^{12}	=	1,000,000,000,000
giga	G	10^{9}	=	1,000,000,000
mega	M	10^{6}	=	1,000,000
kilo	k	10^{3}	=	1,000
hecto	h	10^{2}	=	100
deca	da	10^{1}	=	10
		10^{0}	=	1
deci	d	10^{-1}	=	0.1
centi	c	10^{-2}	=	0.01
milli	m	10^{-3}	=	0.001
micro	µ	10^{-6}	=	0.000001
nano	n	10^{-9}	=	0.000000001
pico	p	10^{-12}	=	0.000000000001
femto	f	10^{-15}	=	0.000000000000001
atto	a	10^{-18}	=	0.000000000000000001

Linear
1 meter (m) = 100 centimeters (cm) = 1000 millimeters (mm)

Area
1 m^2 = 1 × 10^4 cm^2 = 1 × 10^6 mm^2

Volume
1 m^3 = 1 × 10^6 cm^3 = 1 × 10^9 mm^3
1 liter (l) = 1000 cm^3 = 1 × 10^6 mm^3

Mass
1 kilogram (kg) = 1000 grams (g)
  (Approximately the mass of 1 liter of water)
1 metric ton (or tonne) = 1000 kg

Table 22.63
US Customary Units and Conversion Factors

Linear Units
12 inches (in) = 1 foot (ft)
36 inches = 3 feet = 1 yard (yd)
1 rod = 5$\frac{1}{2}$ yards = 16$\frac{1}{2}$ feet
1 statute mile = 1760 yards = 5280 feet
1 nautical mile = 6076.11549 feet

Area
1 ft^2 = 144 in^2
1 yd^2 = 9 ft^2 = 1296 in^2
1 rod^2 = 30$\frac{1}{4}$ yd^2
1 acre = 4840 yd^2 = 43,560 ft^2
1 acre = 160 rod^2
1 mile^2 = 640 acres

Volume
1 ft^3 = 1728 in^3
1 yd^3 = 27 ft^3

Liquid Volume Measure
1 fluid ounce (fl oz) = 8 fluid drams = 1.804 in
1 pint (pt) = 16 fl oz
1 quart (qt) = 2 pt = 32 fl oz = 57$\frac{3}{4}$ in^3
1 gallon (gal) = 4 qt = 231 in^3
1 barrel = 31$\frac{1}{2}$ gal

Dry Volume Measure
1 quart (qt) = 2 pints (pt) = 67.2 in^3
1 peck = 8 qt
1 bushel = 4 pecks = 2150.42 in^3

Avoirdupois Weight
1 dram (dr) = 27.343 grains (gr) or (gr a)
1 ounce (oz) = 437.5 gr
1 pound (lb) = 16 oz = 7000 gr
1 short ton = 2000 lb, 1 long ton = 2240 lb

Troy Weight
1 grain troy (gr t) = 1 grain avoirdupois
1 pennyweight (dwt) or (pwt) = 24 gr t
1 ounce troy (oz t) = 480 grains
1 lb t = 12 oz t = 5760 grains

Apothecaries' Weight
1 grain apothecaries' (gr ap)
  = 1 gr t = 1 gr
1 dram ap (dr ap) = 60 gr
1 oz ap = 1 oz t = 8 dr ap = 480 gr
1 lb ap = 1 lb t = 12 oz ap = 5760 gr

Conversion
Metric Unit = Metric Unit × US Unit

(Length)

mm	25.4	inch
cm	2.54	inch
cm	30.48	foot
m	0.3048	foot
m	0.9144	yard
km	1.609	mile
km	1.852	nautical mile

(Area)

mm^2	645.16	inch^2
cm^2	6.4516	in^2
cm^2	929.03	ft^2
m^2	0.0929	ft^2
cm^2	8361.3	yd^2
m^2	0.83613	yd^2
m^2	4047	acre
km^2	2.59	mi^2

(Mass)   **(Avoirdupois Weight)**

grams	0.0648	grains
g	28.349	oz
g	453.59	lb
kg	0.45359	lb
tonne	0.907	short ton
tonne	1.016	long ton

(Volume)

mm^3	16387.064	in^3
cm^3	16.387	in^3
m^3	0.028316	ft^3
m^3	0.764555	yd^3
ml	16.387	in^3
ml	29.57	fl oz
ml	473	pint
ml	946.333	quart
l	28.32	ft^3
l	0.9463	quart
l	3.785	gallon
l	1.101	dry quart
l	8.809	peck
l	35.238	bushel

(Mass)   **(Troy Weight)**

g	31.103	oz t
g	373.248	lb t

(Mass)   **(Apothecaries' Weight)**

g	3.387	dr ap
g	31.103	oz ap
g	373.248	lb ap

Multiply →
Metric Unit = Conversion Factor × US Customary Unit

← Divide
Metric Unit ÷ Conversion Factor = US Customary Unit

Table 22.64
Voltage-Power Conversion Table

Based on a 50-ohm system

| \-\-\-\-\-\-\-\-\-\-\- Voltage \-\-\-\-\-\-\-\-\-\-\- ||| \-\-\-\-\-\-\-\-\-\-\- Power \-\-\-\-\-\-\-\-\-\-\- ||
RMS	Peak-to-Peak	dBmV	Watts	dBm
0.01 µV	0.0283 µV	−100	2×10^{-18}	−147.0
0.02 µV	0.0566 µV	−93.98	8×10^{-18}	−141.0
0.04 µV	0.113 µV	−87.96	32×10^{-18}	−134.9
0.08 µV	0.226 µV	−81.94	128×10^{-18}	−128.9
0.1 µV	0.283 µV	−80.0	200×10^{-18}	−127.0
0.2 µV	0.566 µV	−73.98	800×10^{-18}	−121.0
0.4 µV	1.131 µV	−67.96	3.2×10^{-15}	−114.9
0.8 µV	2.236 µV	−61.94	12.8×10^{-15}	−108.9
1.0 µV	2.828 µV	−60.0	20.0×10^{15}	−107.0
2.0 µV	5.657 µV	−53.98	80.0×10^{-15}	−101.0
4.0 µV	11.31 µV	−47.96	320×10^{-15}	−94.95
8.0 µV	22.63 µV	−41.94	1.28×10^{-12}	−88.93
10.0 µV	28.28 µV	−40.00	2.0×10^{-12}	−86.99
20.0 µV	56.57 µV	−33.98	8.0×10^{-12}	−80.97
40.0 µV	113.1 µV	−27.96	32.0×10^{-12}	−74.95
80.0 µV	226.3 µV	−21.94	128.0×10^{-12}	−68.93
100.0 µV	282.8 µV	−20.0	200.0×10^{12}	−66.99
200.0 µV	565.7 µV	−13.98	800.0×10^{-12}	−60.97
400.0 µV	1.131 mV	−7.959	3.2×10^{-9}	−54.95
800.0 µV	2.263 mV	−1.938	12.8×10^{-9}	−48.93
1.0 mV	2.828 mV	0.0	20.0×10^{-9}	−46.99
2.0 mV	5.657 mV	6.02	80.0×10^{-9}	−40.97
4.0 mV	11.31 mV	12.04	320×10^{-9}	−34.95
8.0 mV	22.63 mV	18.06	1.28 µW	−28.93
10.0 mV	28.28 mV	20.00	1 2.0 µW	−26.99
20.0 mV	56.57 mV	26.02	8.0 µW	−20.97
40.0 mV	113.1 mV	32.04	32.0 µW	−14.95
80.0 mV	226.3 mV	38.06	128.0 µW	−8.93
100.0 mV	282.8 mV	40.0	200.0 µW	−6.99
200.0 mV	565.7 mV	46.02	800.0 µW	−0.97
223.6 mV	632.4 mV	46.99	1.0 mW	0
400.0 mV	1.131 V	52.04	3.2 mW	5.05
800.0 mV	2.263 V	58.06	12.80 mW	11.07
1.0 V	2.828 V	60.0	20.0 mW	13.01
2.0 V	5.657 V	66.02	80.0 mW	19.03
4.0 V	11.31 V	72.04	320.0 mW	25.05
8.0 V	22.63 V	78.06	1.28 W	31.07
10.0 V	28.28 V	80.0	2.0 W	33.01
20.0 V	56.57 V	86.02	8.0 W	39.03
40.0 V	113.1 V	92.04	32.0 W	45.05
80.0 V	226.3 V	98.06	128.0 W	51.07
100.0 V	282.8 V	100.0	200.0 W	53.01
200.0 V	565.7 V	106.0	800.0 W	59.03
223.6 V	632.4 V	107.0	1,000.0 W	60.0
400.0 V	1,131.0 V	112.0	3,200.0 W	65.05
800.0 V	2,263.0 V	118.1	12,800.0 W	71.07
1000.0 V	2,828.0 V	120.0	20,000 W	73.01
2000.0 V	5,657.0 V	126.0	80,000 W	79.03
4000.0 V	11,310.0 V	132.0	320,000 W	85.05
8000.0 V	22,630.0 V	138.1	1.28 MW	91.07
10,000.0 V	28,280.0 V	140.0	2.0 MW	93.01

Table 22.65
Reflection Coefficient, Attenuation, SWR and Return Loss

Reflection Coefficient (%)	Attenuation (dB)	Max SWR	Return Loss, dB	Reflection Coefficient (%)	Attenuation (dB)	Max SWR	Return Loss, dB
1.000	0.000434	1.020	40.00	45.351	1.0000	2.660	6.87
1.517	0.001000	1.031	36.38	48.000	1.1374	2.846	6.38
2.000	0.001738	1.041	33.98	50.000	1.2494	3.000	6.02
3.000	0.003910	1.062	30.46	52.000	1.3692	3.167	5.68
4.000	0.006954	1.083	27.96	54.042	1.5000	3.352	5.35
4.796	0.01000	1.101	26.38	56.234	1.6509	3.570	5.00
5.000	0.01087	1.105	26.02	58.000	1.7809	3.762	4.73
6.000	0.01566	1.128	24.44	60.000	1.9382	4.000	4.44
7.000	0.02133	1.151	23.10	60.749	2.0000	4.095	4.33
7.576	0.02500	1.164	22.41	63.000	2.1961	4.405	4.01
8.000	0.02788	1.174	21.94	66.156	2.5000	4.909	3.59
9.000	0.03532	1.198	20.92	66.667	2.5528	5.000	3.52
10.000	0.04365	1.222	20.00	70.627	3.0000	5.809	3.02
10.699	0.05000	1.240	19.41	70.711	3.0103	5.829	3.01
11.000	0.05287	1.247	19.17				
12.000	0.06299	1.273	18.42				
13.085	0.07500	1.301	17.66				
14.000	0.08597	1.326	17.08				
15.000	0.09883	1.353	16.48				
15.087	0.10000	1.355	16.43				
16.000	0.1126	1.381	15.92				
17.783	0.1396	1.433	15.00				
18.000	0.1430	1.439	14.89				
19.000	0.1597	1.469	14.42				
20.000	0.1773	1.500	13.98				
22.000	0.2155	1.564	13.15				
23.652	0.2500	1.620	12.52				
24.000	0.2577	1.632	12.40				
25.000	0.2803	1.667	12.04				
26.000	0.3040	1.703	11.70				
27.000	0.3287	1.740	11.37				
28.000	0.3546	1.778	11.06				
30.000	0.4096	1.857	10.46				
31.623	0.4576	1.925	10.00				
32.977	0.5000	1.984	9.64				
33.333	0.5115	2.000	9.54				
34.000	0.5335	2.030	9.37				
35.000	0.5675	2.077	9.12				
36.000	0.6028	2.125	8.87				
37.000	0.6394	2.175	8.64				
38.000	0.6773	2.226	8.40				
39.825	0.75000	2.324	8.00				
40.000	0.7572	2.333	7.96				
42.000	0.8428	2.448	7.54				
42.857	0.8814	2.500	7.36				
44.000	0.9345	2.571	7.13				

$$\rho = \frac{SWR - 1}{SWR + 1}$$

where $\rho = 0.01 \times$ (reflection coefficient in %)

$$\rho = 10^{-RL/20}$$

where RL = return loss (dB)

$$\rho = \sqrt{1 - (0.1^X)}$$

where X = A/10 and A = attenuation (dB)

$$SWR = \frac{1 + \rho}{1 - \rho}$$

Table 22.66
Abbreviations List

A
a—atto (prefix for 10^{-18})
A—ampere (unit of electrical current)
ac—alternating current
ACC—Affiliated Club Coordinator
ACSSB—amplitude-compandored single sideband
A/D—analog-to-digital
ADC—analog-to-digital converter
AF—audio frequency
AFC—automatic frequency control
AFSK—audio frequency-shift keying
AGC—automatic gain control
Ah—ampere hour
ALC—automatic level control
AM—amplitude modulation
AMRAD—Amateur Radio Research and Development Corporation
AMSAT—Radio Amateur Satellite Corporation
AMTOR—Amateur Teleprinting Over Radio
ANT—antenna
ARA—Amateur Radio Association
ARC—Amateur Radio Club
ARES—Amateur Radio Emergency Service
ARQ—Automatic repeat request
ARRL—American Radio Relay League
ARS—Amateur Radio Society (station)
ASCII—American National Standard Code for Information Interchange
ATV—amateur television
AVC—automatic volume control
AWG—American wire gauge
az-el—azimuth-elevation

B
B—bel; blower; susceptance; flux density, (inductors)
balun—balanced to unbalanced (transformer)
BC—broadcast
BCD—binary coded decimal
BCI—broadcast interference
Bd—baud (bids in single-channel binary data transmission)
BER—bit error rate
BFO—beat-frequency oscillator
bit—binary digit
bit/s—bits per second
BM—Bulletin Manager
BPF—band-pass filter
BPL—Brass Pounders League
BPL—Broadband over Power Line
BT—battery
BW—bandwidth
Bytes—Bytes

C
c—centi (prefix for 10^{-2})
C—coulomb (quantity of electric charge); capacitor
CAC—Contest Advisory Committee
CATVI—cable television interference
CB—Citizens Band (radio)
CBBS—computer bulletin-board service
CBMS—computer-based message system
CCITT—International Telegraph and Telephone Consultative Committee
CCTV—closed-circuit television
CCW—coherent CW
ccw—counterclockwise
CD—civil defense
cm—centimeter
CMOS—complementary-symmetry metal-oxide semiconductor
coax—coaxial cable
COR—carrier-operated relay
CP—code proficiency (award)
CPU—central processing unit
CRT—cathode ray tube
CT—center tap
CTCSS—continuous tone-coded squelch system
cw—clockwise
CW—continuous wave

D
d—deci (prefix for 10^{-1})
D—diode
da—deca (prefix for 10)
D/A—digital-to-analog
DAC—digital-to-analog converter
dB—decibel (0.1 bel)
dBi—decibels above (or below) isotropic antenna
dBm—decibels above (or below) 1 milliwatt
DBM—double balanced mixer
dBV—decibels above/below 1 V (in video, relative to 1 V P-P)
dBW—decibels above/below 1 W
dc—direct current
D-C—direct conversion
DDS—direct digital synthesis
DEC—District Emergency Coordinator
deg—degree
DET—detector
DF—direction finding; direction finder
DIP—dual in-line package
DMM—digital multimeter
DPDT—double-pole double-throw (switch)
DPSK—differential phase-shift keying
DPST—double-pole single-throw (switch)
DS—direct sequence (spread spectrum); display
DSB—double sideband
DSP—digital signal processing
DTMF—dual-tone multifrequency
DV—digital voice
DVM—digital voltmeter
DX—long distance; duplex
DXAC—DX Advisory Committee
DXCC—DX Century Club

E
e—base of natural logarithms (2.71828)
E—voltage
EA—ARRL Educational Advisor
EC—Emergency Coordinator
ECL—emitter-coupled logic
EHF—extremely high frequency (30-300 GHz)
EIA—Electronic Industries Alliance
EIRP—effective isotropic radiated power
ELF—extremely low frequency
ELT—emergency locator transmitter
EMC—electromagnetic compatibility
EME—earth-moon-earth (moonbounce)
EMF—electromotive force
EMI—electromagnetic interference
EMP—electromagnetic pulse
EOC—emergency operations center
EPROM—erasable programmable read only memory

F
f—femto (prefix for 10^{-15}); frequency
F—farad (capacitance unit); fuse
fax—facsimile
FCC—Federal Communications Commission
FD—Field Day
FEMA—Federal Emergency Management Agency
FET—field-effect transistor
FFT—fast Fourier transform
FL—filter
FM—frequency modulation
FMTV—frequency-modulated television
FSK—frequency-shift keying
FSTV—fast-scan (real-time) television
ft—foot (unit of length)

G
g—gram (unit of mass)
G—giga (prefix for 10^9); conductance
GaAs—gallium arsenide
GB—gigabytes
GDO—grid- or gate-dip oscillator
GHz—gigahertz (10^9 Hz)
GND—ground

H
h—hecto (prefix for 10^2)
H—henry (unit of inductance)
HF—high frequency (3-30 MHz)
HFO—high-frequency oscillator; heterodyne frequency oscillator
HPF—highest probable frequency; high-pass filter
Hz—hertz (unit of frequency, 1 cycle/s)

I
I—current, indicating lamp
IARU—International Amateur Radio Union
IC—integrated circuit
ID—identification; inside diameter
IEEE—Institute of Electrical and Electronics Engineers
IF—intermediate frequency

22.62   Chapter 22

IMD—intermodulation distortion
in.—inch (unit of length)
in./s—inch per second (unit of velocity)
I/O—input/output
IRC—international reply coupon
ISB—independent sideband
ITF—Interference Task Force
ITU—International Telecommunication Union
ITU-T—ITU Telecommunication Standardization Bureau

J-K

j—operator for complex notation, as for reactive component of an impedance ($+j$ inductive; $-j$ capacitive)
J—joule (kg m^2/s^2) (energy or work unit); jack
JFET—junction field-effect transistor
k—kilo (prefix for 10^3); Boltzmann's constant (1.38×10^{-23} J/K)
K—kelvin (used without degree symbol) absolute temperature scale; relay
kB—kilobytes
kBd—1000 bauds
kbit—1024 bits
kbit/s—1024 bits per second
kbyte—1024 bytes
kg—kilogram
kHz—kilohertz
km—kilometer
kV—kilovolt
kW—kilowatt
kΩ—kilohm

L

l—liter (liquid volume)
L—lambert; inductor
lb—pound (force unit)
LC—inductance-capacitance
LCD—liquid crystal display
LED—light-emitting diode
LF—low frequency (30-300 kHz)
LHC—left-hand circular (polarization)
LO—local oscillator; Leadership Official
LP—log periodic
LS—loudspeaker
lsb—least significant bit
LSB—lower sideband
LSI—large-scale integration
LUF—lowest usable frequency

M

m—meter (length); milli (prefix for 10^{-3})
M—mega (prefix for 10^6); meter (instrument)
mA—milliampere
mAh—milliampere hour
MB—megabytes
MCP—multimode communications processor
MDS—Multipoint Distribution Service; minimum discernible (or detectable) signal
MF—medium frequency (300-3000 kHz)
mH—millihenry
MHz—megahertz

mi—mile, statute (unit of length)
mi/h (MPH)—mile per hour
mi/s—mile per second
mic—microphone
Mil—one-thousandth of an inch
min—minute (time)
MIX—mixer
mm—millimeter
MOD—modulator
modem—modulator/demodulator
MOS—metal-oxide semiconductor
MOSFET—metal-oxide semiconductor field-effect transistor
MS—meteor scatter
ms—millisecond
m/s—meters per second
msb—most-significant bit
MSI—medium-scale integration
MSK—minimum-shift keying
MSO—message storage operation
MUF—maximum usable frequency
mV—millivolt
mW—milliwatt
MΩ—megohm

N

n—nano (prefix for 10^{-9}); number of turns (inductors)
NBFM—narrow-band frequency modulation
NC—no connection; normally closed
NCS—net-control station; National Communications System
nF—nanofarad
NF—noise figure
nH—nanohenry
NiCd—nickel cadmium
NM—Net Manager
NMOS—N-channel metal-oxide silicon
NO—normally open
NPN—negative-positive-negative (transistor)
NPRM—Notice of Proposed Rule Making (FCC)
ns—nanosecond
NTIA—National Telecommunications and Information Administration
NTS—National Traffic System

O

OBS—Official Bulletin Station
OD—outside diameter
OES—Official Emergency Station
OO—Official Observer
op amp—operational amplifier
ORS—Official Relay Station
OSC—oscillator
OSCAR—Orbiting Satellite Carrying Amateur Radio
OTC—Old Timer's Club
oz—ounce ($\frac{1}{16}$ pound)

P

p—pico (prefix for 10^{-12})
P—power; plug
PA—power amplifier
PACTOR—digital mode combining aspects of packet and AMTOR
PAM—pulse-amplitude modulation
PBS—packet bulletin-board system

PC—printed circuit
PD—power dissipation
PEP—peak envelope power
PEV—peak envelope voltage
pF—picofarad
pH—picohenry
PIC—Public Information Coordinator
PIN—positive-intrinsic-negative (semiconductor)
PIO—Public Information Officer
PIV—peak inverse voltage
PLC—Power Line Carrier
PLL—phase-locked loop
PM—phase modulation
PMOS—P-channel (metal-oxide semiconductor)
PNP—positive negative positive (transistor)
pot—potentiometer
P-P—peak to peak
ppd—postpaid
PROM—programmable read-only memory
PSAC—Public Service Advisory Committee
PSHR—Public Service Honor Roll
PTO—permeability-tuned oscillator
PTT—push to talk

Q-R

Q—figure of merit (tuned circuit); transistor
QRP—low power (less than 5-W output)
R—resistor
RACES—Radio Amateur Civil Emergency Service
RAM—random-access memory
RC—resistance-capacitance
R/C—radio control
RCC—Rag Chewer's Club
RDF—radio direction finding
RF—radio frequency
RFC—radio-frequency choke
RFI—radio-frequency interference
RHC—right-hand circular (polarization)
RIT—receiver incremental tuning
RLC—resistance-inductance-capacitance
RM—rule making (number assigned to petition)
r/min (RPM)—revolutions per minute
rms—root mean square
ROM—read-only memory
r/s—revolutions per second
RS—Radio Sputnik (Russian ham satellite)
RST—readability-strength-tone (CW signal report)
RTTY—radioteletype
RX—receiver, receiving

S

s—second (time)
S—siemens (unit of conductance); switch
SASE—self-addressed stamped envelope
SCF—switched capacitor filter
SCR—silicon controlled rectifier
SEC—Section Emergency Coordinator

Component Data and References 22.63

SET—Simulated Emergency Test
SGL—State Government Liaison
SHF—super-high frequency (3-30 GHz)
SM—Section Manager; silver mica (capacitor)
S/N—signal-to-noise ratio
SPDT—single-pole double-throw (switch)
SPST—single-pole single-throw (switch)
SS—ARRL Sweepstakes; spread spectrum
SSB—single sideband
SSC—Special Service Club
SSI—small-scale integration
SSTV—slow-scan television
STM—Section Traffic Manager
SX—simplex
sync—synchronous, synchronizing
SWL—shortwave listener
SWR—standing-wave ratio

T
T—tera (prefix for 10^{12}); transformer
TA—ARRL Technical Advisor
TC—Technical Coordinator
TCC—Transcontinental Corps (NTS)
TCP/IP—Transmission Control Protocol/Internet Protocol
tfc—traffic
TNC—terminal node controller (packet radio)
TR—transmit/receive
TS—Technical Specialist
TTL—transistor-transistor logic
TTY—teletypewriter
TU—terminal unit
TV—television
TVI—television interference
TX—transmitter, transmitting

U
U—integrated circuit
UHF—ultra-high frequency (300 MHz to 3 GHz)
USB—upper sideband
UTC—Coordinated Universal Time (also abbreviated Z)
UV—ultraviolet

V
V—volt; vacuum tube
VCO—voltage-controlled oscillator
VCR—video cassette recorder
VDT—video-display terminal
VE—Volunteer Examiner

VEC—Volunteer Examiner Coordinator
VFO—variable-frequency oscillator
VHF—very-high frequency (30-300 MHz)
VLF—very-low frequency (3-30 kHz)
VLSI—very-large-scale integration
VMOS—V-topology metal-oxide-semiconductor
VOM—volt-ohmmeter
VOX—voice-operated switch
VR—voltage regulator
VSWR—voltage standing-wave ratio
VTVM—vacuum-tube voltmeter
VUCC—VHF/UHF Century Club
VXO—variable-frequency crystal oscillator

W
W—watt (kg m^{2}s^{-3}), unit of power
WAC—Worked All Continents
WAS—Worked All States
WBFM—wide-band frequency modulation
WEFAX—weather facsimile
Wh—watthour
WPM—words per minute
WRC—World Radiocommunication Conference
WVDC—working voltage, direct current

X
X—reactance
XCVR—transceiver
XFMR—transformer
XIT—transmitter incremental tuning
XO—crystal oscillator
XTAL—crystal
XVTR—transverter

Y-Z
Y—crystal; admittance
YIG—yttrium iron garnet
Z—impedance; also see UTC

Numbers/Symbols
5BDXCC—Five-Band DXCC
5BWAC—Five-Band WAC
5BWAS—Five-Band WAS
6BWAC—Six-Band WAC
°—degree (plane angle)
°C—degree Celsius (temperature)
°F—degree Fahrenheit (temperature)
α—(alpha) angles; coefficients, attenuation constant, absorption factor, area, common-base forward current-transfer ratio of a bipolar transistor
β—(beta) angles; coefficients, phase constant, current gain of common-emitter transistor amplifiers
γ—(gamma) specific gravity, angles, electrical conductivity, propagation constant
Γ—(gamma) complex propagation constant
δ—(delta) increment or decrement; density; angles
Δ—(delta) increment or decrement determinant, permittivity
ε—(epsilon) dielectric constant; permittivity; electric intensity
ζ—(zeta) coordinates; coefficients
η—(eta) intrinsic impedance; efficiency; surface charge density; hysteresis; coordinate
θ—(theta) angular phase displacement; time constant; reluctance; angles
ι—(iota) unit vector
κ—(kappa) susceptibility; coupling coefficient
λ—(lambda) wavelength; attenuation constant
Λ—(lambda) permeance
μ—(mu) permeability; amplification factor; micro (prefix for 10^{-6})
μF—microfarad
μH—microhenry
μP—microprocessor
ξ—(xi) coordinates
π—(pi) ≈3.14159
ρ—(rho) resistivity; volume charge density; coordinates; reflection coefficient
σ—(sigma) surface charge density; complex propagation constant; electrical conductivity; leakage coefficient; deviation
Σ—(sigma) summation
τ—(tau) time constant; volume resistivity; time-phase displacement; transmission factor; density
φ—(phi) magnetic flux angles
Φ—(phi) angles
χ—(chi) electric susceptibility; angles
Ψ—(psi) dielectric flux; phase difference; coordinates; angles
ω—(omega) angular velocity 2 πF
Ω—(omega) resistance in ohms; solid angle

Contents

23.1 Electronic Shop Safety
    23.1.1 Chemicals
23.2 Tools and Their Use
    23.2.1 Sources of Tools
    23.2.2 Tool Descriptions and Uses
23.3 Soldering Tools and Techniques
    23.3.1 Soldering Irons
    23.3.2 Solder
    23.3.3 Soldering
    23.3.4 Desoldering
    23.3.5 Soldering Safety
23.4 Surface Mount Technology (SMT)
    23.4.1 Equipment Needed
    23.4.2 Surface-Mount Parts
    23.4.3 SMT Soldering Basics
    23.4.4 Removing SMT Components
    23.4.5 SMT Construction Examples
23.5 Constructing Electronic Circuits
    23.5.1 Electrostatic Discharge (ESD)
    23.5.2 Sorting Parts
    23.5.3 Construction Order
    23.5.4 Component Mounting
    23.5.5 Electronics Construction Techniques
    23.5.6 Printed-Circuit (PC) Boards
    23.5.7 From Schematic to Working Circuit
    23.5.8 Tuning and Alignment
    23.5.9 Other Construction Techniques

23.6 CAD for PCB Design
    23.6.1 Overview of the PCB Design Process
    23.6.2 Types of PCB Design Software
    23.6.3 Schematic Capture
    23.6.4 PCB Characteristics
    23.6.5 PCB Design Elements
    23.6.6 PCB Layout
    23.6.7 Preparation for Fabrication
23.7 Microwave Construction
    23.7.1 Lead Lengths
    23.7.2 Metalworking
    23.7.3 Circuit Construction
    23.7.4 Capacitors for Microwave Construction
    23.7.5 Tuning and "No-Tune" Designs
23.8 Mechanical Fabrication
    23.8.1 Cutting and Bending Sheet Metal
    23.8.2 Finishing Aluminum
    23.8.3 Chassis Working
    23.8.4 Drilling Techniques
    23.8.5 Construction Notes

Chapter 23

Construction Techniques

Home construction of electronics projects and kits can be a fun part of Amateur Radio. A recent ARRL survey shows that more than half of active hams build electronic projects. There are many kit vendors with products ranging from simple introductory projects all the way to complete transceivers. Becoming familiar with building practices will help you repair and install commercial equipment as well.

Even experienced constructors will find valuable tips in this chapter. It discusses tools and their uses, electronic construction techniques, tells how to turn a schematic into a working circuit and then summarizes common mechanical construction practices. This chapter is maintained by Joe Eisenberg, KØNEB based on material originally written and compiled by Ed Hare, W1RFI, and Jim Duffey, KK6MC. Dale Grover, KD8KYZ, maintains the comprehensive introduction to the use of PCB design and layout software.

Chapter 23 — Downloadable Supplemental Content

Supplemental Files
- "A No-Special-Tools SMD Desoldering Technique" by Wayne Yoshida, KH6WZ
- "Surface Mount Technology — You Can Work With It" by Sam Ulbing, N4UAU (Parts 1 - 4)
- Making Your Own Printed Circuit Boards
- "Reflow Soldering for the Radio Amateur" by Jim Koehler, VE5JP
- "Re-purposing Obsolete Instrument Enclosures" by Scott Roleson, KC7CJ

23.1 Electronic Shop Safety

Building, repairing and modifying equipment in home workshops is a longstanding ham radio tradition. In fact, in the early days, building your own equipment was the only option available. While times and interests change, home construction of radio equipment and related accessories remains popular and enjoyable. Building your own gear need not be hazardous if you become familiar with the hazards, learn how to perform the necessary functions and follow some basic safe practices including the ones listed below and in the section on soldering. Let's start with our own abilities:

Consider your state of mind. Working on projects or troubleshooting (especially where high voltage is present) requires concentration. Don't work when you're tired or distracted. Be realistic about your ability to focus on the job at hand. Put another way, if we aren't able to be highly alert, we should put off doing hazardous work until we are able to focus on the hazards.

Think! Pay attention to what you are doing. No list of safety rules can cover all possibilities. Safety is always your responsibility. You must think about what you are doing, how it relates to the tools and the specific situation at hand. When working with tools, avoid creating situations in which you can be injured or the project damaged if things don't go "just right."

Take your time. If you hurry, not only will you make more mistakes and possibly spoil the appearance of your new equipment, you won't have time to think things through. Always plan ahead. Do not work with shop tools if you can't concentrate on what you are doing — it's not a race! Working when you are tired can also lead to problems, such as misidentification of parts or making poor or erroneous connections. Listening to the regular time notices on broadcast radio while you work will prompt you to take plenty of breaks so you do not work when you are too tired.

Protect yourself. Use of drills, saws, grinders and other wood- or metal-working equipment can release small fragments that could cause serious eye damage. Always wear safety glasses or goggles when doing work that might present a flying object hazard and that includes soldering, where small bits of molten solder can be flung a surprising distance. If you use hammers, wire-cutters, chisels and other hand tools, you will also need the protection that safety eyewear offers. Dress appropriately — loose clothing (or even hair) can be caught in exposed rotating equipment such as drill presses.

Don't work alone. Have someone nearby who can help if you get into trouble when working with dangerous equipment, chemicals or voltages.

Know what to do in an emergency. Despite your best efforts to be careful, accidents may still occur from time to time. Ensure that everyone in your household knows basic first aid procedures and understands how to summon help in an emergency. They should also know where to find and how to safely shut down electrical power in your shack and shop. Get medical help when necessary. Every workshop should contain a good first-aid kit. Keep an eye-wash kit near any dangerous chemicals or power tools that can create chips or splinters. If you become injured, apply first aid and then seek medical help if you are not sure that you are okay. Even a small burn or scratch on your eye can develop into a serious problem if not treated promptly.

What about the equipment and tools involved in shop work? Here are some basic safety considerations that apply to them, as well:

Table 23.1
Properties and Hazards of Chemicals often Used in the Shack or Workshop

Generic Chemical Name	Purpose or Use	Hazards	Ways to Minimize Risks
Lead-tin solder	Bonding electrical components	Lead exposure (mostly from hand contact)	Always wash hands after soldering or touching solder.
		Flux exposure (inhalation)	Use good ventilation.
Isopropyl alcohol	Flux remover	Dermatitis (skin rash)	Wear molded gloves suitable for solvents.
		Vapor inhalation	Use good ventilation and avoid aerosol generation.
		Fire hazard	Use good ventilation, limit use to small amounts, keep ignition sources away, dispose of rags only in tightly sealed metal cans.
Freons	Circuit cooling and general solvent	Vapor inhalation	Use adequate ventilation.
		Dermatitis	Wear molded gloves suitable for solvents.
Phenols and methylene chloride	Enameled wire/ paint stripper	Strong skin corrosive	Avoid skin contact; wear suitable molded gloves; use adequate ventilation.
Beryllium oxide	Ceramic insulator found in some power transistors and vacuum tubes that conducts heat well	Toxic when in fine dust form and inhaled	Avoid grinding, sawing or reducing to dust form.
Beryllium metal	Lightweight metal, alloyed with copper	Same as beryllium oxide	Avoid grinding, sawing, welding or reducing to dust. Contact supplier for special procedures.
Various paints	Finishing	Exposures to solvents	Adequate ventilation; use respirator when spraying.
		Exposures to sensitizers (especially urethane paint)	Adequate ventilation and use respirator.
		Exposure to toxic metals (lead, cadmium, chrome, and so on) in pigments	Adequate ventilation and use respirator.
		Fire hazard (especially when spray painting)	Adequate ventilation; control of residues; eliminate ignition sources.
Ferric chloride	Printed circuit board etchant	Skin and eye contact	Use suitable containers; wear splash goggles and molded gloves suitable for acids.
Ammonium persulphate and mercuric chloride	Printed circuit board etchants	Skin and eye contact	Use suitable containers; wear splash goggles and molded gloves suitable for acids.
Epoxy resins	General purpose cement or paint	Dermatitis and possible sensitizer	Avoid skin contact. Mix only amount needed.
Sulfuric acid	Electrolyte in lead-acid batteries	Strong corrosive when on skin or eyes. Will release hydrogen when charging (fire, explosion hazard).	Always wear splash goggles and molded plastic gloves (PVC) when handling. Keep ignition sources away from battery when charging. Use adequate ventilation.

Read instructions and manuals carefully... and follow them. The manufacturers of tools are the most knowledgeable about how to use their products safely. Tap their knowledge by carefully reading all operating instructions and warnings. Avoiding injuries with power tools requires safe tool design as well as proper operation by the user. Keep the instructions in a place where you can refer to them in the future.

Respect safety features of the equipment you work on and use. Never disable any safety feature of any tool. If you do, sooner or later you or someone else will make the mistake the safety feature was designed to prevent.

Keep your shop or work area neat and organized. A messy shop is a dangerous shop. A knife left laying in a drawer can cut someone looking for another tool; a hammer left on top of a shelf can fall down at the worst possible moment; a sharp tool left on a chair can be a dangerous surprise for the weary constructor who sits down.

Keep your tools in good condition. Always take care of your investment. Store tools in a way to prevent damage or use by untrained persons (young children, for example). Keep the cutting edges of saws, chisels and drill bits sharp. Protect metal surfaces from corrosion. Frequently inspect the cords and plugs of electrical equipment and make any necessary repairs. If you find that your power cord is becoming frayed, repair it right away. One solution is to buy a replacement cord with a molded connector already attached.

Make sure your shop is well ventilated. Paint, solvents, cleaners or other chemicals can create dangerous fumes. If you feel dizzy, get into fresh air immediately, and seek medical help if you do not recover quickly.

Respect power tools. Power tools are not forgiving. A drill can go through your hand a lot easier than metal. A power saw can remove a finger with ease. Keep away from the business end of power tools. Tuck in your shirt, roll up your sleeves and remove your tie before using any power tool. If you have long hair, tie it back so it can't become entangled in power equipment.

23.1.1 Chemicals

Chemicals such as cleaners, adhesives, construction materials, and coolants are used every day by amateurs without ill effects. Take the opportunity to become knowledgeable of the hazards associated with these materials and treat them with respect. **Table 23.1** summarizes the uses and hazards of chemicals and other materials used in the ham shack. It includes preventive measures that can minimize risk. For advanced information, the Centers for Disease Prevention and Control maintains an extensive database at **www.cdc.gov/niosh/topics/chemicalsafety**. Meridian Engineering maintains a collection of materials safety information at **www.meridianeng.com/datasheets.html**. When in doubt, contact the manufacturer or distributor of the material for safety information or use an Internet search engine by entering the material name and "safety" into the search window.

Here are a few key suggestions for safely storing, handling, and using chemicals:

Read the information that accompanies the chemical and follow the manufacturer's recommended safety practices. If you would like more information than is printed on the label, ask for a material safety data sheet (MSDS). Manufacturers of brand-name chemical products usually post an MSDS on their product websites.

Store chemicals properly, away from sunlight and sources of heat. Secure their containers to prevent spills and so that children and untrained persons will not gain access. Always keep containers labeled so there is no confusion about the contents. It is best to use the container in which the chemical was purchased. If you transfer solvents to other containers, such as wash bottles, label the new container with exactly what it contains.

Handle chemicals carefully to avoid spills. Clean up any spills or leaks promptly but don't overexpose yourself in the process. Never dispose of chemicals in household sinks or drains. Instead, contact your local waste plant operator, transfer station or fire department to determine the proper disposal procedures for your area. Many communities have household hazardous waste collection programs. Of course, the best solution is to only buy the amount of chemical that you will need, and use it all if possible. Always label any waste chemicals, especially if they are no longer in their original containers. Oil-filled capacitors and transformers were once commonly filled with oil containing PCBs. Never dispose of any such items that may contain PCBs in landfills – contact your county or city recycling office or local electric utility for information on proper disposal.

Always use recommended personal protective equipment (such as gloves, face shield, splash goggles and aprons). If corrosives (acids or caustics) are splashed on you *immediately* rinse with cold water for a minimum of 15 minutes to flush the skin thoroughly. If splashed in the eyes, direct a gentle stream of cold water into the eyes for at least 15 minutes. Gently lift the eyelids so trapped liquids can be flushed completely. Start flushing before removing contaminated clothing. Seek professional medical assistance. If using hazardous chemicals, it is unwise to work alone since people splashed with chemicals need the calm influence of another person.

Food and chemicals don't mix. Keep food, drinks and cigarettes *away* from areas where chemicals are used and don't bring chemicals to places where you eat.

Poison Control

If you think you have a chemical emergency, call your local poison control center immediately. Dial 1-800-222-1222 or use the map at **www.poison.org/otherPC** to find the center in your area or dial 911.

23.2 Tools and Their Use

All electronic construction makes use of tools, from mechanical tools for chassis fabrication to the soldering tools used for circuit assembly. A good understanding of tools and their uses will enable you to perform most construction tasks.

While sophisticated and expensive tools often work better or more quickly than simple hand tools, with proper use, simple hand tools can turn out a fine piece of equipment. **Table 23.2** lists tools indispensable for construction of electronic equipment. These tools can be used to perform nearly any construction task. Add tools to your collection from time to time, as finances permit.

23.2.1 Sources of Tools

Electronic-supply houses, mail-order/web stores and most hardware stores carry the tools required to build or service Amateur Radio equipment. Bargains are available at ham flea markets or local neighborhood sales, but beware! Some flea-market bargains are really shoddy and won't work very well or last very long. Some used tools are offered for sale because the owner is not happy with their performance.

There is no substitute for quality! A high-quality tool, while a bit more expensive, will last a lifetime. Poor quality tools don't last long and often do a poor job even when brand new. You don't need to buy machinist-grade tools, but stay away from cheap tools; they are not the bargains they might appear to be.

CARE OF TOOLS

The proper care of tools is more than a matter of pride. Tools that have not been cared for properly will not last long or work well. Dull or broken tools can be safety hazards. Tools that are in good condition do the work for you; tools that are misused or dull are difficult to use.

Store tools in a dry place. Tools do not fit in with most living room decors, so they are often relegated to the basement or garage.

Table 23.2
Recommended Tools and Materials

Simple Hand Tools
Screwdrivers
Slotted, 3-in, 1/8-in blade
Slotted, 8-in, 1/8-in blade
Slotted, 3-in, 3/16-in blade
Slotted, stubby, 1/4-in blade
Slotted, 4-in, 1/4-in blade
Slotted, 6-in, 5/16-in blade
Phillips, 2½-in, #0 (pocket clip)
Phillips, 3-in, #1
Phillips, stubby, #2
Phillips, 4-in, #2
Long-shank screwdriver with holding clip on blade
Jeweler's set
Right-angle, slotted and Phillips

Pliers, Sockets and Wrenches
Long-nose pliers, 6- and 4-in
Diagonal cutters, 6- and 4-in
Channel-lock pliers, 6-in
Slip-joint pliers
Locking pliers (Vise Grip or equivalent)
Socket nut-driver set, 1/16- to 1/2-in
Set of socket wrenches for hex nuts
Allen (hex) wrench set
Wrench set
Adjustable wrenches, 6- and 10-in
Tweezers, regular and reverse-action
Retrieval tool/parts holder, flexible claw
Retrieval tool, magnetic

Cutting and Grinding Tools
File set consisting of flat, round, half-round, and triangular. Large and miniature types recommended
Burnishing tool
Wire strippers
Wire crimper
Hemostat, straight
Scissors
Tin shears, 10-in
Hacksaw and blades
Hand nibbling tool (for chassis-hole cutting)

Scratch awl or scriber (for marking metal)
Heavy-duty jackknife
Knife blade set (X-ACTO or equivalent)
Machine-screw taps, #4-40 through #10-32 thread
Socket punches, ½ in, 5/8 in, ¾ in, 1 1/8 in, 1¼ in, and 1½ in
Tapered reamer, T-handle, 1/2-in maximum width
Deburring tool

Miscellaneous Hand Tools
Combination square, 12-in, for layout work
Hammer, ball-peen, 12-oz head
Hammer, tack
Bench vise, 4-in jaws or larger
Center punch
Plastic alignment tools
Mirror, inspection
Flashlight, penlight and standard
Magnifying glass
Ruler or tape measure
Dental pick
Calipers
Brush, wire
Brush, soft
Small paintbrush
IC-puller tool

Hand-Powered Tools
Hand drill, 1/4-in chuck or larger
High-speed drill bits, #60 through 3/8-in diameter

Power Tools
Motor-driven emery wheel for grinding
Electric drill, hand-held
Drill press
Miniature electric motor tool (Dremel or equivalent) and accessory drill press

Soldering Tools and Supplies
Soldering station, adjustable temp, assorted tips
Soldering iron, 100 W or higher, 5/8-in tip

Soldering gun, 200 W or higher
Solder, 60/40, rosin core
Desoldering tool
Desoldering wick, 1/8-in and 1/4-in width
Liquid flux, pen or bottle
Isopropyl alcohol for flux removal

Safety
Safety glasses
Hearing protector, earphones or earplugs
Fire extinguisher
First-aid kit

Useful Materials
Medium-weight machine oil
Contact cleaner, liquid or spray can
RTV sealant or equivalent
Electrical tape, vinyl plastic
Sandpaper, assorted
Emery cloth
Steel wool, assorted
Cleaning pad, Scotchbrite or equivalent
Cleaners and degreasers
Contact lubricant
Sheet aluminum, solid and perforated, 16- or 18-gauge, for brackets and shielding.
Aluminum angle stock, ½ × ½-in and ¼-in diameter round brass or aluminum rod (for shaft extensions)
Machine screws: Round-head and flat head, with nuts and lockwashers to fit. Most useful sizes: 4-40, 6-32 and 8-32, in lengths from ¼-in to 1½ in (Nickel-plated steel is satisfactory except in strong RF fields, where brass should be used.)
Bakelite, Lucite, polystyrene and copper-clad PC-board scraps.
Soldering lugs, panel bearings, rubber grommets, terminal-lug wiring strips, varnished-cambric insulating tubing, heat-shrinkable tubing
Shielded and unshielded wire
Tinned bare wire, #22, #14 and #12
Enameled wire, #20 through #30

Unfortunately, many basements or garages are not good places to store tools; dampness and dust are not good for tools. If your tools are stored in a damp place, use a dehumidifier. Sometimes you can minimize rust by keeping your tools lightly oiled, but this is a second-best solution. If you oil your tools, they may not rust, but you will end up covered in oil every time you use them. Wax or silicone spray is a better alternative.

Store tools neatly. A messy toolbox, with tools strewn about haphazardly, can be more than an inconvenience. You may waste a lot of time looking for the right tool and sharp edges can be dulled or nicked by tools banging into each other in the bottom of the box. As the old adage says, every tool should have a place, and every tool should be in its place. If you must search the workbench, garage, attic and car to find the right screwdriver, you'll spend more time looking for tools than building projects.

SHARPENING

Many cutting tools can be sharpened. Send a tool that has been seriously dulled to a professional sharpening service. These services can sharpen saw blades, some files, drill bits and most cutting blades. Touch up the edge of cutting tools with a whetstone to extend the time between sharpening.

Sharpen drill bits frequently to minimize the amount of material that must be removed each time. Frequent sharpening also makes it easier to maintain the critical surface angles required for best cutting with least wear. Most inexpensive drill-bit sharpeners available for shop use do a poor job, either from the poor quality of the sharpening tool or inexperience of the operator. Also, drills should be sharpened at different angles for different applications. Commercial sharpening services do a much better job.

INTENDED PURPOSE

Don't use tools for anything other than their intended purpose! If you use a pair of wire cutters to cut sheet metal, pliers as a vise or a screwdriver as a pry bar, you ruin a good tool and sometimes the work piece, as well. Although an experienced constructor can improvise with tools, most take pride in not abusing them. Having a wide variety of good tools at your disposal minimizes the problem of using the wrong tool for the job.

23.2.2 Tool Descriptions and Uses

Specific applications for tools are discussed throughout this chapter. Hand tools are used for so many different applications that they are discussed first, followed by some tips for proper use of power tools.

SCREWDRIVERS AND NUTDRIVERS

For construction or repair, you need to have an assortment of screwdrivers. Each blade size is designed to fit a specific range of screw head sizes. Using the wrong size blade usually damages the blade, the screw head or both. You may also need stubby sizes to fit into tight spaces. Right-angle screwdrivers are inexpensive and can get into tight spaces that can't otherwise be reached.

Electric screwdrivers are relatively inexpensive and very useful, particularly for repetitive tasks. If you have a lot of screws to fasten, they can save a lot of time and effort. They come with a wide assortment of screwdriver and nutdriver bits. An electric drill can also function as an electric screwdriver, although it may be heavy and over-powered for many applications.

Keep screwdriver blades in good condition. If a blade becomes broken or worn out, replace the screwdriver. A screwdriver only costs a few dollars; do not use one that is not in perfect condition. Save old screwdrivers to use as pry bars and levers, but use only good ones on screws. Filing a worn blade seldom gives good results.

Nutdrivers, the complement to screwdrivers, are often much easier to use than a wrench, particularly for nuts smaller than ⅜ inch. They are also less damaging to the nut than any type of pliers, with a better grip on the nut. Nutdrivers also minimize the chances of damage to front panels when tightening the nuts on control shafts. A set of interchangeable nutdrivers with a shared handle is a very handy addition to the toolbox.

PLIERS AND LOCKING-GRIP PLIERS

Pliers and locking-grip pliers are used to hold or bend things. They are not wrenches! If pliers are used to remove a nut or bolt, the nut or the pliers is usually damaged. To remove a nut, use a wrench or nutdriver. There is one exception to this rule of thumb: To remove a nut that is stripped too badly for a wrench, use a pair of pliers, locking-grip pliers, or a diagonal cutter to bite into the nut and start it turning. Reserve an old tool or one dedicated to just this purpose as it is not good for the tool.

Pliers are not intended for heavy-duty applications. Use a metal brake to bend heavy metal; use a vise to hold a heavy component. If the pliers' jaws or teeth become worn, replace the tool.

There are many different kinds of fine pliers, usually called "needle-nose" pliers or something similar, that are particularly useful in electronics work. These are intended for light jobs, such as bending or holding wires or small work pieces. Two or three of these tools with different sizes of jaws will suffice for most jobs.

WIRE CUTTERS AND STRIPPERS

Wire cutters are primarily used to cut wires or component leads. The choice of blade style depends on the application. Diagonal blades or "dikes" are most often used to cut wire. Some delicate components can be damaged by cutting their leads with dikes because of the abrupt shock of the cut. Scissors or shears designed to cut wire should be used instead.

Specialized wire cutters are available to trim wires leads on circuit boards. These cutters are often called "flush cutters". Their cutting end is *not* designed to cut thicker wires. Use them *only* to clip smaller gauge wires, such as that on components used in circuits.

Wire strippers are available in manual and automatic styles. The manual strippers have a series of holes designed to remove insulation from a specific gauge of wire. Using the holes that are too big or too small will create nicks in the wire, which usually leads to the wire breaking at the nick. Automatic strippers grab and hold the wire for a consistent strip — some even judge the wire thickness automatically. If you strip a lot of wires, an automatic stripper may be worth the extra expense.

Wire strippers are handy, but with a little practice you can usually strip wires using a diagonal cutter or a knife. This is not the only use for a knife, so keep an assortment handy. Do not use wire cutters or strippers on anything other than wire! If you use a cutter to trim a protruding screw head or cut a hardened-steel spring, you will usually damage the blades.

FILES

Files are used for a wide range of tasks. In addition to enlarging holes and slots, they are used to remove burrs, shape metal, wood or plastic and clean some surfaces in preparation for soldering. Files are especially prone to damage from rust and moisture. Keep them in a dry place. The cutting edge of the blades can also become clogged with the material you are removing. Use file brushes (also called file cards) to keep files clean. Most files cannot be sharpened easily, so when the teeth become worn, the file must be replaced.

DRILL BITS

Drill bits are made from carbon steel, high-speed steel or carbide. Carbon steel is more common and is usually supplied unless a specific request is made for high-speed bits. Carbon steel drill bits cost less than high-speed or carbide types; they are sufficient for most equipment construction work. Carbide drill bits last much longer under heavy use. One disadvantage of carbide bits is that they are brittle and break easily, especially if you are using a hand-held power drill. When drilling abrasive material, such as fiberglass, the carbide bits last much longer than the steel bits.

Twist drills are available in a number of sizes listed in **Table 23.3**. Those listed in bold

**Table 23.3
Numbered Drill Sizes**

No.	Diameter (Mils)	Will Clear Screw	Drilled for Tapping from Steel or Brass
1	228.0	12-24	—
2	221.0	—	—
3	213.0	—	14-24
4	209.0	12-20	—
5	205.0	—	—
6	204.0	—	—
7	201.0	—	—
8	199.0	—	—
9	196.0	—	—
10	193.5	—	—
11	191.0	10-24 / 10-32	—
12	189.0	—	—
13	185.0	—	—
14	182.0	—	—
15	180.0	—	—
16	177.0	—	12-24
17	173.0	—	—
18	169.5	—	—
19	166.0	8-32	12-20
20	161.0	—	—
21	159.0	—	10-32
22	157.0	—	—
23	154.0	—	—
24	152.0	—	—
25	149.5	—	10-24
26	147.0	—	—
27	144.0	—	—
28	140.0	6-32	—
29	136.0	—	8-32
30	128.5	—	—
31	120.0	—	—
32	116.0	—	—
33	113.0	4-40	—
34	111.0	—	—
35	110.0	—	—
36	106.5	—	6-32
37	104.0	—	—
38	101.5	—	—
39	099.5	3-48	—
40	098.0	—	—
41	096.0	—	—
42	093.5	—	—
43	089.0	—	4-40
44	086.0	2-56	—
45	082.0	—	—
46	081.0	—	—
47	078.5	—	3-48
48	076.0	—	—
49	073.0	—	—
50	070.0	—	2-56
51	067.0	—	—
52	063.5	—	—
53	059.5	—	—
54	055.0	—	—

type are the most commonly used in construction of amateur equipment. You may not use all of the drills in a standard set, but it is nice to have a complete set on hand. You should also buy several spares of the more common sizes. Although Table 23.3 lists drills down to #54, the series extends to number #80. While the smaller sizes cannot usually be found in hardware stores or home improvement stores, they are commonly available through industrial tool suppliers and through various sources on the Internet.

A "step drill" consists of multiple drill diameters stacked as one bit, looking somewhat like a Christmas tree. These bits are very useful for drilling metal case material used in radio projects as the fluted edge of the bit in between sizes removes most if not all burrs from the hole you are drilling. Use them carefully and slowly to take advantage of their ability to remove burrs. A step drill also has the advantage of being able to drill a number of different standard size holes without having to change the bit.

SPECIALIZED TOOLS

Most constructors know how to use common tools, such as screwdrivers, wrenches and hammers. Although specialized tools usually do a job that can be done with other tools, once the specialty tool is used you will wonder how you ever did the job without it! Let's discuss other tools that are not so common.

A hand nibbling tool is shown in **Figure 23.1**. Use this tool to remove small "nibbles" of metal. It is easy to use; position the tool where you want to remove metal and squeeze the handle. The tool takes a small bite out of the metal. When you use a nibbler, be careful that you don't remove too much metal, clip the edge of a component mounted to the sheet metal or grab a wire that is routed near the edge of a chassis. Fixing a broken wire is easy, but something to avoid if possible. It is easy to remove metal but nearly impossible to put it back. Do it right the first time!

Deburring Tool

A deburring tool is just the thing to remove the sharp edges left on a hole after drilling or punching operations. See **Figure 23.2**. Position the tool over the hole and rotate it around the edge of the hole to remove burrs or rough edges. As an alternative, select a drill bit that is somewhat larger than the hole, position it over the hole, and spin it lightly to remove the burr. Be sure to deburr both sides of the hole.

Socket or Chassis Punches

Greenlee is the most widely known of the socket-punch manufacturers. Most socket punches are round, but they do come in other shapes. To use one, drill a pilot hole large enough to clear the bolt that runs through the punch. Then, mount the punch as shown in **Figure 23.3**, with the cutter on one side of the sheet metal and the socket on the other. Tighten the nut with a wrench until the cutter cuts all the way through the sheet metal. These punches are often sold in sets

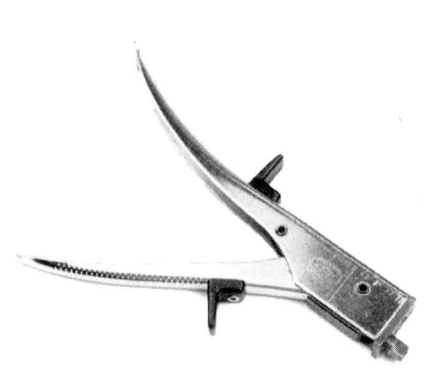

Figure 23.1 — A nibbling tool is used to remove small sections of sheet metal.

Figure 23.2 — A deburring tool is used to remove the burrs left after drilling a hole.

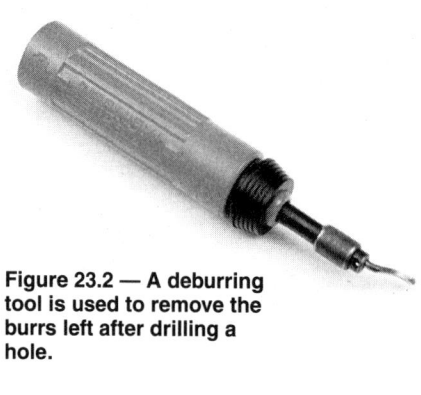

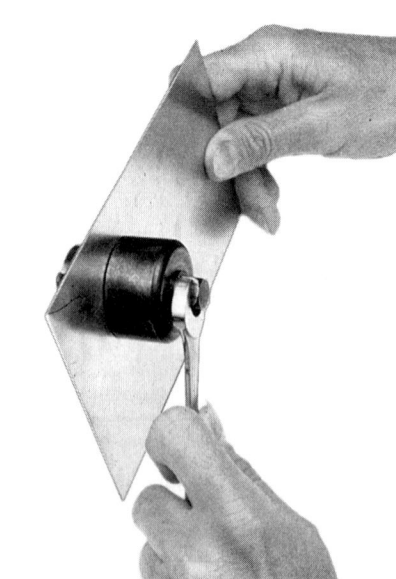

Figure 23.3 — A socket punch is used to punch a clean, round hole in sheet metal.

at a significant discount to the same punches purchased separately. Hand-punches that operate by squeezing will also cut small holes by hand in light-gauge sheet metal, printed-circuit boards, and plastic.

Crimping Tools

The use of crimped connectors is common in the electronics industry. In many commercial and aerospace applications, soldered joints are no longer used. Hams have been reluctant to adapt crimped connections, largely due to mistrust of contacts that are not soldered, the use of cheap crimp connectors on consumer electronics, and the high cost of quality crimping tools or "crimpers." If high quality connectors and tools are used, the crimped connector will be as reliable a connection as a soldered one. The crimped connection is easier to make than a soldered one in most cases.

Crimped coaxial connectors are the most common crimped connector. MIL-spec or equivalent crimp connectors are available for the UHF, BNC, F and N-series MIL-spec connectors. Power connectors, such as the Anderson PowerPoles and Molex connectors are probably the second most commonly used crimped connections.

When purchasing a crimper, look for a ratcheting model with dies that are intended for the connectors you will be using. The common pliers-type crimper designed for household electrical terminals will have trouble crimping power connectors and is unsuitable for coaxial connectors. A good ratcheting crimper can be obtained for $50 to $100 with the necessary interchangeable dies. Large ratcheting crimpers suitable for the larger coaxial connectors can cost several hundred dollars. A good crimper and set of dies is an excellent investment for a club or group of like-minded hams.

Compression tools are now the most common method of installing Type F connectors. (See the **Component Data and References** chapter.) BNC, TNC, and SMA connectors now can be installed using compression connectors and tools, as well. Quad-shielded RG-6 is the most common cable used for this purpose and a compression tool makes the job very easy. A compression crimp tool works differently as it presses an internal sleeve into the body of the connector to make contact with the shield. Most compression tools are lower in cost than conventional ratcheting tools, and are available at most home improvement stores. You will need to purchase compression connectors designed to work with the tool and cable type you selected. Installation instructions are usually provided on the tool's package and with packages of connectors.

Useful Shop Materials

Small stocks of various materials are used when constructing electronics equipment. Most of these are available from hardware or radio supply stores. A representative list is shown at the end of Table 23.2.

Small parts, such as machine screws, nuts, washers and soldering lugs can be economically purchased in large quantities (it doesn't pay to buy more than a lifetime supply). For items you don't use often, many radio supply stores or hardware stores sell small quantities and assortments. Stainless steel hardware can be kept on hand for outdoor use.

Tuning and Alignment Tools

It's helpful to have an assortment of special tools for adjusting variable capacitors, inductors, and potentiometers. See the section Tuning and Alignment later in this chapter.

23.3 Soldering Tools and Techniques

Soldering is used in nearly every phase of electronic construction so you'll need soldering tools. This section discusses the tools and materials used in soldering.

23.3.1 Soldering Irons

A soldering tool must be hot enough to do the job and lightweight enough for agility and comfort. A heavy soldering gun useful for assembling wire antennas is too large for printed-circuit work, for example. A fine-tip soldering iron (sometimes called a "soldering pencil") works well for smaller jobs.

You may need an assortment of soldering irons to do a wide variety of soldering tasks. They range in size from a small 25 W iron for delicate printed-circuit work to larger 100 to 300 W soldering irons and guns. Small "pencil" butane-powered soldering irons and torches are also available, with a variety of soldering-iron tips. Most butane irons are not suited to use over long periods of time, but are ideal for small jobs and for performing tasks suited for a larger soldering iron, as they can be turned up to relatively high heating levels. Most small butane pencil irons can be set to provide as little as 10 W of equivalent heat, or up to 75-100 W. Butane powered irons also perform well outdoors, making them ideal for antenna work. Battery powered irons are available too, but are also not suited for use over long periods.

A 25 W pencil tip iron is adequate for printed circuit board work. A 40 W iron is necessary for larger jobs, such as soldering leads to panel connectors and making splices. These two irons or a temperature-controlled soldering station should handle most electronic homebrew requirements. A 100 W iron is good for bigger jobs, such as soldering antenna connections or soldering to power cables.

You should get several different sizes and shapes of tips when you purchase an iron. While most people prefer a conical tip, the chisel tip is also useful. The lower wattage irons will likely have a good selection of tip sizes and geometries. Irons 100 W and larger usually have a non-interchangeable chisel tip. For printed circuit board work, a good rule of thumb is to use a tip whose point is the same size as the component leads you are soldering.

If you buy an iron for use on circuits that contain electrostatic sensitive components, get one that has a grounded tip. Otherwise, you risk electrostatic damage to the components. Such irons are usually specified as having a grounded tip, and will have a three-prong plug. It is usually not necessary to have a grounded tip on the 100 W iron as it is not used on sensitive components.

Soldering guns are used for larger jobs and are too large for most electronics work. Where the soldering iron tip has an internal heater, the soldering gun tip is heated directly by current flowing in the tip. The nuts connecting the tip to the iron can loosen with each heat cycle, so they need tightening periodically. Soldering guns are available that have high and low heat levels controlled by an extra trigger position. Soldering gun tips are usually copper and do not last as long as the iron-clad tips of the smaller irons.

If you do a lot of building, a *soldering station* with a temperature-controlled tip is a better investment than a simple iron. The iron tip temperature can be precisely controlled and can be varied to the type of work being done. Soldering stations generally reach operating temperature more quickly than conventional irons and can be turned down to idle when you are not soldering. Some even have a digital tip temperature display. Soldering stations are available from numerous manufacturers. It is best to buy from an established manufacturer to insure future availability of tips and other components. Reconditioned soldering stations are often available and are good value.

If the only available soldering iron is a simple pencil type iron, an inexpensive means to vary the temperature of the iron is to use a lamp dimmer A simple control box can be made from a dimmer, wall socket, power cord, and outlet box available at any hardware store. Since a simple soldering iron is a resistive load, a lamp dimmer designed to work with incandescent lamps works well to cool down a soldering iron, and warm it up quickly once it is needed. This allows you to turn down the temperature of the iron while it is idle to prevent oxidation of the tip if left at full heat without being used.

RF-heated irons and hot-air soldering tools are primarily in use by industry and particularly useful for soldering surface-mount devices. The cost of these stations is high, although they are available as used and reconditioned.

TOOLS FOR SOLDERING SURFACE-MOUNT DEVICES

Hot-air soldering stations use a hot-air gun to melt the solder without contacting the pads or traces. This is easier on the fine features of the PC board but requires some skill to avoid overheating an IC or component. The air stream can also blow small parts off the board, as well, so some care and practice is required. Nevertheless, hot-air soldering is quite effective and can solder entire ICs in one operation.

"Hot tweezers" are a dual-tipped soldering iron used to solder and remove surface mount parts. Hot tweezers can make very quick work of removing and replacing most common two- and three-terminal surface mount devices with a lot lower chance of board damage.

Some stations that combine hot tweezers and a hot-air tool with a heating table that allows you to bring the entire circuit board up to a temperature just below the melting point of the solder. This feature allows you to use a hot-air tool with less heating time, reducing the chance of possibly warping the board.

MAINTAINING SOLDERING IRONS

Keep soldering tools in good condition by keeping the tips well-tinned with solder. Tinning is performed by melting solder directly onto the tip and letting it form a coating. Do not keep the tips at full temperature for long periods when not in use.

After each use, remove the tip and clean off any scale that may have accumulated. Clean an oxidized tip by dipping the hot tip in sal ammoniac (ammonium chloride) and then wiping it clean with a rag. Sal ammoniac is somewhat corrosive, so if you don't wipe the tip thoroughly, it can contaminate electronic soldering. There are proprietary "tip tinner" products available that can also be used for this function.

If a tip becomes oxidized during use, it can be restored to its shiny state by wiping the tip with a damp sponge or rag and then re-tinning. (Some tips are not supposed to be cleaned with water — check the manufacturer's recommendations.) A gentle scraping is also useful for stubborn cases. A copper or stainless-steel coil kitchen scrubber (do not use a scrubber that contains soap) works fine for this. Swipe the iron through the scrubber to clean it. A scrubber or sponge is most conveniently used by cramming it into a clean tuna can and placing it next to the solder station.

If a copper tip becomes pitted after repeated use, file it smooth and bright and then tin it immediately with solder. The solder prevents further oxidation of the tip. Modern soldering iron tips are nickel or iron clad and should not be filed, as the cladding protects the tip from pitting.

The secret of good soldering is to use the right amount of heat. Many people who have not soldered before use too little heat, dabbing at the joint to be soldered and making little solder blobs that cause unintended short circuits.

On a printed circuit board, examine your connections closely. If it looks like a rounded blob, reheat it with your soldering iron tip at the base of the connection, drawing the tip away from the connection along the wire lead, forming a desired "Hershey's Kiss" type of appearance. A round blob will often hold the wire in place, but often makes little or no contact with the printed trace on the board's surface. To avoid creating a large "blob" that risks bridging to adjacent pads, remove the solder with a vacuum tool or solder braid and resolder the joint.

23.3.2 Solder

Solders have different melting points, depending on the ratio of tin to lead. Tin melts at 450 °F and lead at 621 °F. Solder made from 63% tin and 37% lead melts at 361 °F, the lowest melting point for a tin and lead mixture. Called 63-37 (or eutectic), this type of solder also provides the most rapid solid-to-liquid transition and the best stress resistance. 63-37 solder also stays in the plastic state for the briefest time, thus making it ideal for hand soldering because it is a lot less likely to cool unevenly.

Solders made with different lead/tin ratios have a plastic state at some temperatures. If the solder is deformed while it is in the plastic state, the deformation remains when the solder freezes into the solid state. Any stress or motion applied to "plastic solder" causes a poor solder joint.

60-40 solder has the best wetting qualities. Wetting is the ability to spread rapidly, coat the surfaces to be joined, and bond materials uniformly. 60-40 solder also has a low melting point. These factors make it the most commonly used solder in electronics. However, 63-37 solder is the best-suited for manual construction techniques.

Some connections that carry high current can't be made with ordinary tin-lead solder because the heat generated by the current would melt the solder. Automotive starter brushes and transmitter tank circuits are two examples. Silver-bearing solders have higher melting points, and so prevent this problem. High-temperature silver alloys become liquid in the 1100 °F to 1200 °F range, and a silver-manganese (85-15) alloy requires almost 1800 °F.

Because silver dissolves easily in tin, tin-bearing solders can leach silver plating from components. This problem can be greatly reduced by partially saturating the tin in the solder with silver or by eliminating the tin. Commercial solders are available which incorporate these features. Tin-silver or tin-lead-silver alloys become liquid at temperatures from 430 °F for 96.5-3.5 (tin-silver), to 588 °F for 1.0-97.5-1.5 (tin-lead-silver). A 15.0-80.0-5.0 alloy of lead-indium-silver melts at 314 °F.

Rosin-core wire-type solder is formed into a tube with a flux compound inside. The resin (usually called "rosin" in solder) in a solder is a *flux*. Flux melts at a lower temperature than solder, so it flows out onto the joint before the solder melts to coat the joint surfaces. The solder used for surface-mount soldering (discussed later) is a cream or paste and flux, if used, must be added to the joint separately.

Flux removes oxide by suspending it in solution and floating it to the top. Flux is not a cleaning agent! Always clean the surfaces to be soldered before soldering. Rubbing alcohol on a cotton swab is a good cleaning aid. Cleaning an entire board before beginning to install components is easy and prepares the surface for the best soldering. Flux is not a part of a soldered connection — it merely aids the soldering process. Don't touch the board with your fingers after cleaning.

After soldering, remove any remaining flux. Rosin flux can be removed with isopropyl or denatured alcohol. A cotton swab is a good tool for applying the alcohol and scrubbing the excess flux away. Commercial flux-removal sprays are available at most electronic-part distributors. Water-soluble fluxes are also available. Solder is now available with "no-clean" flux. This type of flux minimizes the amount of flux left on the board after soldering.

Never use acid flux or acid-core solder for electrical work. It should be used only for plumbing or chassis work. If used on electronics, the flux will corrode and damage the equipment. For circuit construction, only use fluxes or solder-flux combinations that are labeled for electronic soldering.

A basic tutorial on "Soldering 101" including a video demonstration is available from Sparkfun Electronics at **www.sparkfun.com/tutorials/213**.

LEAD-FREE SOLDER

In 2006, the European Union Restriction of Hazardous Substances Directive (RoHS) went into effect. This directive prohibits manufacture and import of consumer electronics which incorporate lead, including the common tin-lead solder used in electronic assembly. California recently enacted a similar RoHS law. As a result of these directives there has been a move to lead-free solders in commercial use. They can contain two or more elements that are not as hazardous as lead, including tin, copper, silver, bismuth, indium, zinc, antimony and traces of other metals. Two lead-free solders commonly used for electronic use are SnAgCu alloy SAC305 and tin-copper alloy Sn100. SAC305 contains 96.5% tin, 3% silver, and 0.5% copper and melts at 217 °C. Sn100 contains 99.3% tin, 0.6% copper, as well as traces of nickel and silver and melts at 228 °C. Both of these melting points are higher than the 176 °C melting point of 60-40 and 63-37 lead-bearing solder, but conventional soldering stations will be able to reach the melting points of the new solders easily. Tin-lead solders are still available, but the move away from them by commercial manufacturers will probably lead to the day when they will be unavailable to hams who build their own gear. Be prepared.

The new RoHS solders can be used in much the same manner as conventional solders. The resulting solder joint appears somewhat duller than a conventional solder joint, and the lead-free solders tend to wick higher than the lead-tin solders. Due to the higher heat, it is important that the soldering iron tip be clean, shiny and freshly tinned so that heat is transferred to the joint to be soldered as quickly as possible to avoid excess heating of the parts being soldered. The soldering iron should be set to between 700 °F and 800 °F.

Solder and soldering equipment vendors provide numerous guides to hand soldering with lead-free solders. Weller's "Weller University" online presentation **www.elexp.com/Images/Weller_Coping_with_Lead_Free.pdf** provides a great deal of detail about how soldering iron tips work with lead-free solder. More information is available from Kester (**www.kester.com**) in the Knowledge Base under the Hand Soldering link.

Most, if not all, RoHS-compliant components can be soldered with lead-tin solder. If the RoHS part has leads that are tinned or coated with an alloy to make soldering easier, it is necessary to use a hotter iron than would normally be required in lead-tin soldering. A soldering iron tip temperature of 315 °C (600 °F) or greater will be adequate for soldering RoHS parts with lead-tin solder.

In contrast, a working tip temperature of 275 °C is generally adequate for working with conventional non-RoHS parts.

23.3.3 Soldering

The two key factors in quality soldering are time and temperature. Rapid heating is desired so that all parts of the joint are made hot enough for the solder to remain molten as it flows over the joint surfaces. Most unsuccessful solder jobs fail because insufficient heat has been applied. To achieve rapid heating, the soldering iron tip should be hotter than the melting point of solder and large enough that transferring heat to the cooler joint materials occurs quickly. A tip temperature about 100 °F (60 °C) above the solder melting point is right for mounting components on PC boards.

Use solder that is sized appropriately for the job. As the cross section of the solder decreases, so does the amount of heat required to melt it. Diameters from 0.025 to 0.040 inch are good for nearly all circuit wiring. The most common sizes suitable for amateur projects are 0.031 or 0.025. Sensitive and smaller components can be damaged or surfaces re-oxidized if heat is applied for too long a period. Solder that is too thick can cause shorts between close-by connections. (A heavier solder is useful for working on antennas, connectors, and light metal work, such as shields.)

If you are a beginner, you may want to start with one of the numerous "Learn to Solder" kits available from many electronics parts and kit vendors. The kits come with a printed-circuit board, a basic soldering iron, solder, and the components to complete a simple electronics project. Or, seek out a group kit building session, such as those put on by the QRP ARCI at the annual Dayton Hamvention or by a local or regional group at a hamfest or specialty convention. Robotics and maker groups often have learn-to-solder sessions, too.

Here's how to make a good solder joint. This description assumes that solder with a flux core is used to solder a typical PC board connection such as an IC pin.

• Prepare the joint. Clean all conductors thoroughly with fine steel wool or a plastic scrubbing pad. Clean the circuit board at the beginning of assembly and individual parts such as resistors and capacitors immediately before soldering. Some parts (such as ICs and surface-mount components) cannot be cleaned easily; don't worry unless they're exceptionally dirty.

• Prepare the tool. It should be hot enough to melt solder applied to its tip quickly (half a second when dry, instantly when wet with solder). Apply a little solder directly to the tip so that the surface is shiny. This process is called "tinning" the tool. The solder coating helps conduct heat from the tip to the joint and prevents the tip from oxidizing.

• Place the tip in contact with one side of the joint. If you can place the tip on the underside of the joint, do so. With the tool below the joint, convection helps transfer heat to the joint.

• Place the solder against the joint directly opposite the soldering tool. It should melt within a second for normal PC connections, within two seconds for most other connections. If it takes longer to melt, there is not enough heat for the job at hand. If you have a variable heat soldering iron, adjust it so that the solder flows quickly for the size of wire and joints you are soldering. Much more heat can damage components and the board.

• Keep the tool against the joint until the solder flows freely throughout the joint. When it flows freely, solder tends to form concave joints called "fillets" between the conductors. With insufficient heat solder does not flow freely; it forms convex shapes — blobs. Once the solder shape changes from convex to concave, remove the tool from the joint. If a fillet won't form, the joint may need additional cleaning. Look for that "Hershey's Kiss" shape to know if it is done correctly.

• Let the joint cool without movement at room temperature. It usually takes no more than a few seconds. If the joint is moved before it is cool, it may take on a dull, satin or grainy appearance that is characteristic of a "cold" solder joint. Reheat cold joints until the solder flows freely and hold them still until cool. Using 63-37 solder will help reduce the time until the solder is solid again.

• When the iron is set aside, or if it loses its shiny appearance, wipe away any dirt with a damp cloth or sponge. If it remains dull after cleaning, tin it again.

• Adafruit has published a good collection of photographs showing many common soldering problems and how to repair them. See **learn.adafruit.com/adafruit-guide-excellent-soldering/common-problems**.

Overheating a transistor or diode while soldering can cause permanent damage, although as you get better at soldering, you'll be able to solder very quickly with little risk to the components. If the soldering iron will be applied for longer than a couple of seconds, use a small heat sink when you solder transistors, diodes or components with plastic parts that can melt. Grip the component lead with a pair of needle-nose pliers up close to the unit so that the heat is conducted away (be careful — it is easy to damage delicate component leads). A rubber-band wrapped around the pliers handles will hold the pliers on the wire. A small alligator clip or a flat spring type paper clip also makes a good heat sink.

Mechanical stress can damage components, too. Mount components so there is no appreciable mechanical strain on the leads. Be especially careful with small glass diodes and small disc capacitors as these components are easy to break when forming the leads.

Installing wire jumpers between connectors or modules and circuit boards can be straightforward or it can lead to a rat's nest. For some excellent advice and guidance about this basic task, read "W8ZR's Tips for Wiring Circuit Board Jumpers" at **w8zr. net/stationpro/images/download%20files/ Tips%20for%20Wiring%20Circuit%20 Board%20Jumpers.pdf**. This is a common task in building equipment so why not learn to do it well?

Soldering to hollow pins, such as found on connectors, can be difficult, particularly if the connector has been used previously or has oxidized. Use a suitable small twist drill to clean the inside of the pin and then tin it. While the solder is still melted, clear the surplus solder from each pin with a whipping motion or by blowing through the pin from the inside of the connector. Watch out for flying hot solder — use safety goggles and protect the work surface and your arms and legs! A glass ashtray or small baking dish works great for catching the loose solder. Do not perform this operation near open electronic equipment as the loose solder can easily form short circuits. If the pin surface is plated, file the plating from the pin tip. Then insert the wire and solder it. After soldering, remove excess solder with a file, if necessary.

When soldering to the pins of plastic connectors or other assemblies, heat-sink the pin with needle-nose pliers at the base where it comes in contact with the plastic housing. Do not allow the pin to overheat; it will loosen and become misaligned. If you need to solder very quickly due to concerns about melting the housing, tin both the pin and wire first. Reheat the pin while inserting the wire. This melts the solder on both the pin and the wire, resulting in a solid connection without overheating the pin.

23.3.4 Desoldering

There are times when soldered components need to be removed. The parts may be bad, they may be installed incorrectly, or you may want to remove them for use in another project.

There are several techniques for desoldering. The easiest way is to use a desoldering braid. Desoldering braid is simply fine copper braid, often containing flux. It is available under a wide variety of trade names wherever soldering supplies are sold. A good rule of thumb is to choose a width and thickness of desoldering braid that matches the size of the connection being desoldered.

The soldering braid is placed against the joint to be desoldered. A hot iron is pressed onto the braid. If you have a variable temperature soldering station, you might get better results by turning up the temperature, as the combination of the wick and the connection absorbs more heat. As the solder melts, it is wicked into the braid and away from the joint. Copper is an excellent conductor of heat, and the braid can get quite hot, so watch your fingers when using braid for desoldering. After all the leads have been treated in this manner the part can be removed. (A thin film of solder may remain, but is easily broken loose through the use of needle-nose pliers.) The part of the braid that wicked up the solder is clipped off.

Do not allow the used portion of the braid get too long, as it will absorb too much heat and not do as good of a job removing solder. When desoldering connections that have been made by using lead-free or "RoHS" solder, it can sometimes be difficult to achieve the high temperature needed to use solder wick, even with the iron heat turned all of the way up. A good tip in this case is to add a small amount of conventional leaded solder to the joint first, allowing it to mix. That lowers the melting point to a level that allows for much easier desoldering using solder wick, or other methods.

A desoldering vacuum pump can also be used. There are two types of desoldering vacuum tools, a simple rubber syringe bulb with a high temperature plastic tip and a desoldering pump. The desoldering pump is a simple manual vacuum pump consisting of a cylinder that contains a spring-loaded plunger attached to a metal rod inside a tip of high temperature plastic on the end of the pump. To desolder a joint, the plunger is pushed down, and locked in place. The tip is placed against the joint to be desoldered along with a soldering iron. When the solder melts, a button on the pump releases the plunger, which pulls the rod back, creating a vacuum that sucks the molten solder through the tip. The part being desoldered can then be removed. Pushing the plunger again ejects the solder from the desoldering tip.

The desoldering bulb employs a similar concept: heat the joint to be desoldered, squeeze the bulb, place the tip on the joint and release it to suck up the solder. Remove the part that was desoldered. If the first application of the desoldering pump doesn't suck up all the solder, reheat the joint and suck up the rest.

If the desoldering tool doesn't seem to be sucking up solder, the tip may be clogged with solder. The tip can be unclogged by pushing the solder through. You may have to clear the tip several times when doing a job that requires desoldering many joints. One can purchase small desoldering irons that contain a bulb on the handle that leads to a tip adjacent to the iron tip. This desoldering iron combination is somewhat easier to handle than the separate bulb and iron and does an effective job. Use a glass ashtray for a container to blow out the excess solder from this tool before using it again, as an ashtray is usually designed to handle heat.

Desoldering stations are also available. One type contains a vacuum pump in a console much like a soldering station. A vacuum line is connected to the tip of the soldering iron. There is a valve trigger on the iron that is used to open the tip to the vacuum when the solder is melted. The solder is sucked up the line into a receptacle in the station or in the hand piece.

DESOLDERING SURFACE-MOUNT DEVICES

Special tools are available for desoldering and replacing surface-mount parts. (See the previous section on Tools for Soldering Surface-Mount Devices.) The two most common are "hot tweezers" which is really a special dual-tipped soldering iron that is squeezed to match the size of the component. Hot tweezers can be used to not only remove, but to replace surface-mount parts. Another tool for this purpose is a hot-air tool with a small tip that focuses the hot air on a single component. This tool can be used to remove a surface mount part as well as to replace one. The hot-air tool heats the joint with hot air so the component can be lifted off with tweezers or needle-nose pliers.

Use surplus circuit boards to practice soldering and desoldering techniques. Old boards from all kinds of electronic items are often at very low cost or free at many flea markets. Use these surplus boards to practice different soldering and desoldering techniques without having to worry about damaging a project. Computer boards are often made with lead-free solder, and are ideal for practicing desoldering methods by adding leaded solder to the connections before desoldering.

23.3.5 Soldering Safety

Soldering requires a certain degree of practice and, of course, the right tools. What potential hazards are involved?

Since the solder used for virtually all electronic components is a lead-tin alloy, the first thing in most people's minds is lead, a well-known health hazard. There are two primary ways lead might enter our bodies when soldering: we could breathe lead fumes into our lungs or we could ingest (swallow) lead or lead-contaminated food. Inhalation of lead fumes is extremely unlikely because the temperatures ordinarily used in electronic soldering are far below those needed to vaporize lead. Nevertheless, since lead is soft and we may tend to handle it with our fingers, contaminating our food is a real possibility. For this reason, wash your hands carefully after any soldering (or touching of solder connections).

Using a small fan can keep the fumes away from your eyes and reduce your exposure to solder smoke. A small computer chipset fan, often only an inch or two wide, can be used. By reducing the voltage that feeds the fan, the speed and noise can be reduced, allowing the fumes to be blown away, yet not creating another problem with the airflow. Look in old computers for these little fans, often attached to video cards or to the bus chips on the motherboard. The CPU or case fans can be also used, but the voltage supplying them will definitely need to be reduced to create the desired level of airflow. There are also commercially available specialized fans with built-in filters designed for this purpose — look for a soldering "fume extractor".

Soldering equipment gets *hot*! Be careful. Treat a soldering iron as you would any other hot object. A soldering iron stand is helpful, preferably one that has a cage that surrounds the hot tip of the iron. Here's a helpful tip — if the soldering iron gets knocked off the bench, train yourself not to grab for it because the chances are good that you'll grab the hot end!

When heated, the flux in solder gives off a vapor in the form of a light gray smoke-like plume. This flux vapor, which often contains aldehydes, is a strong irritant and can cause potentially serious problems to persons who suffer from respiratory sensitivity conditions such as asthma. In most cases it is relatively easy to use a small fan, like the small computer fans described previously to move the flux vapor away from your eyes and face. Opening a window provides additional air exchange.

Solvents are often used to remove excess flux after the parts have cooled to room temperature. Minimize skin contact with solvents by wearing molded gloves resistant to the solvent. If you use a solvent to remove flux, it is best to use the mildest one that does the job. Isopropyl alcohol, or rubbing alcohol, is often sufficient. You can purchase alcohol ranging from 70% to 92% concentration at local drug stores that works well in removing most types of fluxes. Some water-soluble solder fluxes can be removed with water.

Observe these precautions to protect yourself and others:
• Properly ventilate the work area. If you can smell fumes, you are breathing them.
• Wash your hands after soldering, especially before handling food.
• Minimize direct contact with flux and flux solvents. Wear disposable surgical gloves when handling solvents.

For more information about soldering hazards and the ways to make soldering safer, see "Making Soldering Safer," by Brian P. Bergeron, MD, NU1N (Mar 1991 *QST*, pp 28-30) and "More on Safer Soldering," by Gary E. Meyers, K9CZB (Aug 1991 *QST*, p 42).

23.4 Surface Mount Technology (SMT)

Today, nearly all consumer electronic devices are made with surface mount technology. Hams have lagged behind in adopting this technology largely due to the misconception that it is difficult, requires extensive practice and requires special equipment. In fact, surface mount devices can be soldered easily with commonly available equipment. There is no more practice required to become proficient enough to produce a circuit with surface-mount (SM) devices than there is with soldering through-hole (leaded) components.

There are several advantages to working with SMT:

• Projects are much more compact than if through-hole components are used
• SM parts are available that are not available in through-hole packages
• Fewer and fewer through-hole parts are being produced
• Equivalent SM components are often cheaper than through-hole parts, and
• SM parts have less self-inductance, less self-capacitance and better thermal properties.

There are several techniques that can be used effectively to work with SM components: conventional soldering iron, hot air reflow and hot plate/hot air reflow. This section describes the soldering iron technique. On-line descriptions of reflow techniques are available for the advanced builder that wants to try them. As is the case for through-hole soldering, kits are available to teach the beginner how to solder SMT components.

The following material on working with surface-mount technology contains excerpts from a series of *QST* articles, "Surface Mount Technology — You Can Work with It! Part 1" by Sam Ulbing, N4UAU, published in the April 1999 issue. (The entire series of four articles is available with the online supplemental content. Additional information on SMT is available at **www.arrl.org/surface-mount-technology**.) Additional information and illustrations were contributed by George Heron, N2APB.

23.4.1 Equipment Needed

You do not need lots of expensive equipment to work with SM devices.

• A fundamental piece of equipment for SM work is an illuminated magnifying glass. You can use an inexpensive one with a 5 inch diameter lens, and it's convenient to use the magnifier for all soldering work, not just for SM use. Such magnifiers are widely available from about $25. Most offer a 3× magnification and have a built-in circular light. Be sure to use a light that is fluorescent or LED-based. Incandescent lights are much hotter and make it difficult to ascertain the correct color of component markings.

• A low-power, temperature-controlled soldering iron is necessary. Use a soldering iron with a grounded tip as most SM parts are CMOS devices and are subject to possible ESD (static) failure.

• Use of thin (0.020 inch diameter) rosin-core solder is preferred because the parts are so small that regular 0.031 inch diameter solder will flood a solder pad and cause bridging. Solder paste or cream can also be used.

• A flux pen comes in handy for applying just a little flux at a needed spot.

• Good desoldering braid is necessary to remove excess solder if you get too much on a pad. 0.100 inch wide braid works well.

• ESD protective devices such as wrist straps may be necessary if you live in a dry area and static is a problem.

• Tweezers help pick up parts and position them. Nonmagnetic, stainless-steel drafting dividers also work well. The nonmagnetic property of stainless steel means the chip doesn't get attracted to the dividers.

• Some hams prefer to hold components in place with a temporary adhesive such as DAP Blue-Stik while soldering rather than holding the part with tweezers.

23.4.2 Surface-Mount Parts

Figure 23.4 shows some common SM parts. (The **Component Data and References** chapter has more information on component packages.) Resistors and ceramic capacitors come in many different sizes, and it is important to know the part size for two reasons: Working with SM devices by hand is easier if you use the larger parts; and it is important that the PC-board pad size is larger than the part.

Discrete component packaging has shrunk to 0.12 × 0.06 inch, as shown in the "1206" capacitor in **Figure 23.5** compared to a penny. Even smaller packages are common today, requiring much less PC board area for the same equivalent circuits. Integrated circuit packaging has also been miniaturized to cre-

SMT Parts shown actual size

SMT: SOT – 23, SO – 8, SuperSOT – 6, SOT – 223, SuperSOT – 8, SOIC – 16

Non SMT: TO – 220, TO – 92

Some Common Case Size Comparisons

SMT Resistor and Ceramic Capacitors, Some Common Size Codes
Shape and Features

EIA Size Code	Length (Inches)	Width (Inches)
0402	0.04	0.02
0603	0.06	0.03
0805	0.08	0.05
1206	0.12	0.06
1210	0.12	0.10
2512	0.25	0.12

Metal Ends for Soldering

SMT Solid Tantalum Capacitors, Some Case Sizes
Shape and Features

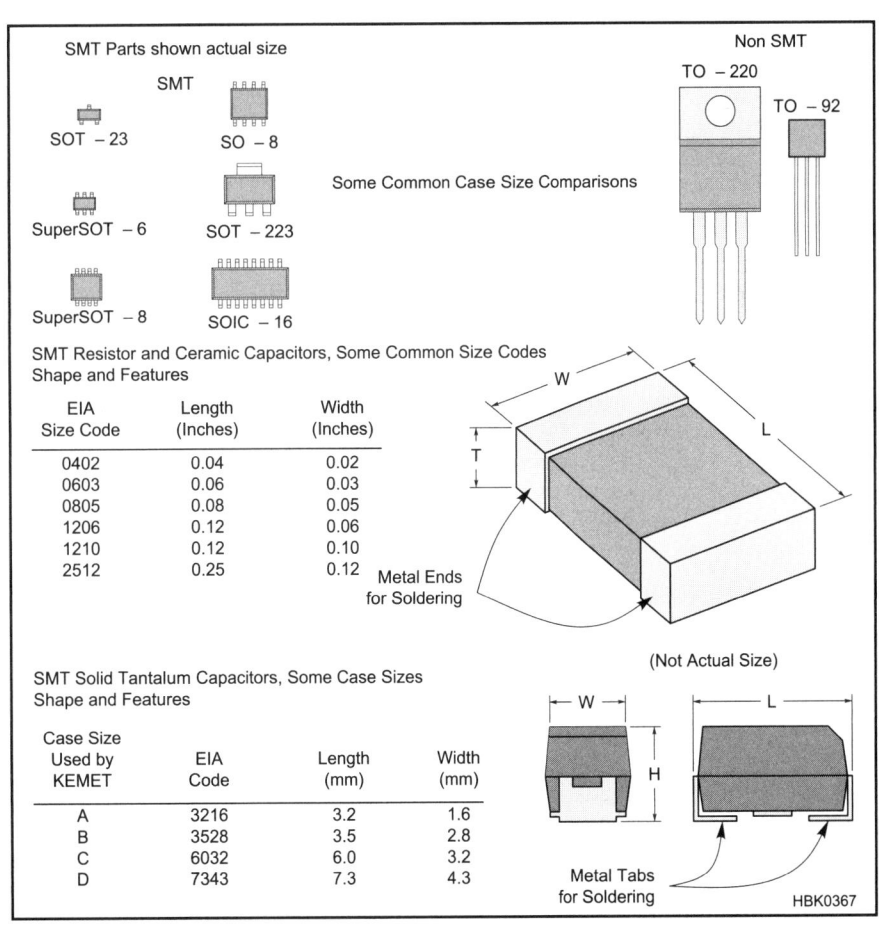

Case Size Used by KEMET	EIA Code	Length (mm)	Width (mm)
A	3216	3.2	1.6
B	3528	3.5	2.8
C	6032	6.0	3.2
D	7343	7.3	4.3

Metal Tabs for Soldering

(Not Actual Size)

HBK0367

Figure 23.4 — Size comparisons of some surface-mount devices and their dimensions. See the Component Data and References chapter for more information about component packages and labeling.

Figure 23.5 — SMT components are small. Clockwise from left: MMIC RF amp, 1206 resistor, SOIC integrated circuit, 1206 capacitor and ferrite inductor.

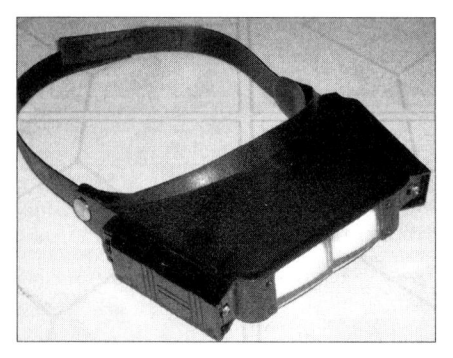

Figure 23.6 — A magnifying visor is great for close-up work on a circuit board. These headsets are often available for less than $10 at hamfests and some even come with superbright LEDs mounted on the side to illuminate the components being soldered.

ate 10 × 5 mm SOIC packages with lead separations of 0.025 inch.

Tantalum capacitors are one of the larger SM parts. Their case code, which is usually a letter, often varies from manufacturer to manufacturer because of different thicknesses. The EIA code for ceramic capacitors and resistors is a measurement of the length and width in inches, but for tantalum parts, those measurements are in millimeters times 10! Keep in mind that tantalum capacitors are polarized; the case usually has a mark or stripe to indicate the positive end. Nearly any part that is used in through-hole technology is available in an SM package.

If you are a beginner, it is probably best to start with the larger sizes — 1206 for resistors and capacitors, SOT-23 for transistors, and SO-8 for ICs. When you get proficient with these parts you can move to smaller ones.

PREPARING FOR SMT WORK

The key to success with any construction project is selecting and using the proper tools. A magnifying lamp is essential for well-lighted, close-up work on the components. **Figure 23.6** shows a convenient magnifying visor. Tweezers or fine-tipped pliers allow you to grab the small chip components with dexterity.

A clean work surface is of paramount importance because SMT components have a tendency to slip from pliers or tweezers and fly off even when held with the utmost care. You'll have the best chance of recovering your wayward part if your table is clear. When the inevitable happens, you'll have lots of trouble finding it if the part falls onto a rug. It's best to have your work area in a room without carpeting, for this reason as well as to protect static-sensitive parts. Using a cookie sheet with a raised lip helps to contain stray SMT parts.

23.4.3 SMT Soldering Basics

If the project contains both SM parts and conventional through-hole parts and you intend to use a heat-gun or oven for reflow soldering, always mount the SM parts first, as through-hole components are not always designed to handle the higher reflow heat levels. Use junk PC boards to practice your soldering and desoldering techniques for SM parts until you are comfortable beginning your own project.

USING A SOLDERING IRON

Let's look at how to solder a surface-mount IC with a soldering iron. Use a little solder to pre-tin the PC board pads if the board is not already pre-tinned. The trick is to add just enough solder so that when you reheat it, it flows to the IC, but not so much that you wind up with a solder bridge. Putting a (very) little flux on the board and the IC legs makes for better solder flow, providing a smooth layer. You can tell if you have the proper soldering-iron tip temperature if the solder melts within 1.5 to 3.5 seconds.

Place the part on the board and then use dividers (or fingers) to push and prod the chip into position. Because the IC is so small and light, it tends to stick to the soldering iron and pull away from the PC board. To prevent this, use the dividers to hold the chip down while tack-soldering two IC legs at diagonally opposite corners. After each tack, check that the part is still aligned. With a dry and clean soldering iron, heat the PC board near the leg. If you do it right, when the solder melts, it will flow to the IC.

The legs of the IC must lie flat on the board. The legs bend easily, so don't press down too hard. Check each connection with a continuity checker placing one tip on the board the other on the IC leg. Check all adjacent pins to ensure there's no bridging. It is easier to correct errors early on, so perform this check often.

If you find that you did not have enough solder on the board for it to flow to the part, add a little solder. It's best to put a drop on the trace near the part, then heat the trace and slide the iron and melted solder toward the part. This reduces the chance of creating a bridge. Soldering resistors and capacitors is similar to soldering an IC's leads, except the resistors and capacitors don't have exposed leads. The reflow method works well for these parts, too.

Attaching wires that connect to points off the board can be a bit of a challenge because even #24 AWG stranded wire is large in comparison to the SM parts. First, make sure all the wire strands are close together, then pre-tin the wire. Pre-tin the pad, carefully place the wire on the pad, then heat it with the soldering iron until the solder melts.

USING REFLOW TECHNIQUES

While SMT projects can be built with conventional solder and a fine-point soldering iron, if you move on to reflow techniques you will need to use solder paste. Solder paste is a grayish looking paste made of a blend of flux and solder. A small dot of solder paste is put on the board at each location a component will need to be soldered. The components are then carefully placed on the board, with the paste loosely holding the parts in position. The whole board is then heated in an oven, or the area of the board being assembled is heated with a heat gun. With sufficient heat, the solder paste melts and flows onto the pad and component contacts, then the board is cooled leaving all of the components soldered in place.

A toaster oven can also be modified to perform reflow soldering as described in the article "Reflow Soldering for the Radio Amateur" by Jim Koehler, VE5FP, in the January 2011 issue of *QST* (this article is included with the online supplemental content). There are many on-line tutorials for adapting and using a toaster oven such as **www.instructables.com/id/Hack-a-Toaster-Oven-for-Reflow-Soldering/** and **www.youtube.com/watch?v=vduU4WWbpbM**. SparkFun also shows how to add a temperature control to a toaster oven at **www.sparkfun.com/tutorials/60**. If you plan on doing a lot of SMT assembly, learning reflow techniques is well worth the effort.

For occasional SMT use, a heat gun is a better choice. Many hobby/crafts stores sell a special heat tool that is used for melting embossing inks used in scrapbooking. Look for an embossing heat tool in the scrapbooking department of these stores. Do not get the heat gun too close to the board, as the airflow may move your components out of place. Hold the tool steady a couple of inches above the board until you see the solder paste turn silver and you see the component appear to be soldered in place, then gradually remove the heat gun. Never use a heat gun designed for paint stripping as the airflow is way too strong for this purpose and will blow the SM parts off the board.

Only a small amount of solder paste is required. Kester Easy Profile 256 is a good solder paste to start with. It is available at reasonable cost in a small syringe with a fine needle-point applicator. As only a small amount is needed for each solder joint, this small amount will last through several medium sized projects. Solder paste must be kept cold or it deteriorates. Kept in a household refrigerator or freezer it has a shelf life of at least a year.

23.4.4 Removing SMT Components

The surface-mount ICs used in commercial equipment are not easy for experimenters to replace. They have tiny pins designed for precision PC boards. Sooner or later, you may need to replace one, though. If you do, don't try to get the old IC out in one piece! This will damage the IC beyond use anyway, and will probably damage the PC board in the process.

Although it requires a delicate touch and small tools, it's possible to change a surface mount IC at home. To remove the old one, use small, sharp wire cutters to cut the IC pins flush with the IC. This usually leaves just enough of the old pin to grab with tweezers. Heat the soldered connection with a small iron and use the pliers to gently pull the pin from the PC board. Use desoldering braid to remove excess solder from the pads and remove and flux with rubbing alcohol. Solder

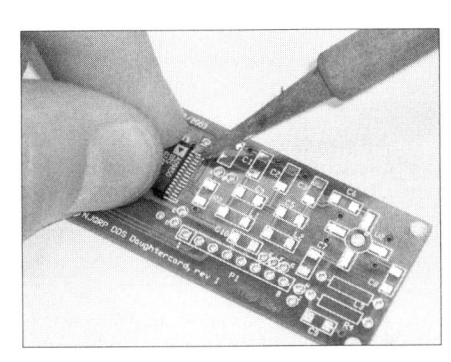

Figure 23.7A — This DDS Daughtercard has all interconnections on the top side. Connections to the ground plane on the backside of the board are made by the use of "vias," wires through the PC board. Pin 28 of the SMT IC is shown being tack-soldered to hold it to the board, keeping all other pins carefully aligned on their pads. Then the other pins are carefully soldered, starting with pin 14 (opposite pin 28). Finally, pin 28 is reheated to ensure a good connection there. If you bridge solder across adjacent pads or pins, use solder wick or a vacuum solder sucker to draw off the excess solder.

Figure 23.7B — Attaching an SMT part. It is a lot easier attaching capacitors, resistors and other discrete components compared to multi-pin ICs. Carefully hold the component in place and properly aligned using needle-nose pliers or tweezers and then solder one end of the component. Then reheat the joint while gently pushing down on the component with the pliers or a Q-tip stick to ensure it is lying flat on the board. Finally, solder the other side of the component.

Figure 23.7C — The fully-populated DDS Daughtercard PC board contains a mix of SMT and through-hole parts, showing how both packaging technologies can be used together.

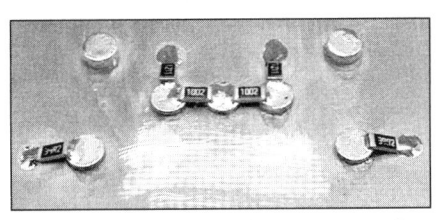

Figure 23.7D — SMT resistors soldered to base board of the Audio Amp in the beginning stages of assembly.

Figure 23.7F — Surface mount ICs can be mounted to general-purpose carrier boards, then attached as a submodule with wires to the base board of the homebrew project.

Figure 23.7E — The completed homebrew Audio Amp assembly shows simple, effective use of SMT components used together with conventional leaded components when constructed "Manhattan-style."

Construction Techniques 23.13

in the new component using the techniques discussed above.

You can also use the embossing heat gun previously described to remove SM parts, especially ICs. Keep in mind that not only the desired component, but some adjacent parts as well may be loosened by this process, so be sure to not move the board during reheating to allow the other components to stay in place. Use a long-handled tweezers to remove a component once you see the solder become silvery again. Be careful to not disturb any adjacent components. Allow the board to thoroughly cool before moving it to prevent inadvertently allowing other components to shift before the solder solidifies again.

To remove individual components without a heat gun, first remove excess solder from the pads by using desoldering braid. Then the component will generally come loose from the pads if gently lifted with a hobby knife or dental tool. If the component remains attached to the pad, touch the pad with the soldering iron and lift the component off the pad. It may take one or two attempts to free the component from all pads. In extreme cases, it may be necessary to add solder to the pad to completely loosen the component. A product called CHIPQUIK (**www.chipquik.com**) reduces the melting point of the existing solder by mixing in a very low temperature solder. Using the flux and solder that comes with a CHIPQUIK kit lets you desolder an SMD easilyt without a hot-air tool.

23.4.5 SMT Construction Examples

The first project example is the DDS Daughtercard — a small module that generates precision RF signals for a variety of projects. This kit has become immensely popular in homebrew circles and is supplied with the chip components contained in color-coded packaging that makes and easy job of identifying the little parts, a nice touch by a kit supplier.

Figure 23.7A shows the DDS PC board, a typical layout for SMT components. All traces are on one side, since the component leads are not "through-hole." The little square pads are the places where the 1206 package-style chips will eventually be soldered. This project demonstrates the reflow technique using a soldering iron. **Figure 23.7B** illustrates how to use this technique.

(a) Pre-solder ("tin") one of the pads on the board where the component will ultimately go by placing a small blob of solder there.

(b) Carefully hold the component in place with small needle-nose pliers or sharp tweezers on the tinned pad.

(c) Reheat the tinned pad and component to reflow the solder onto the component lead, thus temporarily holding the component in place.

(d) Solder the other end of the component to its pad.

(e) Finally, check all connections to make sure there are no bridges or shorts.

Figure 23.7C shows the completed DDS board.

The second project example is the K8IQY Audio Amp — a discrete component audio amplifier that is homebrew-constructed "Manhattan-style" as described later in the chapter in which small pads are glued or soldered to the copper-clad base board wherever you need to attach component leads or wires. See **Figure 23.7D**.

Instead of using little squares or dots of PC board material for pads, you might decide to create isolated connection points by cutting an "island" in the copper using an end mill or pad cutter. No matter how the pads are created, SMT components may be easily soldered from pad-to-pad, or from pad-to-ground plane to build up the circuit. **Figure 23.7E** shows the completed board, combining SMT and leaded components.

Homebrewing with SOIC-packaged integrated circuits is a little trickier and typically requires the use of an "SOIC carrier board" such as the one shown in **Figure 23.7F**, onto which you solder your surface-mount integrated circuit. You can then wire the carrier board onto your base board or whatever you're using to hold your other circuit components.

Full details on the DDS Daughtercard, the K8IQY Islander Audio Amp, and the Islander Pad Cutter may be found online at **www.njqrp.org**.

23.5 Constructing Electronic Circuits

Most of the construction projects undertaken by the average amateur involve electronic circuitry. The circuit is the "heart" of most amateur equipment. It might seem obvious, but in order for you to build it, the circuit must work! Don't always assume that a "cookbook" circuit that appears in an applications note or electronics magazine is flawless. These are sometimes design examples that have not always been thoroughly debugged. Many home-construction projects are one-time deals; the author has put one together and it worked. In some cases, component tolerances or minor layout changes might make it difficult to get a second unit working. Using a solderless breadboard can make it easier to test this type of circuit design. For RF circuits above a few MHz, a solderless breadboard is not always practical due to long lead lengths that result.

Take steps to protect the electronic and mechanical components you use in circuit construction. Some components can be damaged by rough handling. Dropping a ¼ W resistor causes no harm, but dropping a vacuum tube or other delicate subassemblies usually causes damage.

Some components are easily damaged by heat. Some of the chemicals used to clean electronic components (such as flux removers, degreasers or control-lubrication sprays) can damage plastic. Check them for suitability before you use them.

23.5.1 Electrostatic Discharge (ESD)

Some components, especially high-impedance components such as FETs and CMOS gates, can be damaged by electrostatic discharge (ESD). Protect these parts from static charges. Most people are familiar with the static charge that builds up when one walks across a carpet then touches a metal object; the resultant spark can be quite lively. Walking across a carpet on a dry day can generate 35 kV! A worker sitting at a bench can generate voltages up to 6 kV, depending on conditions, such as when relative humidity is less than 20%.

You don't need this much voltage to damage a sensitive electronic component; damage can occur with as little as 30 V. The damage is not always catastrophic. A MOSFET can become noisy, or lose gain; an IC can suffer damage that causes early failure. To prevent this kind of damage, you need to take some precautions.

The energy from a spark can travel inside a piece of equipment to affect internal components. Protection of sensitive electronic components involves the prevention of static build-up together with the removal of any existing charges by dissipating any energy that does build up.

MINIMIZING STATIC BUILD-UP

Several techniques can be used to minimize static build-up. Start by removing any carpet in your work areas. You can replace it with special antistatic carpet, but this is expensive. It's less expensive to treat the carpet with antistatic spray, which is available from electronics wholesalers. Adding humidity to the air can help reduce the presence of static charges as well.

Even the choice of clothing you wear can affect the amount of ESD. Polyester has a much greater ESD potential than cotton.

Many builders who have their workbench on a concrete floor use a rubber mat to minimize the risk of electric shocks from the ac line. Unfortunately, the rubber mat increases the risk of ESD. An antistatic rubber mat can serve both purposes.

Many components are shipped in antistatic packaging. Leave components in their conductive packaging. Other components, notably MOSFETs, are shipped with a small metal ring that temporarily shorts all of the leads together. Leave this ring in place until the device is fully installed in the circuit.

Use antistatic bags to transport susceptible components or equipment. Keep your workbench free of objects such as paper, plastic and other static-generating items. Use conductive containers with a dissipative surface coating for equipment storage. Storing partially assembled projects in antistatic bags is also a good idea.

These precautions help reduce the build-up of electrostatic charges. Other techniques offer a slow discharge path for the charges or keep the components and the operator handling them at the same ground potential.

DISSIPATING STATIC

One of the best techniques is to connect the operator and the devices being handled to earth ground, or to a common reference point. It is not a good idea to directly ground an operator working on electronic equipment, though; the risk of shock is too great. If the operator is grounded through a high-value resistor such as 100 kΩ to 1 MΩ, ESD protection is still offered but there is no risk of shock.

The operator is usually grounded through a conductive wrist strap. This wrist band is equipped with a snap-on ground lead. A 1 MΩ resistor is built into the snap of the strap to protect the user should a live circuit be contacted. Build a similar resistor into any homemade ground strap.

The devices and equipment being handled are also grounded, by working on a charge-dissipating mat that is connected to ground. The mat should be an insulator that has been impregnated with a resistance material. Suitable mats and wrist straps are available from most electronics supply houses. **Figure 23.8** shows

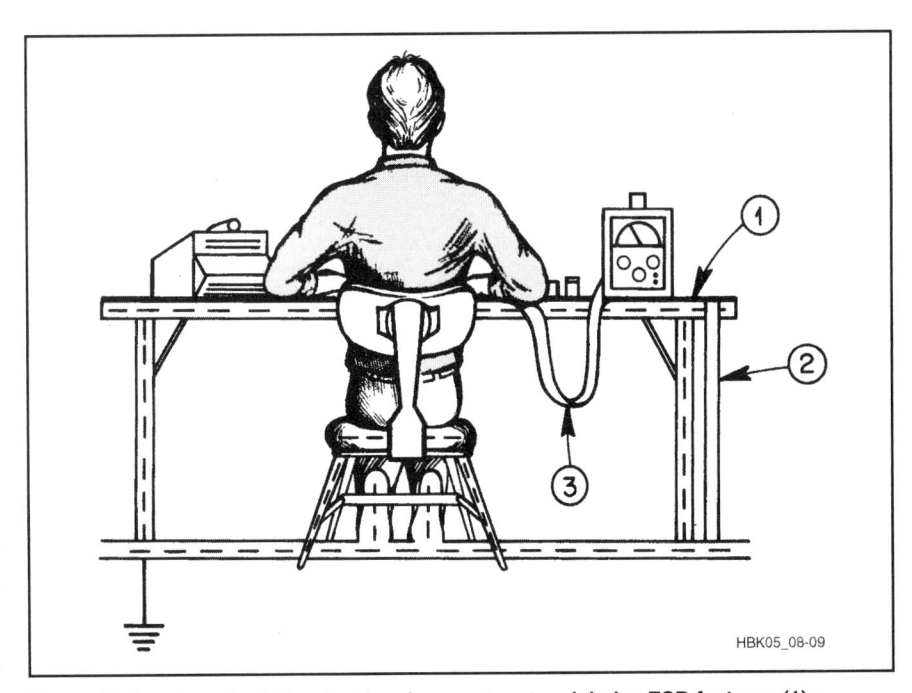

Figure 23.8 — A work station that has been set up to minimize ESD features (1) a grounded dissipative work mat and (2) a wrist strap that (3) grounds the worker through high resistance.

a typical ESD-safe work station.

The work area should also be grounded, directly or through a conductive mat. Use a soldering iron with a grounded tip to solder sensitive components. Most irons that have three-wire power cords are properly grounded. When soldering static-sensitive devices, use two or three jumpers: one to ground you, one to ground the work, and one to ground the iron. If the iron does not have a ground wire in the power cord, clip a jumper from the metal part of the iron near the handle to the metal box that houses the temperature control. Another jumper connects the box to the work. Finally, a jumper goes from the box to an elastic wrist band for static grounding.

23.5.2 Sorting Parts

When building a project, especially one packaged as a kit, finding the appropriate container to sort your components can be a problem. There are a number of things that make this task a lot easier and at a low cost.

Using a plastic egg carton or poking component leads into Styrofoam works quite well for sorting parts, but both methods can lead to ESD damage of sensitive components. Use this method for components such as resistors, capacitors and inductors that are relatively immune to ESD.

Metal cupcake trays are ideal, as the tray itself can be grounded through a 1 MΩ resistor to prevent static buildup. Cupcake trays typically come in three sizes: 6, 12 and 16 cups. The best sorting technique is to place the most common or first-used components in the cups closest to the builder (usually resistors),

---

Common Standard Parts

When building a project or repairing equipment, it is helpful to have an assortment of standard and common parts on hand for use in modifying circuit designs and fine-tuning performance. Making repairs or completing a kit that is missing a part are also good reasons to keep an assortment of parts on hand. It is not possible to have every possible needed part, but the majority of components in any project are usually one of the common standard values.

Assortments of new parts such as resistors, capacitors, and semiconductors are available from electronic distributors, such as DigiKey, Mouser, Newark, and Jameco, and from parts companies such as Velleman. These are often available with a storage container or cabinet, as well. When taking into account the cost of the parts cabinet and the parts themselves, it is very economical to buy standard parts in this manner. If parts cabinets are not available, craft stores as well as fishing supply stores often have low-cost compartmentalized containers ideal for sorting and storing small parts. Tackle boxes are also useful for storing components and materials, particularly if purchased during the end-of-season sales.

Another recommendation is to buy in quantity when ordering parts for a project. Not only can you often get a price break on the individual components but you will be building up your store of components along the way.

Many vendors also have bags of one or more values of surplus parts from electronic manufacturing. It is often less expensive to buy an entire bag of surplus parts than it is to buy even one or two of them elsewhere. Some come as truly random assortments, often called "grab bags," and others may be sold as "tapes" that were prepared for a parts-placement machine. You will have to sort out the components but the price makes it worthwhile!

You can accumulate a good selection of parts at ham radio flea markets. It is common to see parts cabinets available with entire collections of components and hardware! Grab bags and parts junk boxes are also common here and generally a very good value if you are willing to sort through the components.

The tables in this sidebar list common parts used in many projects. It is a good idea to accumulate these parts and keep them on hand. Keep in mind that you do not have to have every one of these parts, but have the list in mind as you shop for parts. (See the **Component Data and Reference**s chapter for more information on part types.)

Resistors (values in ohms)
10	15	18	22	27	33	39	47	56	68	82	100	120
150	180	220	270	390	470	560	680	820				
1.0k	1.2k	1.5k	1.8k	2.2k	2.7k	3.3k	3.9k	4.7k	5.6k	6.8k	8.2k	
10k	12k	15k	18k	22k	27k	33k	39k	47k	56k	68k	82k	
100k	120k	150k	180k	220k	470k	560k	680k	820k	1M	4.7M		

Potentiometers (values in ohms)
500 1k 5k 10k 100k 1M

Ceramic disc capacitors (values in pF)
5	10	18	22	27	33	39	47	56	68	82	100	120
150	220	390	470	560	680	1000	4700

Ceramic disc capacitors (values in µF)
0.001 0.005 0.01 0.022 0.05 0.1

Electrolytic and tantalum capacitors (values in µF)
1 2.2 4.7 10 22 33 47 100 220 470 1000 2200

Diodes and rectifiers
1N34A 1N914 1N4001 1N4007 1N4148 1N5401 1N5819

Transistors
2N2222 2N3055 MJ2955 2N3904 2N3906 2N4401 2N4404 2N7000 IRF510 TIP31C TIP32C

Voltage regulators
78L05 7805 7812 7815 LM317 723

Operational amplifiers and miscellaneous ICs
324 741 747 TL081
555 (timer)
ULN2001 (driver array)

with the least used parts (usually mounting hardware) in the farther cups.

Another great idea for parts sorting is to use a fishing tackle box with removable trays. Inexpensive tackle boxes are available at outdoor supply houses and department stores, and you can often find them on sale. The tackle box has a distinct advantage of allowing you to sort your parts into different compartments within each movable tray, and some trays have pieces that allow you to resize the compartments to better fit the parts for your project. Many tackle boxes have a larger open space in the top which allows you to store your partially finished boards, with the remaining components in the closeable trays below it. This arrangement is ideal to protect your project from damage and can be securely stored between work sessions.

23.5.3 Construction Order

When building a kit or DIY project, the question often arises as to what order the parts need to be mounted. In a kit, the manual often is very explicit, requiring the builder to construct the project stage by stage. Other kit manuals offer only a minimum of directions, leaving it up to the builder. Have the manual handy, either printed or on a laptop or tablet nearby for reference.

In stage by stage construction, each stage in the project is completed in order to allow the builder to test and troubleshoot that area of the project without having a more complex problem to solve with all components mounted. This method also allows the builder to learn the principles involved in the project and how each part of the circuit works from the power supply to the output. This is a great aid to future modification and repair.

When building a kit in stages, it is often better to sort the parts by stages as well, placing the parts from each stage in their own space. That way, when each stage is completed, there should be no extra parts left over in that stage's container. Number the stages, if they are not already numbered in the manual, and place a small piece of paper with that number in each compartment, indicating the stage that those parts belong to.

When given a minimum of assembly instructions, the best approach is to mount the resistors first, then the capacitors, and then the semiconductors, followed by the more unique components. This way, the majority of parts are mounted early in the process, so finding the remaining part locations is a lot easier. This technique also allows the builder to double check the usage of parts. Try to mount large parts after the smaller surrounding parts so as not to possibly block your ability to properly mount all of them.

Inventory the parts before commencing construction. In kits or DIY projects, if a change is introduced after a number of kits have been assembled, there is a chance of errors so that the parts list or board layouts do not reflect changes in the design of the circuit. Sometimes, a number of extra parts are supplied with a kit to facilitate different options, such as the choice of bands covered. Sometimes parts are eliminated or substituted with a change of other components in the circuit. Be sure to ask the kit supplier if you are not sure as to why you have an empty space or surplus parts. Sometimes new parts values are added to substitute for old values already packed in the kit, making the old values surplus. Resolve questions about component placement before powering up a completed project.

23.5.4 Component Mounting

When working with a large number of components, there are a few techniques that can be helpful should troubleshooting be required. Although resistors are not polarized, it is a good idea to mount them with the color codes reading the same direction to make it easier to spot a part that is not in its correct position. Polarity-sensitive parts, such as diodes, electrolytic capacitors and ICs, must be placed in their specified direction. In general, mount components so their values are readable without having to remove the component from the board or bending it, causing possible damage.

Axial-lead components such as resistors are mounted in one of two methods, upright and flat. To save space on a PC board, resistors are often mounted upright with one lead bent double in a manner resembling a hairpin. The best practice is to make this bend so that the color stripes denoting the resistor value begin at the top and the precision stripe (often silver or gold) is at the bottom, making it easier to read the values once mounted. Components with alphanumeric markings, such as diodes, should be mounted with the markings visible.

Non-polarized capacitors are best placed with markings facing in the same direction, unless the markings would be blocked by another component.

For polarized parts, always double-check its positioning before soldering. A commercially-prepared PC board often has stripes on the diode labels, indicating which end to place the cathode stripe on the diode. A "+" sign on the board inside or next to the circle for a capacitor denotes the positive lead which will often be longer. LEDs will have a flat spot on or a notch on a lead to identify the cathode. See the **Component Data and References** chapter and manufacturers' data sheets for more information on component body styles.

When mounting ICs, using a pin straightener helps align the leads for insertion. If one is not available, use a flat surface to align them at once. Be sure a pin does not get bent inward and that all pins go into the socket or PC board holes.

Straight-pin "header" connectors are commonly used in projects and kits. Unless you have a specialized jig for this purpose, soldering this type of connector can appear to be difficult. An easy technique is to simply solder one pin to hold the part on the board, without regard to how exactly straight the connector is. Using a finger, apply pressure on an unsoldered pin or pins, and reheat the solo pin that was previously soldered. You can feel when the connector is moved into place, straight and vertical. Be sure to only touch a pin that is not being heated as it can become very hot! (KØNEB has contributed photos that are available in the book's online supplemental material as additional guidance.)

Once the connector is in the correct position with only one pin soldered, the other pins can be soldered, completing the connector. This same process can also be used for soldering things like plugs and jacks to a PC board. Temporarily or "tack" solder one pin, then reheat it while adjusting its position, followed by completing the other pins on the connector.

23.5.5 Electronics Construction Techniques

Several different point-to-point wiring techniques or printed-circuit boards (PC boards) can be used to construct electronic circuits. Most circuit projects use a combination of techniques. The selection of techniques depends on many different factors and builder preferences.

For one-time construction, PC boards are really not necessary. It takes time to lay out, drill and etch a PC board. Alterations are difficult to make if you change your ideas or make a mistake.

The simple audio amplifier shown in **Figure 23.9** will be built using various point-to-point or PC-board techniques. This shows

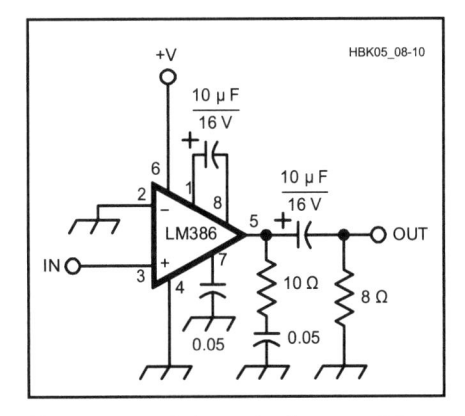

Figure 23.9 — Schematic diagram of the audio amplifier used as a design example of various construction techniques.

Construction Techniques 23.17

how the different construction methods are applied to a typical circuit. (Surface-mount techniques are discussed in the previous section.)

POINT-TO-POINT TECHNIQUES

Point-to-point techniques include all circuit construction techniques that rely on tie points and wiring, or component leads, to build a circuit. This is the technique used in most home-brew construction projects. It is sometimes used in commercial construction, such as old vacuum-tube receivers and modern tube amplifiers.

Point-to-point wiring is also used to connect the "off-board" components used in a printed-circuit project. It can be used to interconnect the various modules and printed-circuit boards used in more complex electronic systems. Most pieces of electronic equipment have at least some point-to-point wiring.

GROUND-PLANE CONSTRUCTION

A point-to-point construction technique that uses the leads of the components as tie points for electrical connections is known as "ground-plane," "dead-bug" or "ugly" construction. "Dead-bug construction" gets its name from the appearance of an IC with its leads sticking up in the air. In most cases, this technique uses copper-clad circuit-board material as a foundation and ground plane on which to build a circuit using point-to-point wiring, so in this chapter it is called "ground-plane construction." An example is shown in **Figure 23.10**.

Ground-plane construction is quick and simple: You build the circuit on an unetched piece of copper-clad circuit board. Wherever a component connects to ground, you solder it to the copper board. Ungrounded connections between components are made point-to-point. Once you learn how to build with a ground-plane board, you can grab a piece of circuit board and start building any time you see an interesting circuit.

A PC board has strict size limits; the components must fit in the space allotted. Ground-plane construction is more flexible; it allows you to use the parts on hand. The circuit can be changed easily — a big help when you are experimenting. The greatest virtue of ground-plane construction is that it is fast.

Ground-plane construction is something like model building, connecting parts using solder almost — but not exactly — like glue. In ground-plane construction you build the circuit directly from the schematic, so it can help you get familiar with a circuit and how it works. You can build subsections of a large circuit on small ground-plane modules and string them together into a larger design.

Circuit connections are made directly, minimizing component lead length. Short lead lengths and a low-impedance ground conductor help prevent circuit instability. There is usually less inter-component capacitive coupling than would be found between PC-board traces, so it is often better than PC-board construction for RF, high-gain or sensitive circuits.

Use circuit components to support other circuit components. Start by mounting one component onto the ground plane, building from there. There is really only one two-handed technique to mount a component to the ground plane. Bend one of the component leads at a 90° angle, and then trim off the excess. Solder a blob of solder to the board surface, perhaps about 0.1 inch in diameter, leaving a small dome of solder. Using one hand, hold the component in place on top of the soldered spot and reheat the component and the solder. It should flow nicely, soldering the component securely. Remove the iron tip and hold the component perfectly still until the solder cools. You can then make connections to the first part.

Connections should be mechanically secure before soldering. Bend a small hook in the lead of a component, then "crimp" it to the next component(s). Do not rely only on the solder connections to provide mechanical strength; sooner or later one of these connections will fail, resulting in a dead circuit.

In most cases, each circuit has enough grounded components to support all of the components in the circuit. This is not always

Figure 23.10 — The example audio amplifier of Figure 23.9 built using ground-plane construction.

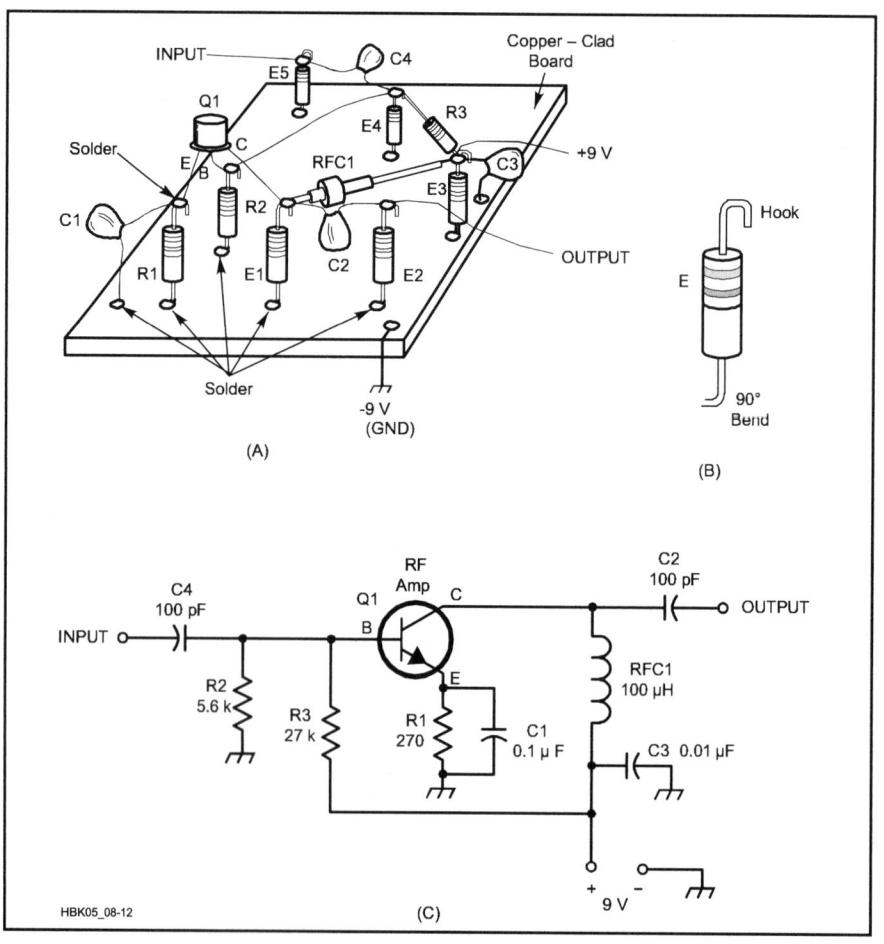

Figure 23.11 — Pictorial view of a circuit board that uses ground-plane construction is shown at A. A close-up view of one of the standoff resistors is shown at B. Note how the leads are bent. The schematic diagram at C shows the circuit displayed at A.

possible, however. In some circuits, high-value resistors can be used as standoff insulators. One resistor lead is soldered to the copper ground plane; the other lead is used as a circuit connection point. You can use ¼ or ½ W resistors in values from 1 to 10 MΩ. Such high-value resistors permit almost no current to flow, and in low-impedance circuits they act more like insulators than resistors. As a rule of thumb, resistors used as standoff insulators should have a value that is at least 10 times the circuit impedance at that point in the circuit.

Figure 23.11A shows how to use the standoff technique to wire the circuit shown at Figure 23.11C. Figure 23.11B shows how the resistor leads are bent before the standoff component is soldered to the ground plane. Components E1 through E5 are resistors that are used as standoff insulators. They do not appear in the schematic diagram. The base circuitry at Q1 of Figure 23.11A has been stretched out to reduce clutter in the drawing. In a practical circuit, all of the signal leads should be kept as short as possible. E4 would, therefore, be placed much closer to Q1 than the drawing indicates.

No standoff posts are required near R1 and R2 of Figure 23.11. These two resistors serve two purposes: They are not only the normal circuit resistances, but function as standoff posts as well. Follow this practice wherever a capacitor or resistor can be employed in the dual role.

"MANHATTAN" CONSTRUCTION

Another solution to building up a circuit is called "Manhattan" construction, shown previously in the Surface-Mount Components section as Figure 23.7E. This method got its name from the appearance of the finished product, resembling the tall buildings in a city. Manhattan construction uses plain, unetched copper clad PC board material to make both the main board and the component connection points. The PC board material used may be single or double-sided.

After cutting the desired size and shape of the board required for the project, use the scraps left over to make the insulated contact pads. These pads can be made a number of ways, the most common being cutting the material into tiny squares about ¼ or ⅜ inch across. Another method to create the pads is to use a heavy-duty hole punch. This kind of punch often has changeable dies to create various sizes of round holes in materials such as sheet metal, and is available at many tool dealers. Once cut, the pads can be glued to the board in a pattern that accommodates the lead lengths of the parts to be connected.

Pads can be glued to the base board or soldered if the pads are double-sided PC board material. Use a tiny drop of instant glue, such as a cyanoacrylate "super glue" to mount the pads to the board. When soldering to the pads, use the minimum amount of heat required to avoid loosening the pads.

Component leads are soldered to the pads, and additional leads can be added to a pad by simply reheating the connection already there. The main board is used as the ground plane with all ground leads soldered to the board. This method of construction works well with RF circuits up to UHF.

WIRED TRACES — THE LAZY PC BOARD

If you already have a PC-board design, but don't want to copy the entire circuit — or you don't want to make a double-sided PC board — then the easiest construction technique is to use a bare board or perfboard and hardwire the traces.

Drill the necessary holes in a piece of single-sided board, remove the copper ground plane from around the holes, and then wire up the back using component leads and bits of wire instead of etched traces (**Figure 23.12**).

To transfer an existing board layout, make a 1:1 photocopy and tape it to your piece of PC board. Prick through the holes with an automatic (one-handed) center punch or by firm pressure with a sharp scriber, remove the photocopy and drill all the holes. Holes for ground leads are optional — you generally get a better RF ground by bending the component lead flat to the board and soldering it down. Remove the copper around the rest of the holes by pressing a drill bit lightly against the hole and twisting it between your fingers. A drill press can also be used, but either way, don't remove too much board material. Then wire up the circuit beneath the board. The results look very neat and tidy — from the top, at least!

Circuits that contain components originally designed for PC-board mounting are good candidates for this technique. Wired traces would also be suitable for circuits involving multi-pin RF ICs, double-balanced mixers and similar components. To bypass the pins of these components to ground, connect a miniature ceramic capacitor on the bottom of the board directly from the bypassed pin to the ground plane.

A wired-trace board is fairly sturdy, even though many of the components are only held in by their bent leads and blobs of solder. A drop of cyanoacrylate "super glue" can hold down any larger components, components with fragile leads or any long leads or wires that might move.

PERFORATED CONSTRUCTION BOARD

A simple approach to circuit building uses

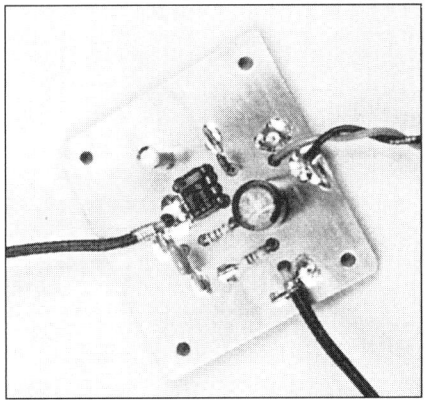

Figure 23.12 — The audio amplifier built using wired-traces construction.

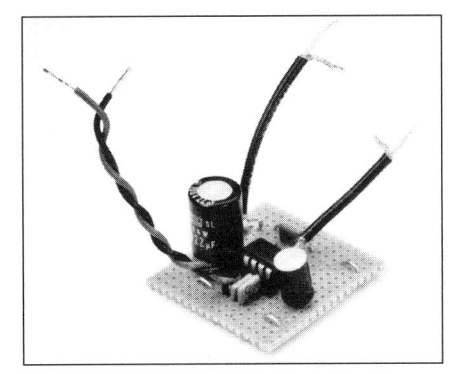

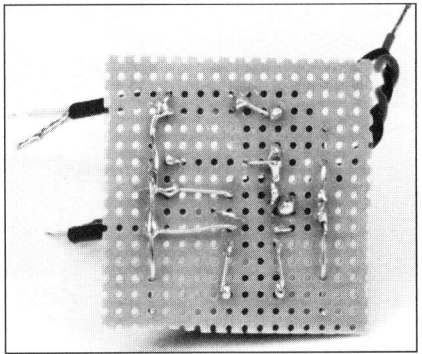

Figure 23.13 — The audio amplifier built on perforated board. Top view at left; bottom view at right.

a perforated phenolic or epoxy resin board known as perfboard. Perfboard is available with many different hole patterns. Choose the one that suits your needs. Perfboard is usually unclad, although it is made with pads that facilitate soldering.

Circuit construction on perforated board is easy. Start by placing the components loosely on the board and moving them around until a satisfactory layout is obtained. Most of the construction techniques described in this chapter can be applied to perfboard. The audio amplifier of Figure 23.9 is shown constructed with this technique in **Figure 23.13**.

Perfboard and accessories are widely available. Accessories include mounting hardware and a variety of connection terminals for solder and solderless construction.

TERMINAL AND WIRE

A perfboard is usually used for this technique. Push terminals are inserted into the hole in a perfboard. Components can then be easily soldered to the terminals. As an alternative, drill holes into a bare or copper-clad board wherever they are needed (**Figure 23.14**). The components are usually mounted on one side of the board and wires are soldered to the bottom of the board, acting as wired PC-board "traces." If a component has a reasonably rigid lead to which you can attach other components, use that instead of a push terminal — a modification of the ground-plane construction technique.

If you are using a bare board to provide a ground plane, drill holes for your terminals with a high-speed PC-board drill and drill press. Mark the position of the hole with a center punch to prevent the drill from skidding. The hole should provide a snug fit for the push terminal.

Mount RF components on top of the board, keeping the dc components and much of the interconnecting wiring underneath. Make dc feed-through connections with terminals having bypass capacitors on top of the board. Use small solder-in feedthrough capacitors for more critical applications.

SOLDERLESS PROTOTYPE BOARD

One construction alternative that works well for audio and digital circuits is the solderless prototype board (protoboard), shown in **Figure 23.15**. It is usually not suitable for RF circuits above a few MHz.

A protoboard has rows of holes with spring-loaded metal strips inside the board. Circuit components and hookup wire are inserted into the holes, making contact with the metal strips. Components that are inserted into the same row are connected together. Component and interconnection changes are easy to make. Pre-made and color-coded jumpers make wiring these boards easier. (A length of phone system cable with four solid-conductor wires makes an excellent source of colored jumper wire.) Look for a protoboard that has power supply terminals already mounted on them for easier connection.

Protoboards have some minor disadvantages. The metal strips add stray capacitance to the circuit and jumper lengths can be long. Large-diameter component leads can deform the metal contacts of the strips — be sure to insert wire no larger than the manufacturer recommends.

WIRE-WRAP CONSTRUCTION

Wire-wrap techniques can be used to quickly construct a circuit without solder. Low- and medium-speed digital circuits are often assembled on a wire-wrap board. The technique is not limited to digital circuits, however. **Figure 23.16** shows the audio amplifier built using wire wrap. Circuit changes are easy to make, yet the method is suitable for permanent assemblies.

Wire wrap is done by wrapping a wire around a small square post to make each connection. A wrapping tool resembles a thick pencil. Electric wire-wrap guns are convenient when many connections must be made. The wire is almost always #30 AWG wire

Figure 23.14 — The audio amplifier built using terminal-and-wire construction.

Figure 23.15 — The audio amplifier built on a solderless prototyping board.

Figure 23.16 — The audio amplifier built using wire-wrap techniques.

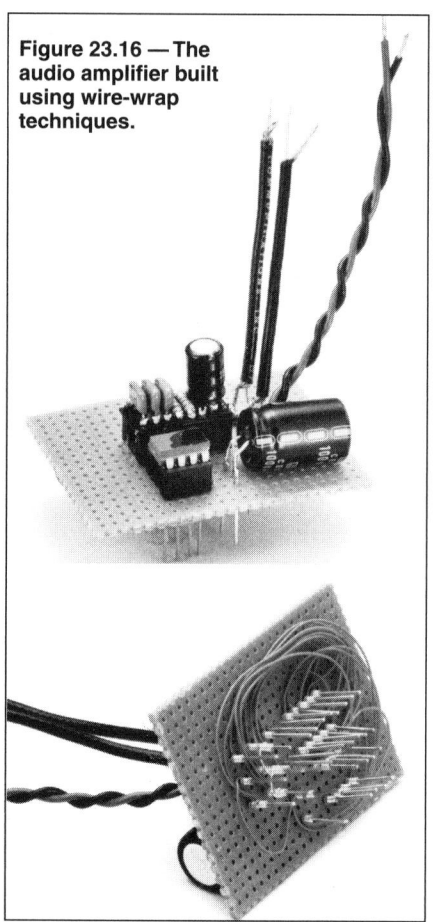

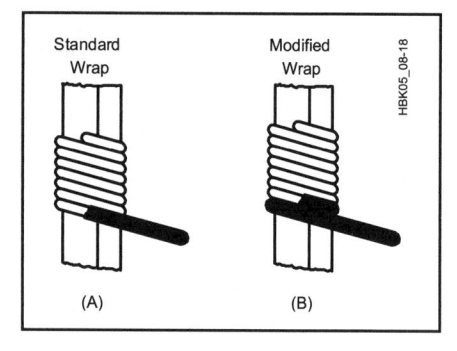

Figure 23.17 — Wire-wrap connections. Standard wrap is shown at A; modified wrap at B.

with thin insulation. Two wire-wrap methods are used: the standard and the modified wrap (**Figure 23.17**). The modified wrap adds a turn of insulated wire which provides a bit of stress relief to the connection. The wrap-post terminals are square (wire wrap works only on posts with sharp corners). They should be long enough for at least two connections. Figure 23.17 and **Figure 23.18** show proper and improper wire-wrap techniques. Mount small components on an IC header plug. Insert the header into a wire-wrap IC socket as shown in Figure 23.16. The large capacitor in that figure has its leads soldered directly to wire-wrap posts.

"READY-MADE" UTILITY PC BOARDS

"Utility" PC boards are an alternative to custom-designed etched PC boards. They offer the flexibility of perforated board construction and the mechanical and electrical advantages of etched circuit connection pads. Utility PC boards can be used to build anything from simple passive filter circuits to computers.

Circuits can be built on boards on which the copper cladding has been divided into connection pads. Power supply voltages can be distributed on bus strips. Boards like those shown in **Figure 23.19** are commercially available.

An audio amplifier constructed on a utility PC board is shown in **Figure 23.20**. Component leads are inserted into the board and soldered to the etched pads. Wire jumpers connect the pads together to complete the circuit.

Utility boards with one or more etched plugs for use in computer-bus, interface and general purpose applications are widely available. Connectors, mounting hardware and other accessories are also available. Check with your parts supplier for details.

23.5.6 Printed-Circuit (PC) Boards

PC boards are everywhere — in all kinds of consumer electronics, in most of your Amateur Radio equipment. They are also used in most kits and construction projects. A newcomer to electronics might think that there is some unwritten law against building equipment in any other way!

The misconception that everything needs to be built on a printed-circuit board is often a stumbling block to easy project construction. In fact, a PC board is probably the worst choice for a one-time project. In actuality, a moderately complex project (such as a QRP transmitter) can be built in much less time using other techniques such as those described in the preceding section. The additional design, layout and manufacturing is usually much more work than it would take to build the project by hand.

So why does everyone use PC boards? The most important reason is that they are reproducible. They allow many units to be mass-produced with exactly the same layout, reducing the time and work of conventional wiring and minimizing the possibilities of wiring errors. If you can buy a ready-made PC board or kit for your project, it can save a lot of construction time. This is true because someone else has done most of the real work involved — designing the PC board layout and fixing any "bugs" caused by inter-trace capacitive coupling, ground loops and similar problems. In most cases, if a ready-made board is not available, ground-plane construction is a lot less work than designing, debugging and then making a PC board.

Using a PC board usually makes project construction easier by minimizing the risk of wiring errors or other construction blunders. Inexperienced constructors usually feel more confident when construction has been simplified to the assembly of components onto a PC board. One of the best ways to get started with home construction (to some the best part of Amateur Radio) is to start by assembling a few kits using PC boards. A list of kit manufacturers can be found on the QRP ARCI website, **www.qrparci.org**, under "Links." Then click on "QRP Kits Bits and Supplies". Another web page listing kits is at **www.w0ch.net/kits/kits.htm**.

ON-LINE PC BOARD FABRICATION SERVICES

In the past few years, on-line PC board fabrication services have become popular among hobbyists and professional designers. See the CAD for PCB Design section of this chapter for a discussion of PCB design software and services. These services specialize in fast turnaround (two or three days, typically) of small boards in low quantities. Some accept artwork files in standard interchange formats and others have proprietary software packages. The cost per board is quite reason-

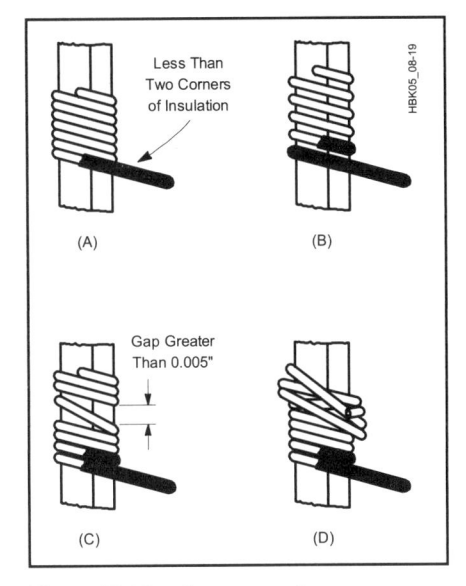

Figure 23.18 — Improper wire-wrap connections. Insufficient insulation for modified wrap is shown at A; a spiral wrap at B, where there is too much space between turns; an open wrap at C, where one or more turns are improperly spaced and an overwrap at D, where the turns overlap on one or more turns.

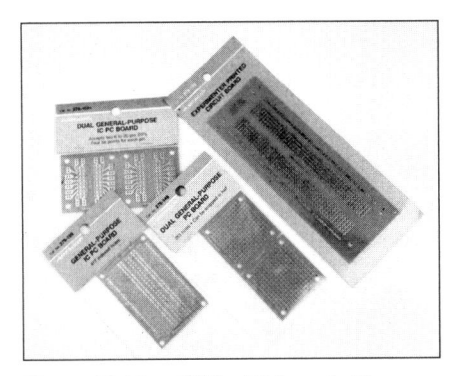

Figure 23.19 — Utility PC boards like these are available from many suppliers.

Figure 23.20 — The audio amplifier built on a multipurpose PC breadboard. Top view at A; bottom view at B.

Construction Techniques 23.21

able, considering the expense of maintaining the tools and techniques needed to construct boards in a home shop. The results are professional and high-quality.

PC-BOARD ASSEMBLY TECHNIQUES

Cleanliness

Make sure your PC board and component leads are clean. Clean the entire PC board before assembly; clean each component before you install it. Corrosion looks dark instead of bright and shiny. Don't use sandpaper to clean your board. Use a piece of fine steel wool or a Scotchbrite cleaning pad to clean component leads or PC board before you solder them together.

Installing Components

In a construction project that uses a PC board, most of the components are installed on the board. Installing components is easy — stick the components in the right board holes, solder the leads, and cut off the extra lead length. Most construction projects have a parts-placement diagram that shows you where each component is installed.

Getting the components in the right holes is called "stuffing" the circuit board. Inserting and soldering one component at a time takes too long. Some people like to put the components in all at once, and then turn the board over and solder all the leads. If you bend the leads a bit (about 20°) from the bottom side after you push them through the board, the components are not likely to fall out when you turn the board over.

Start with the shortest components — horizontally mounted diodes and resistors. Larger components sometimes cover smaller components, so these smaller parts must be installed first. If building a kit, follow the suggested order of mounting your parts if provided. Use adhesive tape to temporarily hold difficult components in place while you solder.

PC-Board Soldering

To solder components to a PC board, bend the leads at a slight angle; apply the soldering iron to one side of the lead, and flow the solder in from the other side of the lead. See **Figure 23.21A**. Too little heat causes a bad or "cold" solder joint; too much heat can damage the PC board. Practice a bit on some spare copper stock before you tackle your first PC board project. After the connection is soldered properly, clip the lead flush with the solder.

Make sure you have the components in the right holes before you solder them. Components that have polarity, such as diodes, ICs and some capacitors must be oriented as shown on the parts-placement diagram.

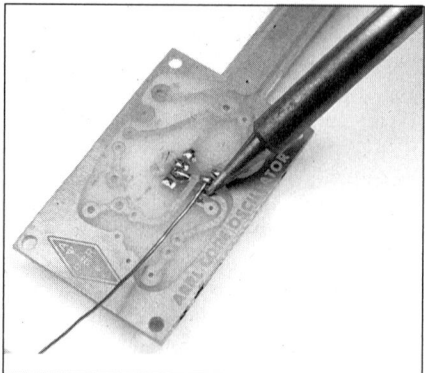

Figure 23.21 — The top photo shows how to solder a component to a PC board. Make sure that the component is flush with the board on the other side. Below is a solder bridge has formed a short circuit between PC board traces.

Inspect solder connections. A bad solder joint is much easier to find before the PC board is mounted to a chassis. Look for any damage caused to the PC board by soldering. Look for solder "bridges" between adjacent circuit-board traces. Solder bridges (Figure 23.21B) occur when solder accidentally connects two or more conductors that are supposed to be isolated. It is often difficult to distinguish a solder bridge from a conductive trace on a tin-plated board. If you find a bridge, re-melt it and the adjacent trace or traces to allow the solder's surface tension to absorb it. Double check that each component is installed in the proper holes on the board and that the orientation is correct. Make sure that no component leads or transistor tabs are touching other components or PC board connections. Check the circuit voltages before installing ICs in their sockets. Ensure that the ICs are oriented properly and installed in the correct sockets.

23.5.7 From Schematic to Working Circuit

Turning a schematic into a working circuit is more than just copying the schematic with components. One thing is usually true — you can't build it the way it looks on the schematic. The schematic describes the electrical connections, but it does not describe the mechanical layout of the circuit. Many design and layout considerations that apply in the real world of practical electronics don't appear on the schematic.

HOW TO DESIGN A GOOD CIRCUIT LAYOUT

A circuit diagram is a poor guide toward a proper layout. Circuit diagrams are drawn to be readable and to describe the electrical connections. They follow drafting conventions that have very little to do with the way the circuit works. On a schematic, ground and supply voltage symbols are scattered all over the place. The first rule of RF layout is — *do not lay out RF circuits as their schematics are drawn!* How a circuit works in practice depends on the layout. Poor layout can ruin the performance of even a well-designed circuit.

The easiest way to explain good layout practices is to take you through an example. **Figure 23.22** is the circuit diagram of a two-stage receiver IF amplifier using dual-gate MOSFETs. It is only a design example, so the values are only typical. To analyze which things are important to the layout of this circuit, ask these questions:

• Which are the RF components, and which are only involved with AF or dc?

• Which components are in the main RF signal path?

• Which components are in the ground return paths?

Use the answers to these questions to plan the layout. The RF components that are in the main RF signal path are usually the most critical. The AF or dc components can usually be placed anywhere. The components in the ground return path should be positioned so they are easily connected to the circuit ground. Answer the questions, apply the answers to the layout and then follow these guidelines:

• Avoid laying out circuits so their inputs and outputs are close together. If a stage's output is too near a previous stage's input, the output signal can feedback into the input and cause problems.

• Keep component leads as short as practical. This doesn't necessarily mean as short as possible, just consider lead length as part of your design.

• Remember that metal transistor cases conduct, and that a transistor's metal case is usually connected to one of its leads. Prevent cases from touching ground or other components, unless called for in the design.

In our design example, the RF components are shown in heavy lines, though not all of these components are in the main RF signal path. The RF signal path consists of T1/C1, Q1, T2/C4, C7, Q2, T3/C11. These need to be positioned in almost a straight line, to avoid feedback from output to input. They form the backbone of the layout, as shown in **Figure 23.23A**.

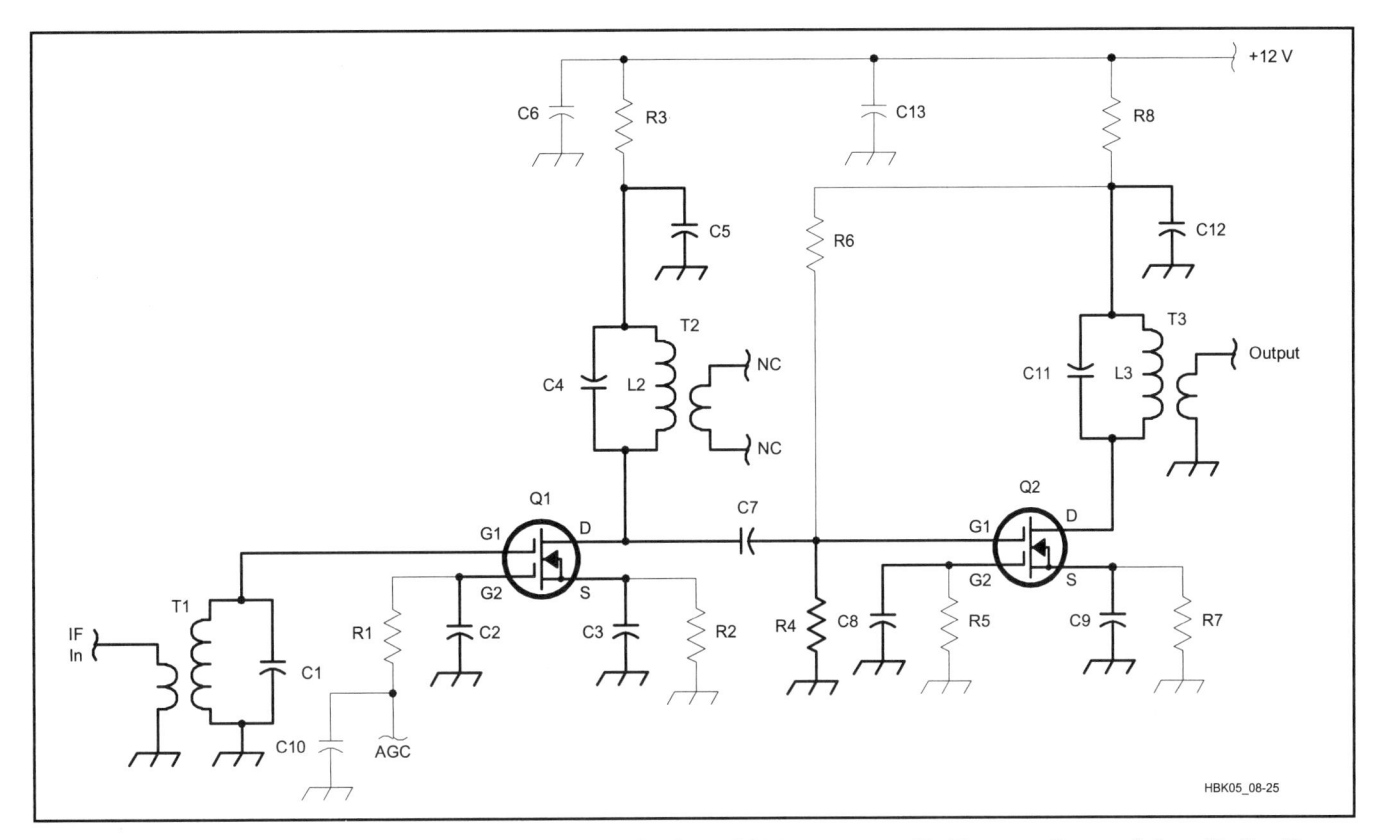

Figure 23.22 — The IF amplifier used in the design example. C1, C4 and C11 are not specified because they are internal to the IF transformers.

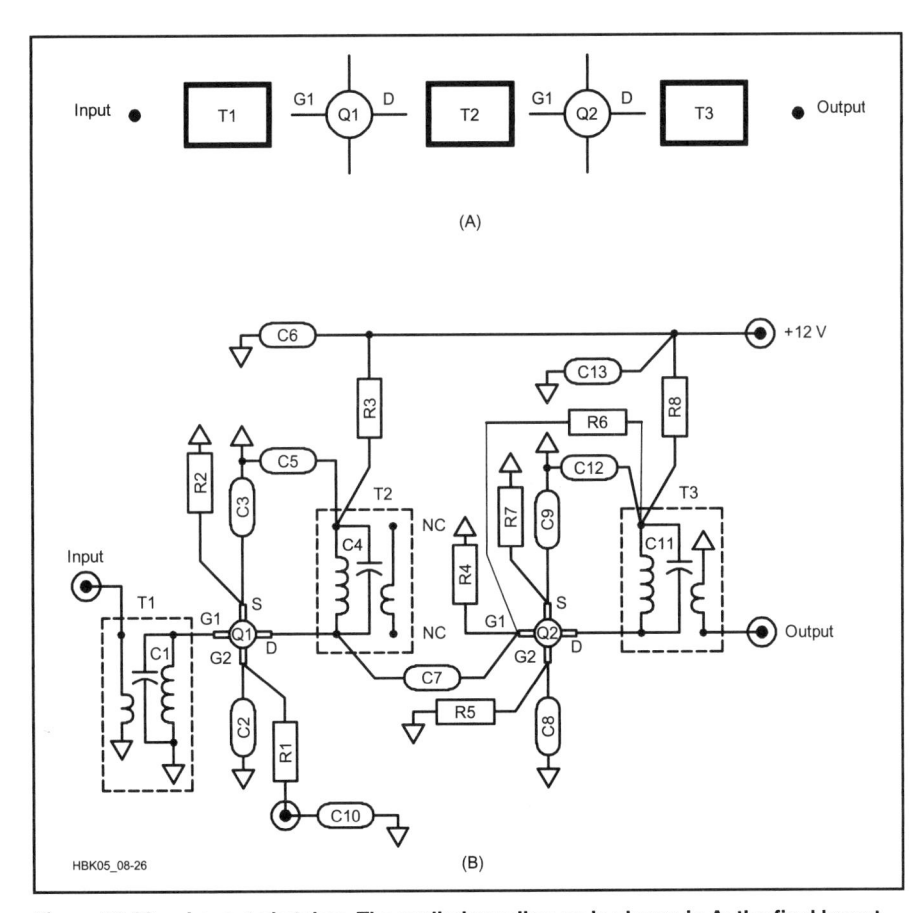

Figure 23.23 — Layout sketches. The preliminary line-up is shown in A; the final layout in B.

The question about ground paths requires some further thought — what is really meant by "ground" and "ground-return paths"? Some points in the circuit need to be kept at RF ground potential. The best RF ground potential on a PC board is a copper ground plane covering one entire side. Points in the circuit that cannot be connected directly to ground for dc reasons must be bypassed ("decoupled") to ground by capacitors that provide ground-return paths for RF.

In Figure 23.23, the components in the ground-return paths are the RF bypass capacitors C2, C3, C5, C8, C9 and C12. R4 is primarily a dc biasing component, but it is also a ground return for RF so its location is important. The values of RF bypass capacitors are chosen to have a low reactance at the frequency in use; typical values would be 0.1 μF at LF, 0.01 μF at HF and 0.001 μF or less at VHF. Not all capacitors are suitable for RF decoupling; the most common are disc ceramic capacitors. RF decoupling capacitors should always have short leads. Surface mount capacitors with no leads are ideal for bypassing.

Almost every RF circuit has an input, an output and a common ground connection. Many circuits also have additional ground connections, both at the input side and at the output side. Maintain a low-impedance path between input and output ground connections. The input ground connections for Q1

Construction Techniques 23.23

are the grounded ends of C1 and the two windings of T1. The two ends of an IF transformer winding are generally not interchangeable; one is designated as the "hot" end, and the other must be connected or bypassed to RF ground.) The capacitor that resonates with the adjustable coil is often mounted inside the can of the IF transformer, leaving only two component leads to be grounded as shown in Figure 23.22B.

The RF ground for Q1 is its source connection via C3. Since Q1 is in a plastic package that can be mounted in any orientation, you can make the common ground either above or below the signal path in Figure 23.23B, although the circuit diagram shows the source at the bottom. The practical circuit works much better with the source at the top, because of the connections to T2.

It's a good idea to locate the hot end of the main winding close to the drain lead of the transistor package, so the other end is toward the top of Figure 23.23B. If the source of Q1 is also toward the top of the layout, there is a common ground point for C3 (the source bypass capacitor) and the output bypass capacitor C5. Gate 2 of Q1 can safely be bypassed toward the bottom of the layout.

C7 couples the signal from the output of Q1 to the input of Q2. The source of Q2 should be bypassed toward the top of the layout, in exactly the same way as the source of Q1. R4 is not critical, but it should be connected on the same side as the other components. Note how the pinout of T3 has placed the output connection as far as possible from the input. With this layout for the signal path and the critical RF components, the circuit has an excellent chance of working properly.

DC Components

The rest of the components carry dc, so their layout is much less critical. Even so, try to keep everything well separated from the main RF signal path. One good choice is to put the 12 V connections along the top of the layout, and the AGC connection at the bottom. The source bias resistors R2 and R7 can be placed alongside C3 and C9. The gate-2 bias resistors for Q2, R5 and R6 are not RF components so their locations aren't too critical. R7 has to cross the signal path in order to reach C12, however, and the best way to avoid signal pickup would be to mount R7 on the opposite side of the copper ground plane from the signal wiring. Generally speaking, ⅛ W or ¼ W metal-film or carbon-film resistors are best for low-level RF circuits.

Actually, it is not quite accurate to say that resistors such as R3 and R8 are not "RF" components. They provide a high impedance to RF in the positive supply lead. Because of R8, for example, the RF signal in T2 is conducted to ground through C5 rather than ending up on the 12 V line, possibly causing unwanted RF feedback. Just to be sure, C6 bypasses R3 and C13 serves the same function for R8. Note that the gate-1 bias resistor R6 is connected to C12 rather than directly to the 12 V supply, to take advantage of the extra decoupling provided by R8 and C13.

If you build something, you want it to work the first time, so don't cut corners! Some commercial PC boards take liberties with layout, bypassing and decoupling. Don't assume that you can do the same. Don't try to eliminate "extra" decoupling components such as R3, C6, R8 and C13, even though they might not all be absolutely necessary. If other people's designs have left them out, put them in again. In the long run it's far easier to take a little more time and use a few extra components, to build in some insurance that your circuit will work. For a one-time project, the few extra parts won't hurt your pocket too badly; they may save untold hours in debugging time.

A real capacitor does not work well over a large frequency range. A 10-µF electrolytic capacitor cannot be used to bypass or decouple RF signals. A 0.1-µF capacitor will not bypass UHF or microwave signals. Choose component values to fit the range. The upper frequency limit is limited by the series inductance, L_S. In fact, at frequencies higher than the frequency at which the capacitor and its series inductance form a resonant circuit, the capacitor actually functions as an inductor. This is why it is a common practice to use two capacitors in parallel for bypassing, as shown in **Figure 23.24**. At first glance, this might appear to be unnecessary. However, the self-resonant frequency of C1 is usually 1 MHz or less; it cannot supply any bypassing above that frequency. However, C2 is able to bypass signals up into the lower VHF range. (This technique should not be applied under all circumstances as discussed in the section on Bypassing in the **RF Techniques** chapter.)

Let's summarize how we got from Figure 23.22 to Figure 23.23B:

• Lay out the signal path in a straight line.

• By experimenting with the placement and orientation of the components in the RF signal path, group the RF ground connections for each stage close together, without mixing up the input and output grounds.

• Place the non-RF components well clear of the signal path, freely using decoupling components for extra measure.

Practical Construction Hints

Now it's time to actually construct a project. The layout concepts discussed earlier can be applied to nearly any construction technique. Although you'll eventually learn from your own experience, the following

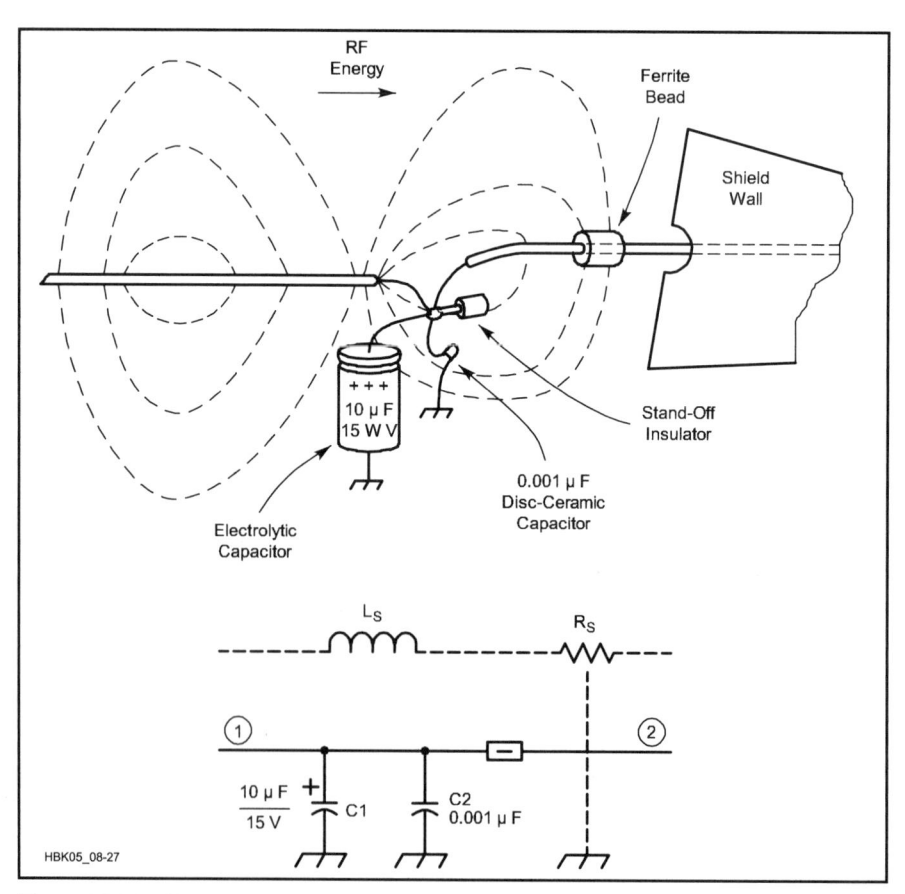

Figure 23.24 — Two capacitors in parallel afford better bypassing across a wide frequency range.

guidelines give a good start:

• Divide the unit into modules built into separate shielded enclosures — RF, IF, VFO, for example. Modular construction improves RF stability, and makes the individual modules easier to build and test. It also means that you can make major changes without rebuilding the whole unit. RF signals between the modules can usually be connected using small coaxial cable.

• Use a full copper ground plane. This is your largest single assurance of RF stability and good performance.

• Keep inputs and outputs well separated for each stage, and for the whole unit. If possible, lay out all stages in a straight line. If an RF signal path doubles back or re-crosses itself it usually results in instability.

• Keep the stages at different frequencies well-separated to minimize interstage coupling and spurious signals.

• Use interstage shields where necessary, but don't rely on them to cure a bad layout.

• Make all connections to the ground plane short and direct. Locate the common ground for each stage between the input and the output ground. Single-point grounding may work for a single stage, but it is rarely effective in a complex RF system.

• Locate frequency-determining components away from heat sources and mount them so as to maximize mechanical strength.

• Avoid unwanted coupling between tuned circuits. Use shielded inductors or toroids rather than open coils. Keep the RF high-voltage points close to the ground plane. Orient air-wound coils at right angles to minimize mutual coupling.

• Use lots of extra RF bypassing, especially on dc supply lines.

• Try to keep RF and dc wiring on opposite sides of the board, so the dc wiring is well away from RF fields.

• Compact designs are convenient, but don't overdo it! If the guidelines cited above mean that a unit needs to be bigger, make it bigger.

COMBINING TECHNIQUES

You can use a mixture of construction techniques on the same board and in most cases you probably should. Even though you choose one style for most of the wiring, there will probably be places where other techniques would be better. If so, do whatever is best for that part of the circuit. The resulting hybrid may not be pretty (these techniques aren't called "ugly construction" for nothing), but it will work!

Mount dual-in-line package (DIP) ICs in an array of drilled holes, then connect them using wired traces as described earlier. It is okay to mount some of the components using a ground-plane method, push pins or even wire wrap. On any one board, you may use a combination of these techniques, drilling holes for some ICs, or gluing others upside down, then surface mounting some of the pins, and other techniques to connect the rest. These combination techniques are often found in a project that combines audio, RF and digital circuitry.

A Final Check

No matter what construction technique is chosen, do a final check before applying power to the circuit! Things do go wrong, and a careful inspection minimizes the risk of a project beginning and ending its life as a puff of smoke! Check wiring carefully. Make a photocopy of the schematic and mark each connection and lead on the schematic with a red X or use highlighter to mark the circuit when you've verified that it's connected properly.

23.5.8 Tuning and Alignment

The task of performing adjustment or alignment can be difficult unless you are using the proper tools. There are variable inductors of various sizes and types and different types of variable capacitors as well as specialized potentiometers to adjust. Each different type of adjustable component requires its own specialized tool for making the adjustment. Failure to use the proper tool in the proper manner can result in damage to the component.

In RF circuits, the proximity of your hand or a metal object can greatly influence the apparent value of the variable component and make it difficult, if not impossible to adjust. For this reason, a number of plastic or ceramic tools are available to make this task as easy as possible and at a very low cost. As example is the Velleman "Plastic Tuning Needle Set" which can be found online (**www.velleman.eu**) and is widely available for a few dollars. Sources such as Mouser, Digi-Key, Newark, and Allied sell both individual tools and assortments of tools. Specialized tools, if required, are usually available from the same vendor selling the adjustable component.

When choosing a tuning tool, use the tool that best fits the adjustment hole or slot. Tips that are too small can end up damaging the inside of the adjustment slot or hole, and tools that are too large can also damage these small components or their adjustment mechanism. Choose a tuning tool with a tip that exactly matches the component.

VARIABLE INDUCTORS

Most variable inductors used in low-power RF circuits are a tiny coil of wire wound around a plastic form, with a threaded ferrite (or sometimes brass) slug in the center. For ferrite slug coils, inserting the slug into the coil increases the inductance and vice versa. (Brass slugs work oppositely and are uncommon.) Some variable inductors are inside metal cans, which act as a shield to reduce coupling to nearby components. The slug either has a hexagonal hole or a slot for a tuning tool to adjust the position of the slug like turning a screw.

Do not use small metal screwdrivers or hex keys (Allen wrenches) to adjust these coils. The metal tool will alter the inductance when inserted, making adjustment unpredictable and frustrating. A metal tool can also damage the slug by cracking it as ferrite slugs are quite brittle, ruining the inductor. Plastic or plastic-tipped tools allow you to make the adjustment while keeping your hand far away and not damaging the slug. Most tuning tools also have a mark on them in the form of a dimple, a logo/identification or a stripe to help you count the number of times you rotate the tool.

VARIABLE CAPACITORS

Variable capacitors not tuned with a shaft and knob usually have a screw-slot for adjustment. These include ceramic and mica trimmers, piston trimmers, and small air variables. Try using a plastic tool first but these adjustments are sometimes too stiff to use a plastic tool. Ceramic and plastic-tipped tools are available but not common in most electronics stores. Metal screwdrivers introduce enough capacitance to alter the value of these small capacitors but may be used in a series of small adjustments.

POTENTIOMETERS

Multi-turn miniature potentiometers (a.k.a "trimpots") usually have small metal adjusting screws. Resistance values are rarely sensitive to metal tools and so a miniature jeweler's screwdriver can be used. For RF circuits, however, use a plastic or ceramic screwdriver to avoid any possible interactions with the signals.

Larger potentiometers that are found inside equipment and that do not have a shaft are designed to be adjusted with a screwdriver-style tool. While a metal screwdriver can be used, a plastic tool eliminates any chance that the metal screwdriver could slip and come in contact with nearby components or leads. The metal screwdriver's shaft can also make accidental contact with wiring inside equipment.

ADJUSTING HIGH VOLTAGE CIRCUITS

If high voltages are involved, such as during tube neutralization or bias voltage adjustment, safety precautions are important. If the adjustable component is located near an RF stage, the presence of your hand can influence the circuit, as well. Use plastic or ceramic screwdrivers for both slotted and Philips-type screws. Be sure to use a tool that is long enough to keep your hands well away from any high voltage source! There are extra long tools available for use in high voltage areas. Shops that repair vacuum tube musical instrument amplifiers may be able to help locate suitable tools — safety first!

RESPECT ADJUSTMENT LIMITS

When making adjustments on any variable component, be sure not to force an adjustment beyond its range as that can cause permanent damage. For example, turning a slug all the way into or out of an adjustable inductor can begin to strip the tiny threads that hold the slug, making it difficult to perform future adjustments. If you feel resistance, stop, then look to see if the adjustment is at a limit. When an adjustment reaches a component's limit, that is usually an indication of a problem somewhere else in the circuit or, less frequently, that the component value has changed. Determine whether either is the case before proceeding.

In some circuits, adjustment is quite smooth and easy while others can be quite touchy, requiring patience and a steady hand to get the circuit adjusted properly. Take your time and watch your meter or oscilloscope for the desired changes. Use the dimples or marks on the tool to give a visual indication of how the adjustment is set or to count turns of a multi-turn adjustment. Keep notes if you are making multiple adjustments or if different adjustments interact.

Finally, don't be a "screwdriver technician" who adjusts components seemingly at random, hoping to get lucky and correct a problem. That usually results in more problems and even a completely non-functional piece of equipment requiring professional realignment or repair. Make small adjustments and if you don't see the results you were expecting, stop and figure out why before proceeding.

23.5.9 Other Construction Techniques

WIRING

Select the wire used in connecting amateur equipment by considering: the maximum current it must carry, the voltage its insulation must withstand and its use.

To minimize leakage of RF that causes EMI, the power wiring and low-level signal wiring of all transmitters should use shielded wire or coaxial cable. Receiver and audio circuits may also require the use of shielded wire at some points for stability or the elimination of coupling to adjacent circuits. Coaxial cable is recommended for all 50 Ω circuits. It can also be used for *short* runs of high-impedance audio wiring.

When choosing wire, consider how much current it will carry. (See the Copper Wire Specifications table in the **Component Data and References** chapter for maximum current-carrying capability, called *ampacity*.) Stranded wire is usually preferred over solid wire because stranded wire better withstands the inevitable bending that is part of building and troubleshooting a circuit. Solid wire is more rigid than stranded wire; use it where mechanical rigidity is needed or desired.

Wire with typical plastic insulation is good for voltages up to about 500 V. Use Teflon-insulated or other high-voltage wire for higher voltages. Teflon insulation does not melt when a soldering iron is applied. This makes it particularly helpful in tight places or large wiring harnesses. Although Teflon-insulated wire is more expensive, it is often available from industrial surplus houses.

Solid wire is often used to wire RF circuits in both receivers and transmitters. Bare soft-drawn tinned wire, #22 to #12 AWG (depending on mechanical requirements) is suitable. Avoid kinks by stretching a piece 10 or 15 feet long and then cutting it into short, convenient lengths. Run RF wiring directly from point to point with a minimum of sharp bends and keep the wire well-spaced from the chassis or other grounded metal surfaces. Where the wiring must pass through a chassis wall or shield, cut a clearance hole and line it with a rubber grommet. If insulation is necessary, slip spaghetti insulation or heat-shrink tubing over the wire. For power-supply leads, bring the wire through walls or barriers via a feedthrough capacitor.

In transmitters where the peak voltage does not exceed 500 V, shielded wire is satisfactory for power circuits. Shielded wire is not readily available for higher voltages — use point-to-point wiring instead. In the case of filament circuits carrying heavy current, it is necessary to use #10 or #12 AWG bare or enameled wire. Slip the bare wire through spaghetti then cover it with copper braid pulled tightly over the spaghetti. Slide the shielding back over the insulation and flow solder into the end of the braid; the braid will stay in place, making it unnecessary to cut it back or secure it in place. Clean the braid first so solder will flow into the braid with a minimum of heat.

ENAMELED WIRE

When connecting enameled wire leads, care must be taken to be sure a good connection is made. There are two methods that can be used to remove the insulation. With Thermaleze-type enamel, the heat from a soldering iron can be used to remove the insulation. You will first need to turn up the heat on your soldering iron for best results. After adding some melted solder to your soldering tip, move the drop slowly along the desired length of the wire lead. Moving it slowly gives the insulation time to melt and the solder a chance to tin the now-exposed wire. The tinned leads will then easily solder to a PC board or other mounting system.

If using other kinds of enameled wire, an emery board or small file can be used to remove the insulation. (Using a knife to scrape off the enamel usually nicks the wire which will eventually break at that point.) Be sure you have removed it completely from the desired lead. Follow that up with your soldering iron and solder to tin the wire using a thin coating of solder. Be sure to not make the tinned surface so thick that the lead cannot fit through the PC board holes. Preparing the leads in this manner will give the best possibility for a clean and secure connection.

HIGH-VOLTAGE TECHNIQUES

High-voltage wiring and construction requires special care. Read and follow the guidelines for high-voltage construction in the **Power Sources** chapter. You must use wire with insulation rated for the voltage it is carrying. Most standard hookup wire is inadequate above 300 or 600 V. High-voltage wire is usually insulated with Teflon or special multilayer plastic. Some coaxial cable is rated at 3700 V_{RMS} (or more) *internally* between the center conductor and shield but the outer jacket rating is usually considerably lower.

CABLE ROUTING

Where power or control leads run together for more than a few inches, they present a better appearance when bound together in a single cable. Plastic cable ties or tubing cut into a spiral are used to restrain and group wiring. Check with your local electronic parts supplier for items that are in stock.

To give a commercial look to the wiring of any unit, route any dc leads and shielded signal leads along the edge of the chassis. If this isn't possible, the cabled leads should then run parallel to an edge of the chassis. Further, the generous use of the tie points mounted parallel to an edge of the chassis, for the support of one or both ends of a resistor or fixed capacitor, adds to the appearance of the finished unit. In a similar manner, arrange the small components so that they are parallel to the panel or sides of the chassis.

Tie Points

When power leads have several branches in the chassis, it is convenient to use fiber-insulated terminal strips as anchors for junction points. Strips of this kind are also useful as insulated supports for resistors, RF chokes and capacitors. Hold exposed points of high-voltage wiring to a minimum; otherwise, make them inaccessible to accidental contact.

WINDING COILS

A detailed tutorial for winding coils by Robert Johns, W3JIP, titled "Homebrew Your Own Inductors!" from August 1997 *QST* can be found in the Radio Technology section of the ARRL TIS at **www.arrl.org/**

radio-technology-topics under Circuit Construction. Understanding these techniques greatly simplifies coil construction.

Close-wound coils are readily wound on the specified form by anchoring one end of the length of wire (in a vise or to a doorknob) and the other end to the coil form. Straighten any kinks in the wire and then pull to keep the wire under slight tension. Wind the coil to the required number of turns while walking toward the anchor, always maintaining a slight tension on the wire.

To space-wind the coil, wind the coil simultaneously with a suitable spacing medium (heavy thread, string or wire) in the manner described above. When the winding is complete, secure the end of the coil to the coilform terminal and then carefully unwind the spacing material. If the coil is wound under suitable tension, the spacing material can be easily removed without disturbing the winding. Finish space-wound coils by judicious applications of RTV sealant or hot-melt glue to hold the turns in place.

The "cold" end of a coil is the end at (or close to) chassis or ground potential. Wind coupling links on the cold end of a coil to minimize capacitive coupling.

Winding Toroidal Inductors

Toroidal inductors and transformers are specified for many projects in this *Handbook*. The advantages of these cores include compactness and a self-shielding property. **Figures 23.25** and **23.26** illustrate the proper way to wind and count turns on a toroidal core.

The task of winding a toroidal core, when more than just a few turns are required, can be greatly simplified by the use of a homemade bobbin upon which the wire is first wound. A simple yet effective bobbin can be fashioned from a wooden popsicle stick. Cut a "V" notch at each end and first wind the wire coil on the popsicle stick lengthwise through the notches. Once this is done, the wound bobbin can be easily passed through the toroid's inside diameter. While firmly grasping one of the wire ends against the toroidal core, the bobbin can be moved up, around, and through the toroidal core repeatedly until the wire has been completely transferred from the bobbin. The choice of bobbin used is somewhat dependent on the inside diameter of the toroid, the wire size, and the number of turns required.

Another method is to create a holder that allows you to grip the core, yet thread the wire easily around it. When winding toroids, be sure to seat the wire so it hugs the shape of the core and do not allow turns to overlap unless part of a twisted group of wires as in bifilar or trifilar windings. Do not pull the wire too tight as the thin wire used in some toroids can break if pulled too tightly.

When you wind a toroid inductor, count each pass of the wire through the toroid center as a turn. You can count the number of turns by counting the number of times the wire passes through the center of the core. See Figure 23.26A.

Multiwire Windings

A bifilar winding is one that has two identical lengths of wire, which when placed on the core result in the same number of turns for each wire. The two wires are wound on the core side by side at the same time, just as if a single winding were being applied. An easier

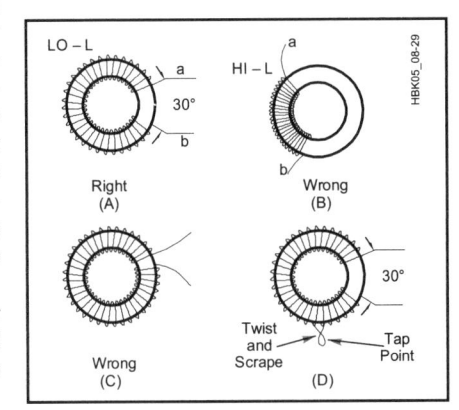

Figure 23.25 — The maximum-Q method for winding a single-layer toroid is shown at A. A 30° gap is best. Methods at B and C have greater distributed capacitance. D shows how to place a tap on a toroidal coil winding.

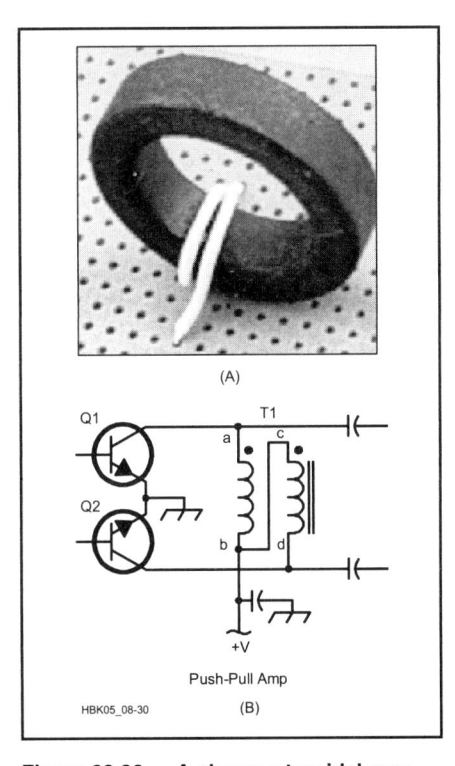

Figure 23.26 — A shows a toroidal core with two turns of wire (see text). Large black dots, like those at T1 in B, indicate winding polarity (see text).

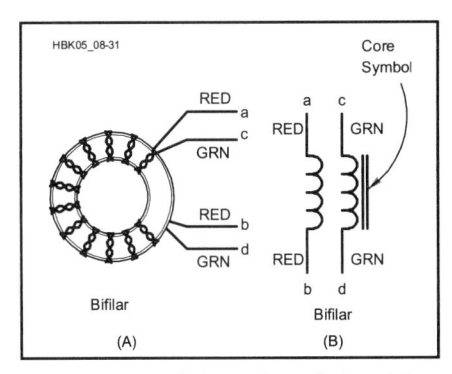

Figure 23.27 — Schematic and pictorial presentation of a bifilar-wound toroidal transformer.

and more popular method is to twist the two wires (8 to 15 turns per inch is adequate), then wind the twisted pair on the core. The wires can be twisted handily by placing one end of each in a bench vise. Tighten the remaining ends in the chuck of a small hand drill and turn the drill to twist the pair.

A trifilar winding has three wires, and a quadrifilar winding has four. The procedure for preparation and winding is otherwise the same as for a bifilar winding. **Figure 23.27** shows a bifilar toroid in schematic and pictorial form. The wires have been twisted together prior to placing them on the core. It is helpful, though by no means essential, to use wires of different color for multifilar windings. It is more difficult to identify multiple windings on a core after it has been wound. Various colors of enamel insulation are available, but it is not easy for amateurs to find this wire locally or in small-quantity lots. This problem can be solved by taking lengths of wire (enameled magnet wire), cleaning the ends to remove dirt and grease, then spray painting them. Ordinary aerosol-can spray enamel works fine. Spray lacquer is not as satisfactory because it is brittle when dry and tends to flake off the wire.

You may also identify bifilar and trifilar toroid lead pairs of identical colors by using a continuity checker. It is a good idea to check all toroids with an ohmmeter or continuity tester to be sure there are no shorts between different windings and that there is a good connection on the ends of each winding. Testing the leads after mounting can be difficult due to the circuit layouts, so be sure to test all toroids before mounting.

The winding sense of a multifilar toroidal transformer is important in most circuits. Figure 23.26B illustrates this principle. The black dots (called phasing dots) at the top of the T1 windings indicate polarity. That is, points a and c are both start or finish ends of their respective windings. In this example, points a and d are of opposite polarity to provide push-pull voltage output from Q1 and Q2.

Construction Techniques 23.27

23.6 CAD for PCB Design

[With numerous PCB design software packages available and low quantity, low cost PCB manufacturing services accepting orders electronically, the development of PCBs has never been easier for the amateur. As with any assembly or manufacturing process, it is important to understand the vocabulary and technology in order to achieve the desired result. Thus, this section provides a detailed description of the entire process of PCB design. — *Ed.*]

The primary goal of using software for printed circuit board (PCB) design is the production of so-called PCB artwork — the graphic design used to create the patterns of traces that establish connectivity on the PCB. Historically, PCB artwork was created by hand on clear film using black tape and special decals which were then photographically reduced. However, free and low cost programs specifically for the PCB design process are now widely available. These programs not only allow the creation of artwork efficiently and accurately, but produce the required ancillary files for commercial production, exchange information with schematic capture software, produce Bills of Materials (parts lists), and even include such features as three dimensional visualization of the finished board. While artwork files can be shared with other people for PCB production, the "source" files used by the CAD program can typically only be used by other people who share the same program.

The decision to produce a PCB must take into account the nature of the circuit itself (for example, high frequency, low noise and high current circuits require additional care). Other considerations are time available, expense, available alternatives, quantity required, ability to share and replicate the design, and nonelectrical characteristics such as thermal and mechanical, as well as desired robustness.

23.6.1 Overview of the PCB Design Process

The PCB design process begins with establishing the list of components in the circuit, the connections between the components, the physical outline/size of the board, and any other physical, thermal and electrical constraints or design goals. Much of the connectivity and component information is reflected in the schematic for a circuit, so in many cases the PCB layout process begins by entering the schematic in a schematic capture program which may be integrated with the PCB CAD program or standalone. (Schematic capture is not required for PCB layout.) Once the schematic is entered, there may be other options possible such as simulating the circuit as described in the preceding sections. A clean, well organized schematic that is easily modified is an asset regardless of the circuit production and construction methods.

With input from the schematic and other information, the board outline is created, mounting and other holes placed, the components positioned, and the pattern of traces created. Once the layout is complete, in many cases it is possible to run a design rules check — the equivalent of a "spell checker." Design rules include component connections and other information to check for problems related to connectivity and manufacturability. This step can save a great deal of time and expense by catching errors that could be fixed by hand, but would otherwise negate some of the benefits of a PCB.

The final step in the PCB layout program is to produce the collection of up to a dozen or so different files required for PCB production. In brief, the list includes the artwork for the pattern of traces, files for producing the board outline, solder masks, silk screens and holes.

The user then uploads the set of files to a PCB manufacturer. As quickly as two to three days later an envelope will be delivered with the freshly minted boards ready for assembly! Alternatively, the user may create the board "in house" using photomechanical or other processes based on the output files from the software.

23.6.2 Types of PCB Design Software

PCB software varies in features, function and cost, but for the radio amateur, the most interesting software for introductory use fall into the following categories: (See **Table 23.4**)

1) Open Source: PCB design software such as *GNU PCB* (**pcb.gpleda.org** for *Linux*, Mac OS X) and *KiCad* (**kicad.sourceforge.net/wiki/index.php/Main_Page**, for *Linux*, Mac OS X, and *Windows*, includes schematic capture) are free to use and have no artificial restrictions. Support is through user forums. Source code is available for the user to modify. *gschem* is a schematic capture sister program to *GNU PCB*.

2) Free, restricted use/restricted feature commercial: At least one company makes a version of their PCB and schematic software that is free to use for noncommercial purposes. Though it is restricted in number of layers (two) and maximum board size (4 × 3.2 inches), *Eagle PCB* is very popular among hobbyists. Files can be shared with others; the resulting industry standard files can be sent to nearly any PCB manufacturer. *Eagle* also contains a schematic entry program.

3) Free, restricted output commercial: Several PCB manufacturers offer schematic and PCB software with a proprietary output format tied to their PCB manufacturing service. *PCB123* from Sunstone Circuits (**www.sunstone.com**, for *Windows*) is one such offering, including schematic capture and layout software with up to four layers and board sizes up to 12 × 18 inches (double sided). For an additional fee (per design), industry standard files can be exported. Schematic entry is included. *Express PCB* (**www.expresspcb.com**, for *Windows*) also provides schematic capture and PCB layout capability, tied to the Express PCB board fabrication services, including the fixed size (3.8 × 2.5 inches) Miniboard service. Advanced Circuit's proprietary *PCB Artist* software (**www.4pcb.com**, for *Windows*) includes the ability to import netlists.

4. Low cost commercial: Many companies offer PCB and schematic software at a range of prices from $50 to many thousands of dollars. Several versions are typically offered from each company, usually based on limitations on board size, schematic size/complexity and features such as auto-routing. Schematic entry may be included in some packages, or be a separate purchase.

PCB design software manuals and tutorials discuss the basic operation but also special

---

Table 23.4
Some Sources of Freeware/Demoware PCB CAD Software

Source	Address	Resource
Autodesk	www.autodesk.com/products/eagle/overview	EAGLE schematic and layout design
Cadence Design Systems	www.orcad.com	OrCAD (schematic, SPICE simulator, layout [PCB] design)
Kicad	kicad-pcb.org/	GPLed full-function schematic and layout design

keystrokes and other shortcuts that make operations such as routing traces much more efficient.

The first time designing and ordering a PCB can be daunting, so keep the initial job simple and pay attention to details (and read the instructions). When starting to use a specific software package, join a user's support group or forum if one is available. Request sample designs from other users and experiment with them to see how they are constructed and what files are required in the output data set. Once you are comfortable with the tools, you can begin on a design of your own.

23.6.3 Schematic Capture

The first step in PCB design is to create a schematic. It is possible to design a layout directly from a paper schematic, but it is much easier if the schematic is entered (or "captured") in electronic form. Schematic capture software has two outputs — the visual schematic and the component and connectivity data for subsequent PCB layout. These two separate requirements can make some operations during schematic entry more complicated than what would seem at first glance necessary. Bear in mind however, that the user is creating not only a clear graphic representation of the circuit, but of the underlying electrical connectivity.

Schematics are generally entered on a (virtual) page usually corresponding to common paper sizes — for example, 11 × 17 inches. More complicated schematics can span multiple pages, using special labels or components to indicate both visual and electrical connectivity. Often one can group logically related elements into a module that can then be referenced as a "black box" on a higher level schematic. For complex circuits, these features are extremely useful and make the difference between a jumbled diagram that is difficult to use and an organized, compact diagram that efficiently communicates the function and operation of the circuit.

COMPONENTS

The components (resistors, capacitors, etc) on a schematic are either selected from an existing library or created by the user and stored in a custom library. It is also possible to find components and/or additional libraries on the Internet, although each program has its own specific format.

Each component includes a great deal more than shape and pin numbers. A typical component library entry includes:

Symbol — This is the graphic representation shown on the schematic. Many components may have the same symbol (eg, the op amp symbol may be shared by many different types of op amps)

Pins — For each pin or point of electrical connection, the component model may specify the pin number, label (eg, "V_{DD}"), pin type (inverting, noninverting) or pin functions (common).

PCB footprint — A given component may be available in a number of different packages (eg, DIP or surface mount). Many components may have the same physical footprint (eg, op amps, comparators and optoisolators could all map to the same eight-pin DIP footprint). Footprints include the electrical connections (pins) as well as mechanical mounting holes and pad sizes, and the component outline.

Value — Many components such as resistors and capacitors will have identical information except for a difference in value. All ¼ W resistors may be instances of the same component, differing only in value and designator.

Designator — The unique reference to the component, such as R1, C7, D3. This is assigned when the component is used (often automatically and in sequence).

Source information — Part number, vendor, cost, etc. This information is for the Bill of Materials.

Components are typically placed on the schematic by opening a library and searching for the desired component. It may be tempting for the beginner to select a component that looks "about right" when faced by a long list of components in some libraries. However, even at this early stage, the physical PCB often must be taken into account. For example, either "1/8W Resistor, Axial" or "1W Resistor, Upright" will result in the same neatly drawn resistor symbol on the schematic but in the subsequent step of using the component data to create a PCB, the footprints will be dramatically different.

It is not at all uncommon to add new components to the library in the course of creating a schematic. Since many components are closely related to existing devices, the process often consists of selecting an existing schematic symbol, editing the shape and/or component data, creating a new label, and associating the part with an existing footprint. Adding a specific type of op amp is an example. This usually only needs to be done once since symbols can be saved in a personal library (and shared with others). It is usually easier to modify a part that is close to what is desired than to "build" a new part from scratch.

Component symbols can generally be rotated and flipped when placing the component instance on the schematic. Designators (R1, T34, etc) can be assigned and modified by the user although the default designators are usually selected sequentially.

CONNECTIONS

The schematic software will have a mode for making electrical connections, called "nets." For example, one might click on the "draw net" symbol then draw a line using the mouse from one pin to another pin, using intermediate mouse clicks to route the line neatly with 90° turns on a uniform grid. Internally, the software must not only draw the visual line, but recognize what electrical connectivity that connection represents. So one must click (exactly) on a component pin to start or end a line or when making a connection between two lines that intersect, explicitly indicate a net-to-net connection (often with a special "dot" component). The connections on a schematic can often be assigned additional information, such as the desired width of the trace for this connection on the PCB or a name assigned by the user, such as "input signal."

Not all connections on a schematic are drawn. To make any schematic — electronic or hand drawn — more readable, conventions are often employed such as ground or power symbols or grouping similar connections into busses. Schematic capture software often supports these conventions. In some cases, components may be created with implicit power connections; in these cases the connections may not even be noted on the schematic but will be exported to the PCB software. However, as a general rule, software aimed at beginning PCB designers will not require the use of these advanced features.

Since it is often possible for component pins to be assigned attributes such as "power input", "output," "input," and so on, some schematic entry programs allow one to do an early design check. The program can then flag connections between two outputs, inputs that are missing connections, and so on. This is not nearly as helpful or complete as the Design Rule Check discussed below.

Free text can be placed on the schematic and there will be a text block in a corner for date, designer, version, title and the other information that identifies the schematic.

NETLISTS

Once the components are placed and connections made, the schematic may be printed and any output files for the PCB layout software produced. The connectivity and component information needed for PCB layout is captured in a *netlist* file. The flow from schematic entry to PCB may be tightly integrated, in which case the user may switch between schematic and PCB like two views of the same design (which they are). However, most schematic software will generate a separate netlist to be used by PCB layout software, whether integrated or a separate program. The netlist can also be exported to an external circuit simulation program or be used by an integrated simulator program. (See the

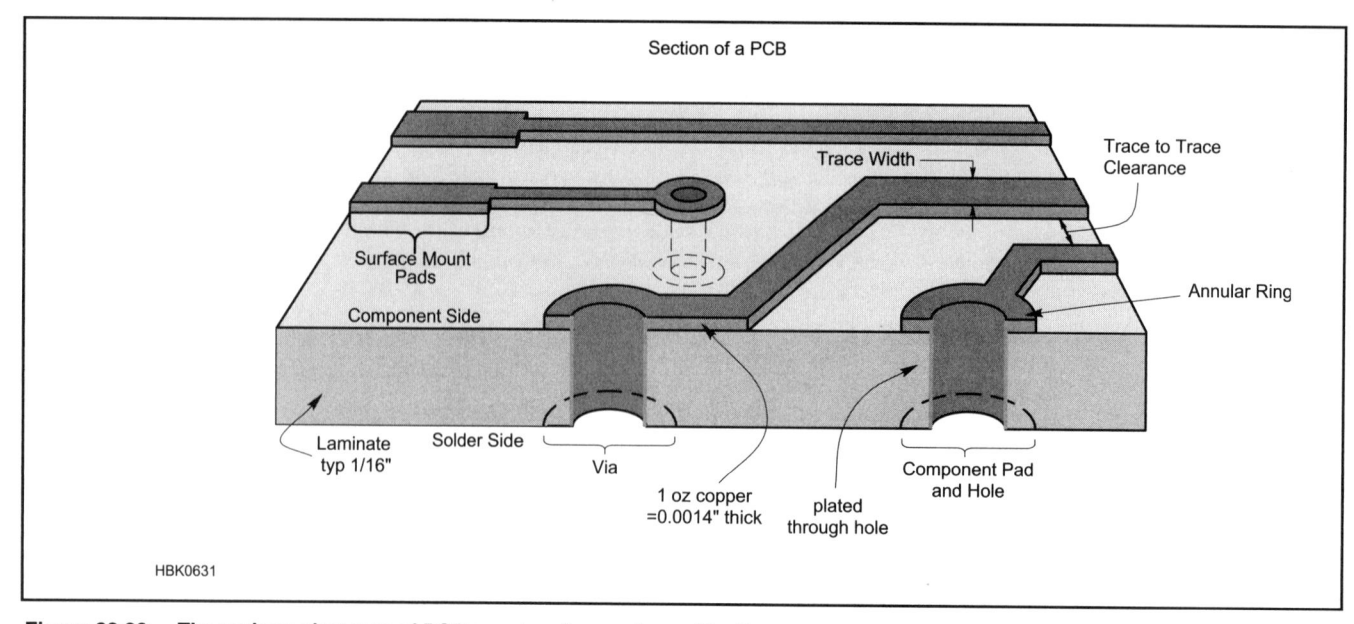

Figure 23.28 — The various elements of PCB construction and specification.

Computer-Aided Circuit Design chapter for more information on circuit simulation.)

Netlists are often human readable text files and in most cases it is possible to create a netlist file manually. In the absence of a schematic entry program, this allows the user to take a hand drawn schematic, extract the connectivity information, and create the netlist for the PCB program to perform design rule checks. However, a netlist is generally not required for the PCB layout software; the user will also have the option to create a PCB on-the-fly, adding components and connections as they wish.

ANNOTATION AND BILL OF MATERIALS

The important features of *forward* and *backward annotation* enter at the interface between schematic entry and PCB layout. It is not uncommon during the PCB layout process to either come across some design deficiency or realize that a change to the schematic could produce a design that would be easier to lay out. Likewise, a review of the schematic partway through the PCB layout process could reveal some needed design change. In the case of changes to the PCB (perhaps changing some pins on a connector to make routing easier), back annotation can propagate the changes "backward" to the schematic. The connectivity data will be updated; however the user may need to manually route the connection lines to neaten up the schematic. Likewise, changes to the schematic when the PCB is already (partially) routed are known as forward annotations and like the schematic, while the connectivity is updated the user will likely need to manually route the traces. Neither forward nor back annotation is necessary, but is useful in keeping the schematic and PCB consistent. In their absence, the user is strongly urged to keep the schematic and PCB up to date manually to avoid time consuming problems later on.

Finally, the underlying data in the schematic can be used to produce a *Bill of Materials* (BOM). A BOM lists all the components of the schematic, typically ordered by reference designator(s), and may even be exportable for online ordering.

23.6.4 PCB Characteristics

PCB CONSTRUCTION

It is useful to know a little bit about PCB construction in order to make sense of the PCB design process. **Figure 23.28** shows the basic structure of a PCB and some of its design elements (discussed in later sections). The laminate material provides a stable, insulating substrate with other known characteristics (thermal, dielectric, etc). Copper is bonded to one or both sides and selectively removed (usually chemically) to leave traces and pads. The pads provide points of connection for components. Though electrical connectivity is crucial, it is important to remember that the solder and pads provide mechanical and thermal connectivity as well. Pads may be drilled for mounting *through-hole* components or left undrilled for *surface-mount* components.

A separate electrochemical process plates the inside surface of *plated-through holes* to provide connectivity between upper and lower pads. Plated-through holes whose sole purpose is to provide electrical connectivity between layers of a PCB are known as *vias*,

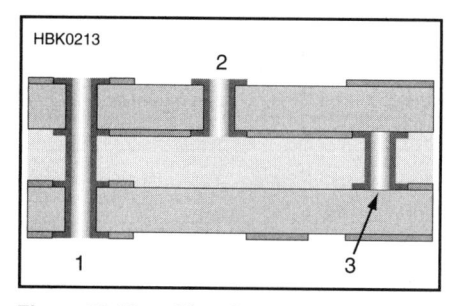

Figure 23.29 — *Via* refers to a plated-through hole that connects one board layer to another. Vias are used for signal, power, or ground connections and even for ventilation. Different via types include through-hole (1); blind (2), and buried (3).

shown in **Figure 23.29**. Since they do not need to accommodate a component lead, their hole and pad size are smaller.

While two layer boards can mount components on either side, most PCBs will have a primary side called the *component side* upon which most of the components will be placed, and a *solder side* dominated by soldered pins and traces. Where high density is required, surface mount (and sometimes through-hole) devices are mounted on both sides, but this is considerably more complex.

Multi-layer boards are essentially a stack of two or more two-layer boards, with an insulating layer between each board. Plated-through holes make connections possible on every layer, and the laminate material is proportionally thinner so the entire multi-layer board is roughly the same thickness as a regular two-layer board. Vias that join selected, adjacent copper layers without connecting the entire stack of layers are called "buried" or "blind" vias and are typically only needed for very

23.30   Chapter 23

dense designs. Multi-layer boards provide much more flexibility in routing signals and some other benefits such as dedicated layers for power distribution and grounding, but at often substantial additional cost.

PCB MANUFACTURING SPECIFICATIONS

Unless the board is manufactured by the hobbyist, the PCB files are sent out to be manufactured by a *board house*. The most important issue for the amateur may be the pricing policies of the board house. Board size, quantity, delivery time, number of layers, number and/or density of holes, presence of solder masks and silk screens, minimum trace/separation width, type of board material, and thickness of copper will all influence pricing. One cost saving option of the past, a single-layer board, may not be offered with low-cost, low-volume services — two layers may be the simplest option and it results in a more robust board. [Note that most ordering specifications use English units of inches and ounces. Offshore board houses may use both English and metric units, or be metric-only. English units are used here because they are the most common encountered by hobbyists. — *Ed.*]

The second issue to consider is manufacturing capabilities and ordering options. These will vary with pricing and delivery times, but include the following:

Board material and thickness — FR-4 is the most popular board material for low volume PCBs; it consists of flame-resistant woven fiberglass with epoxy binder. Typical thickness is 0.062 inch (¹⁄₁₆ inch), but thinner material is sometimes available. Flexible laminates are also available at greater cost and longer delivery time. Special board laminates for microwave use or high-temperature applications are also available.

Copper thickness — Expressed in ounces per square foot, typical values are 1-2 oz (1 oz corresponds to 0.0014 inch of thickness.) Other values may not be available inexpensively for small volumes. Inner layers on multi-layer boards may be thinner — check if this is important. Most board designs can assume at least 1 oz copper for double-sided boards; trace width is then varied to accommodate any high current requirements.

Layers — Two-layer boards are the most common. Because of the way PCBs are manufactured, the number of copper layers will be multiples of two. For quick-turn board houses, usually only two or four layer boards are available. PCBs with more than two layers will always be more expensive and often take longer to manufacture.

Minimum hole size, number, and density of holes — Minimum hole size will rarely be an issue, but unusual board designs with high hole density or many different hole sizes may incur additional costs. Be sure to include vias when specifying minimum hole size. Some board houses may have a specific list of drill sizes they support. Note that you can often just edit the drill file to reduce the number of different drill sizes.

Minimum trace width and clearance — Often these two numbers are close in value. Most board houses are comfortable with traces at least 0.010 inch in width, but 0.008 and 0.006 inch are often available, sometimes at a higher cost.

Minimum annular ring — A minimum amount of copper is required around each plated-through hole, since the PCB manufacturing process has variations. This may be expressed as the ratio of the pad size to hole size, but more commonly as the width of the ring.

Edge clearances — Holes, pads, and traces may not be too close to the edge of the board.

Board outline and copies — There may be options to route the outline of the board in other shapes than a rectangle, perhaps to accommodate a specific enclosure or optimize space. If multiple copies of a board are ordered, some board houses can *panelize* a PCB, duplicating it multiple times on a single larger PCB (with a reduction in cost per board). These copies may be cut apart at the board house or small tabs left to connect the boards so assembly of multiple boards can be done as a single unit.

Tin plating — Once the traces and pads have been etched and drilled, tin plating is usually applied to the exposed copper surfaces for good soldering.

Solder mask — This is a solder-resistant coating applied after tin plating to both sides of the board covering everything except the component mounting pads. It prevents molten solder from bridging the gaps between pads and traces. Solder mask is offered except by the quickest turn services. Green is the most common color, but other colors may be available.

Silkscreen — This is the ink layer, usually white, on top of the solder mask that lays out component shapes and designators and other symbols or text. A minimum line width may be specified — if not specified, try to avoid thin lines. All but the quickest turn services typically offer silk screening on one or both sides of the PCB.

23.6.5 PCB Design Elements

The schematic may not note the specific package of a part, nor the width or length of a connection. The PCB, being a physical object, is composed of specific instances of components (not just "a resistor," but a "¼ W, axial-lead resistor mounted horizontally," for example) plus traces — connections between pins of components with a specific width and separation from other conductors. Before discussing the process of layout, we briefly discuss the nature of components and connections in a PCB.

COMPONENTS

A component in a PCB design is very similar to its counterpart on the schematic. **Figure 23.30** shows the PCB footprint of an opto-interrupter, including graphics and connectivity information. The footprint of a component needs to specify what the footprint is like on all applicable copper layers, any necessary holes including non-electrical mounting holes or slots, and any additional graphics such a silkscreen layer.

Take a common ¼ W axial-lead resistor as an example. This footprint will have two pins, each associated with a pad, corresponding to the resistor's two leads. This pad will appear on both the top and bottom layers of the board, but will also have a smaller pad associated with inner layers, should there be any. The hole's size will be based on the nominal lead diameter, plus some allowance (typically 0.006 inch). The pad size will be big enough to provide a reasonable annular ring, but is usually much larger so as to allow good quality soldering. The pins will be labeled in a way that corresponds to the pin numbering on the schematic symbol (even though for this component, there is no polarity). A silkscreen layer will be defined, usually a box within which the value or designator will appear. The silkscreen layer is particularly useful for indicating orientation of parts with polarity.

More complicated parts may require additional holes which will not be associated with a schematic pin (mounting hole, for example). These are usually added to the part differently than adding a hole with a pad — in this case, the hole is desired without any annular ring or plating. The silkscreen layer may be used to outline the part above and

---

PCB Design and EMC

While amateur projects are rarely subject to electromagnetic compatibility (EMC) standards, using good engineering practices when designing the board still reduces unwanted RF emissions and susceptibility to RF interference. For example, proper layout of a microprocessor circuit's power and ground traces can reduce RF emissions substantially. Proper application of ground planes, bypass capacitors and especially shield connections can have a dramatic effect on RFI performance. (See the **RF Interference** chapter for more on RFI.) A good reference on RFI and PCB design is *Electromagnetic Compatibility Engineering*, by Henry Ott, WA2IRQ.

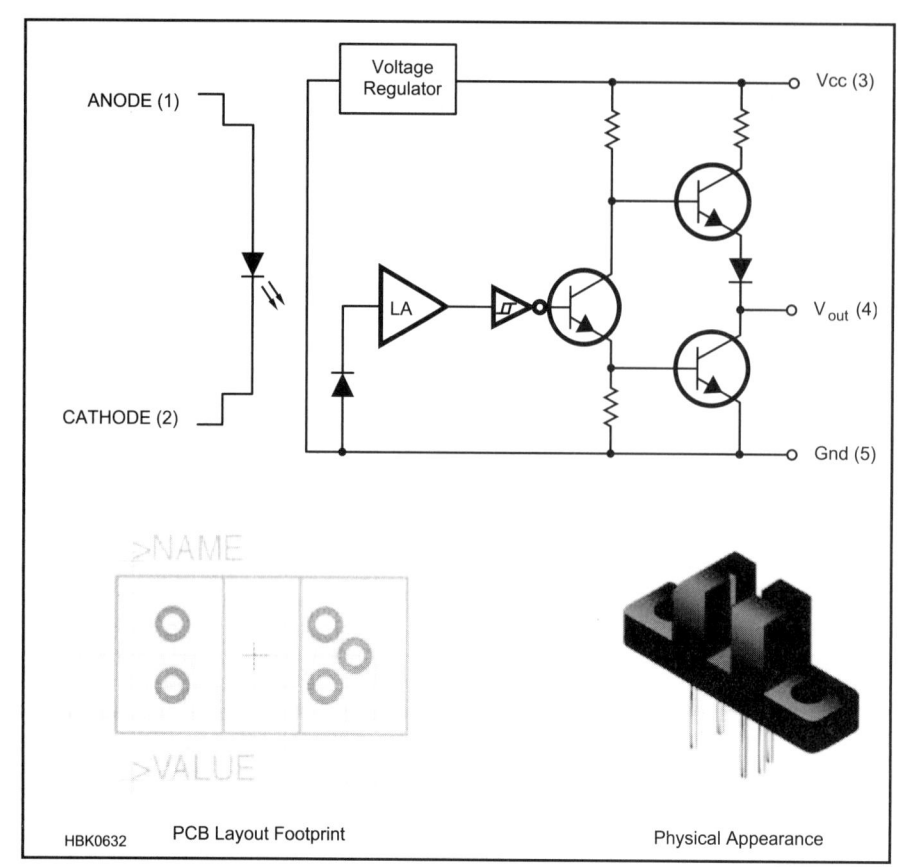

Figure 23.30 — The PCB footprint for a component, such as the opto-interrupter shown here, combines electrical connectivity as defined in the part's schematic and the part's physical attributes.

beyond what is obvious from the pads, for example, a TO-220 power transistor laying on its back, or the plastic packaging around the opto-interrupter in Figure 23.30.

As with schematic entry, it is not uncommon to have to modify or create a new PCB footprint. Good technical drawings are often available for electronic parts; when possible the user should verify these dimensions against a real part with an inexpensive dial caliper. It is also useful to print out the finished circuit board artwork at actual size and do a quick check against any new or unusual parts.

TRACES

Traces are the other main element of PCB construction — the copper pathways that connect components electrically. PCB traces are merely planar, flat wires — they have no magical properties when compared to an equivalent thickness of copper wire. At VHF/UHF/microwave frequencies and for high-speed digital signals, PCB traces act as transmission lines and these properties need to be accounted for, and can be used to advantage, in the design.

There are few constraints on traces apart from those such as minimum width and clearance imposed by the board house. They are created by chemical etching and can take arbitrary shapes. In fact, text and symbols may be created on copper layers which may be handy if a silkscreen is not included. Traces may be of any length, vary in width, incorporate turns or curves, and so on. However, most traces will be a uniform width their entire length (a width they will likely share with other traces carrying similar signals), make neat 45° or 90° corners, and on two-layer boards have a general preference for either horizontal travel on the component side or vertical travel on the solder side.

The same considerations when building a circuit in other methods applies to PCB design, including current capacity (width of trace, thickness of copper), voltage (clearance to other signals), noise (shielding, guarding, proximity to other signals), impedance of ground and power supplies, and so on.

23.6.6 PCB Layout

With a schematic and netlist ready and all of the PCB characteristics defined, the actual layout of the PCB can begin.

BOARD SIZE AND LAYERS

The first step in PCB layout is to create the board outline to contain not only the circuit itself and any additional features such as mounting holes. For prototype or one-off designs, the board is often best made a bit larger to allow more space between components for ease in testing and debugging. (Some low cost or freeware commercial PCB software imposes limits on board size and number of components.) The board outline may be provided in a default size that the user can modify, or the user may need to enter the outline from scratch.

As discussed above, rectangular board shapes are generally acceptable, but many board houses can accommodate more complex outlines, including curves. These outlines will be routed with reasonable accuracy and may save an assembly step if the PCB needs a cutout or odd shape to fit in a specific location.

While the software may not require deciding at the start how many layers the PCB will use, this is a decision the user should make as early as possible, since the jump from two to four or more will have a big impact on routing the traces as well as cost!

For your initial design, start with a two layer board for a simple circuit that you have already built and tested. This will reduce the number of decisions you have to make and remove some of the unknowns from the design process.

COMPONENT PLACEMENT

Good component placement is more than half the battle of PCB layout. Poor placement will require complicated routing of traces and make assembly difficult, while good placement can lead to clean, easy-to-assemble designs.

The first elements placed should be mounting holes or other fixed location features. These are often placed using a special option selected from a palette of tools in the software rather than as parts from a library. Holes sufficient for a #4 or #6 screw are usually fine; be sure to leave room around them for the heads of the screws and nut driver or standoff below. These will be non-plated-through holes with no pad (though the board house may plate all the holes in a board, regardless).

Depending on the software and whether schematic capture was performed, the board outline may already contain the footprints of all the circuit components (sometimes stacked in a heap in one corner of the board) and the netlist will already be loaded. In this case, components may be placed by clicking and dragging the components to the desired location on the board. Most PCB programs have a "rat's nest" option that draws a straight line for each netlist connection of a component, and this is a great aid in placement as the connections between components are apparent as the components are moved around. (See **Figure 23.31**) However, connections are shown to the nearest pin sharing that electrical connection; thus, components such as decoupling capacitors (which are often meant

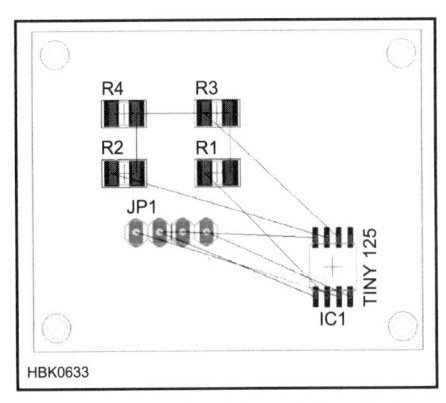

Figure 23.31 — The rat's nest view during PCB layout shows the direct connections between component pins. This helps the designer with component placement and orientation for the most convenient routing.

to be near a specific component) will show rats nest connections to the nearest power and ground pins and not the pins the designer may have intended. These will have to be manually edited.

The PCB layout software may offer *auto-placement* in which the components are initially arranged automatically. The beginner should certainly feel free to experiment and see how well this tool performs, but it is likely not useful for the majority of designs.

PCBs need not be arranged to precisely mimic the schematic, but it is appropriate to place components in a logical flow when possible so as to minimize the length of traces in the signal path. Sensitive components may need to be isolated or shielded from other components, and grounding and decoupling attended to, just as one would do with a point-to-point soldered version.

If the PCB is being designed "on-the-fly" or using an imported netlist, components may need to be selected and placed on the board manually using the libraries of parts in the PCB software. Not all design software makes this task simple or fast — in particular, the description of component footprints may be confusing. The use of highly condensed industry standard or non-uniform naming conventions often means the user needs to browse through the component library to see the different types of components. Resistors, diodes and capacitors seem particularly prone to a propagation of perplexing options. One solution is to open an example PCB layout and see what library element that designer used for resistors, LEDs and so on. Here, the PCB layout software directed at hobbyists may be superior in that there are fewer options than in professional programs.

During placement the user will find that different orientations of components simplify routing (for example, minimizing the number of traces that have to cross over each other or reducing the trace lengths). Components are generally rotated in increments of 90°, although free rotation may be an option. The user is strongly urged to maintain the same orientation on like devices as much as possible. Mixing the position of pin 1 on IC packages, or placing capacitors, diodes, and LEDs with random orientation invites time consuming problems during assembly and testing that can be minimized by consistent, logical layout.

Placement and orientation of components can also affect how easily the final PCB can be assembled. Allow plenty of space for sockets, for example, and for ICs to be inserted and removed. Components with a mechanical interface such as potentiometers and switches should be positioned to allow access for adjustment. Any components such as connectors, switches, or indicators (eg, LEDs) should be positioned carefully, especially if they are to protrude through a panel. Often this will involve having the component overhang the edge of the PCB. (Beware of the required clearance between copper traces and pads to the edge of the PCB.)

Components should include a silkscreen outline that shows the size of the whole component — for example, a transistor in a TO-220 package mounted flat against the PCB should have an outline that shows the mounting hole and the extent of the mounting tab. The user should also consider the clearance required by any additional hardware for mounting a component, such as nuts and bolts or heatsinks — including clearance for nut drivers or other assembly tools.

Take care to minimize the mechanical stress on the PCB, since this can result in cracked traces, separated pads, or other problems. Utilize mounting holes or tabs when possible for components such as connectors, switches, pots. Use two-layer boards with plated-through holes even if the design can be single-layer. Component leads soldered to plated-through holes produce much stronger mechanical connections than single-layer boards in which the soldered pad is held only by the bond between copper and laminate and is easily lifted if too much heat or stress is imposed.

When prototyping a new design, add a few unconnected pads on the circuit board for extra components (eg, a 16 pin DIP, 0.4 inch spaced pads for resistors and other discrete components). Include test points and ground connections. These can be simply pads to which cut off leads can be soldered to provide convenient test points for ground clips or to monitor signals.

Wires or cables can be directly soldered to the PCB, but this is inconvenient when swapping out boards, and is not very robust. Connectors are much preferred when possible and often provide strain relief for the wire or cable. However, if a wire is directly soldered to the PCB, the user should consider adding an unplated hole nearby just large enough to pass the wire including insulation. The wire can then be passed from the solder side through the unplated hole, then soldered into the regular plated-through hole. This provides some measure of strain relief which can be augmented with a dollop of glue if desired.

ROUTING TRACES

After placing components, mounting holes and other fixed location features that limit component or trace placement, traces can be *routed*. That is, to complete all the connections between pins without producing short circuits.

Most PCB design programs allow components and traces to be placed on a regular grid, similarly to drawing programs. There may be two grids — a visible coarse pitch grid, and a "snap" fine pitch grid, to which components and other objects will be aligned when placed. It is good practice to use a 0.1 or 0.050 inch grid for component placement and to route traces on a 0.025 inch grid. While the "snap to grid" feature can usually be turned off to allow fine adjustment of placement, a board routed on a grid is likely to look cleaner and be easier to route.

The trace starts at a component pin and wends its way to any other pins to which it should be connected. Traces should start and end at the center of pads, not at the edge of a pad, so that the connection is properly recorded in the program's database. If a netlist has been loaded, most PCB software will display a rat's nest line showing a direct connection between pads. Once the route is completed, the rat's nest line for that connection disappears. The rat's nest line is rarely the desired path for the trace and often not the correct destination. For example, when routing power traces, the user should use good design sense rather than blindly constructing a Byzantine route linking pins together in random order. For this reason, routing the power and ground early is a good practice.

High speed, high frequency, and low noise circuits will require additional care in routing. In general, traces connecting digital circuits such as microprocessors and memories should not cross or be in close proximity to traces carrying analog or RF signals. Please refer to the **RF Techniques** chapter and earlier sections of this chapter, and the references listed at the end of this section.

Manual routing is a core skill of PCB design, whether or not auto-routing is used. The process is generally made as simple as possible in the software, since routing will take up most of the PCB design time. A trace will be routed on the copper layer currently selected. For a single-sided board, there is only one layer for routing; for a two-layer board the component side and solder side can have traces; and for multi-layer boards additional inner layers can have traces. Often a single keystroke can change the active copper layer (sometimes automatically inserting a via if a route is in progress). The trace is drawn in straight segments and ends at the destination pin. When routing, 90° corners are normally avoided — a pair of 45° angles is the norm. **Figure 23.32** shows some sample traces.

It is good practice on a double-sided board to have one side of the board laid out with mostly horizontal traces, and the other side laid out with mostly vertical traces. A trace that needs to travel primarily vertically can do so on the side with vertical traces and use a via to move to the other side to complete the horizontal part of the route.

It is easiest during testing and debugging to route most traces on the bottom (solder) side of the board — traces on the component side often run under ICs or other components, making them hard to access or follow. It is often much clearer to connect adjacent IC or connector pins by routing a trace that leaves one pad, moves away from the IC or connector, then heads back in to the adjacent pad to connect. This makes it clear the connection on the assembled board is not a solder bridge, which a direct connection between the two pads would resemble.

It may be the case that no amount of vias or wending paths can complete a route. The one remaining tool for the PCB designer is a jumper — a wire added as a component during assembly just for the purpose of making a connection between two points on the board. Jumpers are most often required for single-sided boards; when the "jump" is rather small, uninsulated wire can be used. Jumpers are usually straight lines, and can be horizontal or vertical. Professional production PCBs use machine-insertable zero-ohm resistors as jumpers. Jumpers on double-sided boards are usually not viewed very favorably, but this is an aesthetic and efficiency issue, not a functional one.

Multi-layer boards clearly offer additional routing options, but again having some dominant routing direction (vertical or horizontal) on each layer is recommended, since mixing directions tends to cause routing problems. However, it is not uncommon to devote one or two inner layers to power and ground, rather than merely be additional layers for routing signals. This allows power and ground to be routed with minimal resistance and exposes the traces carrying interesting signals on the component and solder sides where they are available to be probed or modified. It is very difficult to modify traces on inner layers, needless to say!

Before routing too many traces, it is helpful to run the *Design Rule Check (DRC)* on the board. (See the section on Design Rule Checking below.) Applied early and often, DRC can identify areas of concern when it is easiest to correct. For example, a given trace width may provide insufficient clearance when passing between two IC pads.

Some PCB design packages offer *auto-router* capability in which the software uses the component and connectivity data of the netlist and attempts to route the traces automatically. There are some circumstances when they save time, but view these tools with some caution. Auto-routers are good at solving the routing puzzle for a given board, but merely connecting all the pins correctly does not produce a good PCB design. Traces carrying critical signals may take "noisy" routes; components that should have short, low resistance connections to each other may have lengthy traces instead, and so on. More sophisticated auto-routers can be provided with extensive lists of "hints" to minimize these problems. For the beginner, the time spent conveying this design information to the auto-router is likely better spent manually routing the traces.

If an auto-router is used, at a minimum, critical connections should be first routed manually. These include sensitive signals, connections whose length should be minimized, and often power and ground (for both RFI and trace width reasons). Better still is to develop a sense of what a good layout looks like (which will come with practice and analyzing well designed boards), and learn at what stage the auto-router can be "turned loose" to finish the routing puzzle.

TRACE WIDTH AND SPACING

All traces will have some width — the width may be the default width, the last width selected, or a width provided from data in the netlist. It may be tempting to route all but the power traces using the smallest trace width available from the board house (0.008 inch or smaller), since this allows the highest density of traces and eases routing. A better design practice is to use wider traces to avoid hard-to-detect trace cracking and improve board reliability. The more common traces 0.012 inch wide can be run in parallel on a 0.025 inch grid and can pass between many pads on 0.1 inch centers. Even wider traces will make the board easier to produce "in house," though the exact process used (CNC routing, chemical etching, etc) will limit the resolution. Note that it is possible to "neck down" traces where they pass between IC or connector pads — that is, the regular, thick trace is run up close to the narrow gap between the pads, passes between the pads with a narrow width, then expands back to the original width. There is little reason to use traces wider than 0.030 inch or so for most signals (see **Table 23.5**) but power and ground trace widths should be appropriate for the current.

All traces have resistance, and this resistance is a function of the cross section of the trace (width times thickness) and the length. This resistance will convert electrical power to heat. If the heat exceeds a relatively high threshold, the trace becomes a fairly expensive and difficult-to-replace fuse. The

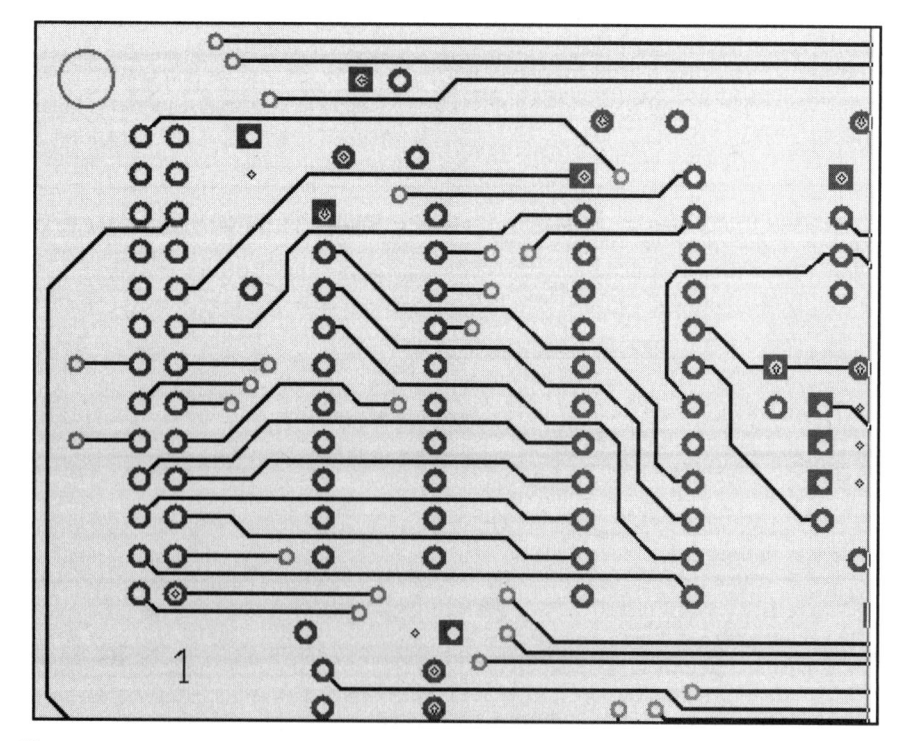

Figure 23.32 — This example shows traces on the side of the PCB for horizontal routing. Traces are routed between pins of ICs. The smaller pads are for vias to a different layer of the PCB.

trace width should be selected such that for the worst case expected current, heat rise is limited to some threshold, often 10 °C. In practice, power traces (especially grounds) are often made as wide as practical to reduce resistance, and they greatly exceed the width required by heat rise limits alone.

Table 23.5 summarizes maximum currents for external (component and solder side) and internal traces for some common trace widths. Internal traces (on inner layers of multi-layer boards) can carry only about half the current of external traces for the same width since the internal layers do not dissipate heat to the ambient air like external traces can. (Note that trace widths are also sometimes expressed in "mils." 1 mil = 0.001 inch; it is shorthand for "milli-inch", not millimeter!)

There is no upper bound on the effective trace width. It is common to have large areas of the board left as solid copper. These *copper fill* areas can serve as grounds, heat sinks, or may just simplify board production (especially homemade boards). It is not a good idea to place a component hole in the middle of a copper fill — the copper is a very efficient heat sink when soldering. Instead, a "wagon wheel" pattern known as a thermal relief is placed (sometimes automatically) around the solder pad, providing good electrical connectivity but reducing the heat sinking. Often, copper fill areas can be specified using a polygon and the fill will automatically flow around pads and traces in that area, but can lead to isolated pads of copper.

In practice, most boards will have only two or perhaps three different trace widths; narrow widths for signals, and a thicker width for power (usually with a healthy margin).

One final note on trace width — vias are typically one size (ie, small), but multiple vias can be used to create low resistance connections between layers. Spacing the vias so their pads do not touch works well; the pads are then shorted on both top and bottom layers.

Voltage also figures into the routing equation, but instead of trace width, higher voltages should be met with an increased clearance between the trace and other copper. The IPC-2221 standard calls for a clearance of 0.024 inch for traces carrying 31-150 V (peak) and 0.050 inch for traces carrying 151-300 V (peak); these are external traces with no coating. (With the appropriate polymer solder mask coating, the clearances are 0.006 inch for 31-100 V and 0.016 inch for 101-300 V. Internal traces also have reduced clearance requirements.) Fully addressing the safety (and regulatory) issues around high voltage wiring is outside the scope of this brief review, however, and the reader is urged to consult UL or IPC standards.

SILKSCREEN AND SOLDER MASK

The silkscreen (or "silk") layer contains the text and graphics that will be silkscreened on the top of the board, shown in **Figure 23.33**. Components will generally have elements on the silkscreen layer that will automatically appear, such as designators and values, but other elements must be created and placed manually. Common silkscreen elements include: Circuit name, date, version, designer (and call sign), company name, power requirements (voltage, current, and fusing), labels for connections (eg, "Mic input"), warnings and cautions, labels for adjustments and switches. A solid white rectangle on the silkscreen layer can provide a good space to write a serial number or test information.

The board house will specify the minimum width for silkscreen lines, including the width of text. Text and graphics can be placed anywhere on the solder mask, but not on solder pads and holes.

Many quick-turn board houses omit the silkscreen for prototype boards. As noted earlier, many of the text elements above can be placed on the external copper layers. Component outlines are not possible since the resulting copper would short out traces, but component polarization can be noted with symbols such as a hand-made "+" made from two short traces, or a "1" from a single short trace. (Note that some component footprints follow a practice of marking the pad for pin 1 with a square pad while others are round or oval.)

The solder mask is a polymer coating that is screened onto the board before the silkscreen graphics. As shown in Figure **23.34**, it covers the entire surface of the board except for pads and vias. Solder masking prevents solder bridges between pads and from pads to traces during assembly and is particularly important for production processes that use wave soldering or reflow soldering. There is one solder mask layer for the top layer and another for the bottom layer. Internal layers do not need a solder mask. Solder masking may be omitted for a prototype board, but care must be taken to keep solder from creating unwanted bridges or short circuits.

Table 23.5
Maximum Current for 10 °C Rise, 1 oz/ft² Copper
Based on IPC-2221 standards (not an official IPC table)

Trace Width (inches)	Max. Current (External Trace) (A)	Max. Current (Internal Trace) (A)	Resistance (ohms/inch)
0.004	0.46	0.23	0.13
0.008	0.75	0.38	0.063
0.012	1.0	0.51	0.042
0.020	1.5	0.73	0.025
0.040	2.4	1.2	0.013
0.050	2.8	1.4	0.010
0.100	4.7	2.4	0.0051
0.200	7.8	3.9	0.0025
0.400	13	6.4	0.0013

IPC-2221 Generic Standard on Printed Circuit Design, Institute for Interconnecting and Packaging Electronic Circuits, **www.ipc.org**

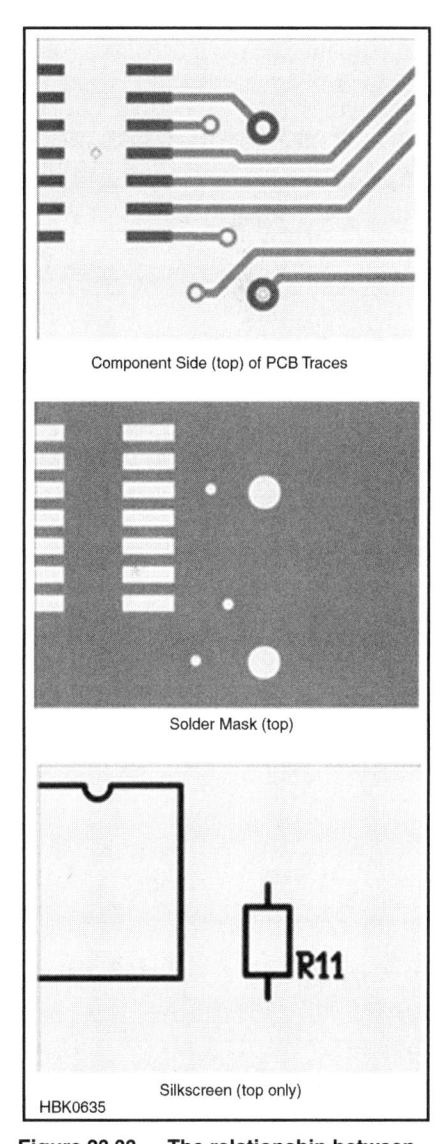

Figure 23.33 — The relationship between the layout's top copper layer with traces and pads, the solder mask that covers the copper (a separate solder mask is required for the top and bottom layers of the PCB) and the silkscreen information that shows component outlines and designators.

During the PCB layout process, solder mask layers are generally not shown because they do not affect connectivity. **Figure 23.34** shows a typical PCB as it appears when the PCB layout process is complete.

DESIGN RULE CHECK

If a netlist has been provided from the schematic capture program, a *design rule check* (*DRC*) can be made of the board's layout. The PCB software will apply a list of rules to the PCB, verifying that all the connections in the netlist are made, that there is sufficient clearance between all the traces, and so on. These rules can be modified based on the specific board house requirements. As stated above, it is useful to run the DRC even before all the traces have been routed — this can identify clearance or other issues that might require substantial re-routing or a different approach.

If the user has waited until all the routing is done before running the DRC, the list of violations can be daunting. However, it is often the case that many if not all of the violations represent issues that may prevent the board from operating as wished. Whenever possible, all DRC violations should be rectified before fabrication.

23.6.7 Preparation for Fabrication

LAYOUT REVIEW

Once the board has passed DRC, the electrical connectivity and basic requirements for manufacturability have likely been satisfied. However, the design may benefit from an additional review pass. Turn off all the layers but one copper layer and examine the traces — often simplifications in routing will be apparent without the distractions of the other copper layers. For example, a trace can be moved to avoid going between two closely spaced pins. Densely spaced traces could be spaced farther apart. There may be opportunities to reduce vias by routing traces primarily on one layer even if that now means both vertical and horizontal travel. Repeat the exercise for all the copper layers.

Review the mechanical aspects of the board as well, including the proximity of traces to hardware. If your prototype PCB does not have a solder mask, traces that run underneath components such as crystals in a conductive case or too close to mounting hardware can form a short circuit. An insulator must be provided or the trace can be re-routed.

GENERATING OUTPUT FILES

Once the PCB design is complete, the complete set of design description files can be generated for producing the PCB. These are:

Copper layers — One file per copper layer. These are known as *Gerber files* and were text files of commands originally intended to drive a *photoplotter*. Gerber was the primary manufacturer of photoplotters, machines that moved a light source of variable width (apertures) from one location to another to draw patterns on photographic film. While photoplotters have been replaced by digital technology, the format used by Gerber has been standardized as RS-274X and is universally used except by PCB software tied to a specific manufacturer. RS-274X is related to RS-274D ("G-Code") used by machinists to program CNC machinery but is an *additive* description (essentially saying "put copper here"), rather than describing the movements of a tool to remove material. A program is thus required to translate between Gerber and G-Code if a CNC machine is used to make a PCB by mechanically removing copper.

Drill file — The file containing the coordinates and drill sizes for all the holes, plated or not. Also called the *NC* or *Excellon* file, some board houses may require a specific format for the coordinates, but these are usually available to be set as options in the PCB program. There is only one drill file for a PCB, since the holes are drilled from one side. (Exotic options such as buried vias will require more information.) Like RS-274X apertures, the drill file will generally contain a drill table.

Silkscreen — Also in RS-274 format. Some board houses can provide silkscreen on both sides of the board, which will require two files.

Solder mask — The solder mask file is used by the board house to create the solder mask. One file per side is required.

A Gerber preview program such as *Gerbv* (**gerbv.gpleda.org**, open source, *Linux*, Mac OS X) or *GC-Prevue* (**www.graphicode.com**, *Windows*) can be used to review the trace layout Gerber files. This is a good test — the board house will make the boards from the Gerber files, not the PCB design file. Gerber previewers can import the copper layers, silkscreen and drill files to verify they correspond and make sense.

Any of the layers can usually be printed out within the PCB program (and/or Gerber preview program) for reference and further inspection.

In addition to files for PCB production, PCB layout programs can also generate assembly diagrams, and in some cases can provide 3D views of what the assembled board will look like. These can be useful for documentation as well as verification of mechanical issues such as height clearance.

Sending the files to the PCB manufacturer or board house and ordering PCBs is explained on the manufacturing website or a customer service representative can walk you through the process. Some firms accept sets of files on CD-ROM and may also offer a design review service for first-time customers or on a fee basis.

PCB CAD REFERENCES

Analog Devices, *High Speed Design Techniques*, Analog Devices, 1996.

Johnson, Howard, and Graham, Martin, *High Speed Digital Design: A Handbook of Black Magic*, Prentice Hall, 1993.

Ott, Henry, *Electromagnetic Compatibility Engineering*, Wiley Press, 2009.

Pease, Robert A, *Troubleshooting Analog Circuits*, Butterworth-Heinemann, 1991.

Silver, W. NØAX, "Hands-On Radio Experiments 107-110: PCB Layout," *QST*, Dec 2011 through Mar 2010.

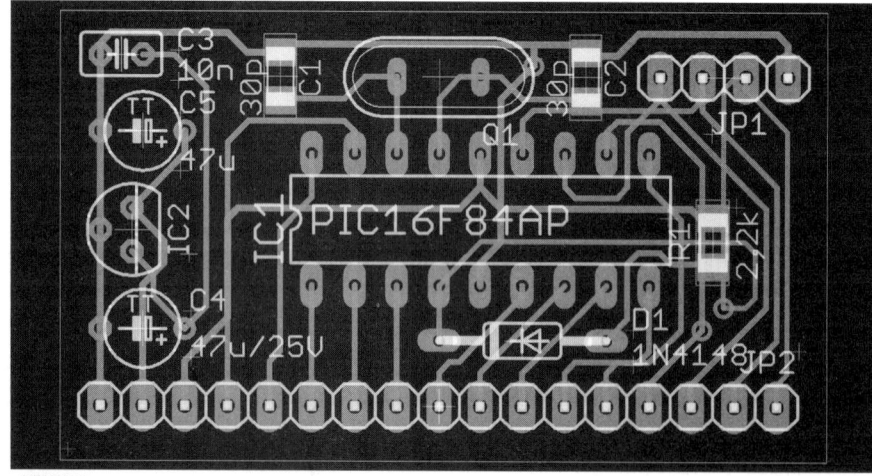

Figure 23.34 — A completed microprocessor board as it is seen in a typical PCB layout editor (Eagle). Solder mask layers are omitted for visibility. Traces that appear to cross each other are on different sides of the board and are in different colors in the layout software. The silkscreen layer is shown in white.

23.7 Microwave Construction

Paul Wade, W1GHZ, updated this short tutorial to construction practices suitable for microwave frequency operation originally written by ARRL Laboratory Engineer, Zack Lau, W1VT. For more information on microwave equipment, read Paul's series of columns, "Microwavelengths," in *QST*.

Microwave construction is not only fun, but within the capabilities of most amateurs. To get on the air requires some degree of construction, since you can't buy a ready to go box. At a minimum, a few modules must be connected together with coax and power cables. At the other extreme, the whole station may be homebrewed from scratch, or from a kit.

The growth of mobile phones and wireless networking has caused a proliferation of microwave integrated circuits offering high performance at low cost. Some of these are also useful for ham applications, so that microwave construction has evolved from traditional waveguide "plumbing" to printed circuitry requiring surface-mount assembly of tiny components. Waveguide techniques are still valuable for some components, such as filters and antennas, so proficiency in both types of construction is valuable.

A problem we all face when building new microwave equipment is finding a nearby station to try it out. One solution is to convince a buddy to build a similar system, so that you will both have someone to work. If you have complementary skills, say one with metal and the other with surface-mount soldering, you can help each other. A larger group or club effort can be even better — someone with experience and test equipment can be an Elmer for the group.

In addition to the material here and in magazine columns, several excellent references for amateurs interested in working on microwave frequencies include:
- *Microwave Know How*, by Andy Barter, G8ATD (RSGB)
- *International Microwave Handbook*, by Andy Barter, G8ATD (RSGB)
- *The ARRL UHF/Microwave Experimenter's Manual* (out of print but available used)
- *The ARRL UHF/Microwave Projects* CD (out of print but available used)

23.7.1 Lead Lengths

Microwave construction is becoming more popular, but at these frequencies the size of physical component leads and PC-board traces cannot be neglected. Microwave construction techniques either minimize these stray values or make them part of the circuit design.

The basic consideration in microwave

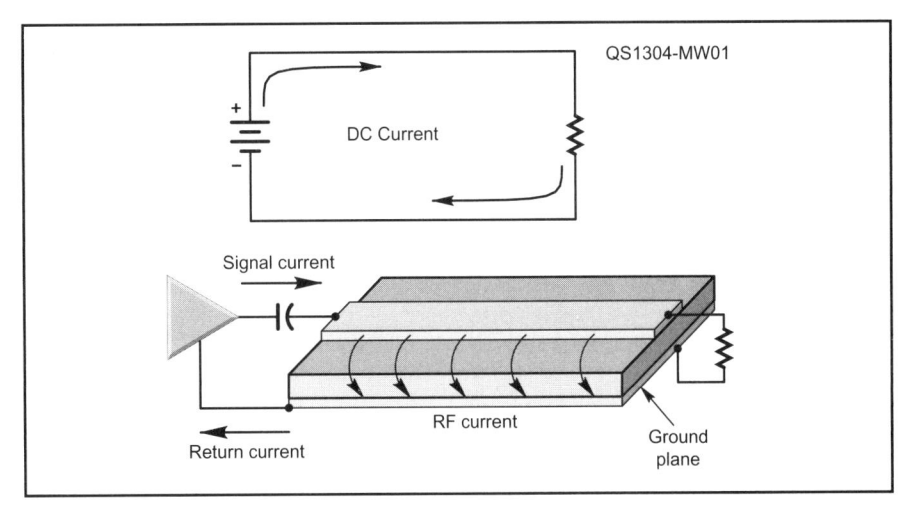

Figure 23.35— Current must always flow in a complete loop. This is particularly important at microwave frequencies where wavelengths are very short.

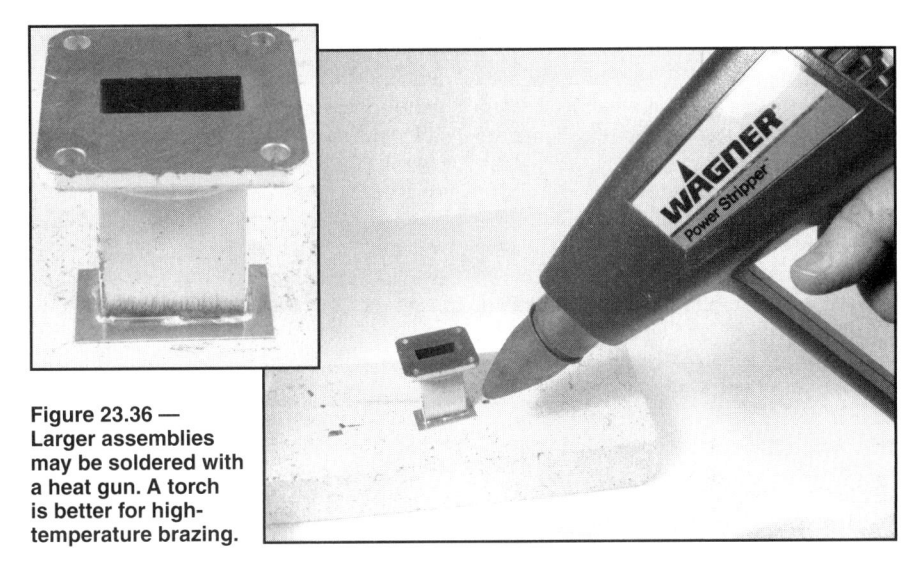

Figure 23.36 — Larger assemblies may be soldered with a heat gun. A torch is better for high-temperature brazing.

circuitry is short lead lengths, particularly for ground returns. Current always flows in a complete loop with a return path through the "ground". (See **Figure 23.35**) The loop must be much smaller than a wavelength for a circuit to work properly — as the frequency gets higher, dimensions must get smaller. One area that requires particular care to ensure good ground return continuity is the transition from coax cable outside a cabinet to a PC board inside the cabinet.

At microwave frequencies, the mechanical aspects and physical size of circuits become very much a part of the design. A few millimeters of conductor has significant reactance at these frequencies. This even affects VHF and HF designs in which the traces and conductors resonate on microwave frequencies. If a high-performance FET has lots of gain in this region, a VHF preamplifier might also function as a 10 GHz oscillator if the circuit stray reactances were just right (or wrong!). You can prevent this by using shields between the input and output or by adding microwave absorptive material to the lid of the shielded module. (SHF Microwave sells absorptive materials.)

23.7.2 Metalworking

Waveguide construction requires some basic metalworking skills, which are also useful for assembly and packaging of microwave systems. Some minimal tools would be a hacksaw, drills, files, and layout tools. While a hand drill can suffice, an inexpensive drill press will make work more precise as well as safer. In metals, Dewalt Pilot Point drill bits make clean, accurate holes. Files and nibbling tools can make rectangular or odd-shaped holes.

Solder has a poor reputation for microwave losses — but, of course, it is essential. It does have higher resistance than copper or aluminum, but that only matters in locations of high current, for instance, the ground end of a high-Q quarter-wave resonator. Horn antennas and most waveguide structures have low Q so a clean solder joint, without excess blobs, has no effect. Traditional tin-lead solder works well; the silver solder with 1% silver has no performance advantage but looks pretty.

For things like waveguide and antennas that are too large for a soldering iron, a hot air gun does an excellent job. **Figure 23.36** shows the backshort of a waveguide transition as it is being soldered with a hot air gun. A small amount of paste flux (Kester SP-44) was applied to the waveguide end, and a ring of solder placed along the joint. Then heat is applied to the whole area until the solder melts and flows into the joint.

A torch can also be used for soldering, but tends to cause more oxidation of the metal. However, when a high-temperature brazed joint is desired, a torch is required. A MAPP gas torch and Silvaloy 15 (or Harris Stay-silv 15) silver brazing material, which requires no flux, are suitable for small and medium-sized components.

Many hams seem to think that silver plating is desirable, but it rarely makes a difference — it just looks much prettier. The only application in which silver plating has been shown to make a significant difference is in UHF cavities with sliding contacts. In most other places, copper losses are low enough so that little improvement is possible, and aluminum is fine for most uses.

23.7.3 Circuit Construction

Modular construction is a useful technique for microwave circuits. Often, circuits are tested by connecting their inputs and output to known 50 Ω sources and loads. Modules are typically kept small to prevent the chassis and PC board from acting as a waveguide, providing a feedback path between the input and output of a circuit, resulting in instability.

PRINTED-CIRCUIT BOARDS AT MICROWAVES

A microwave printed circuit board (PCB) is typically double-sided, with transmission-line circuitry printed on one side and a ground plane on the far side. The ground return path is best provided by plated-thru holes (PTH) connecting the two sides with minimum length. Surface-mount components — integrated circuits, chip capacitors, and chip resistors — are soldered directly to printed pads and transmission lines, and to ground pads with embedded PTH. Many of the microwave integrated circuits come in really tiny packages, with lead pitch as small as 25 mils. See the section on Surface-Mount Technology earlier in this chapter for more information on this type of construction.

When using glass-epoxy PC board at microwave frequencies, the crucial board parameter is the thickness of the dielectric. It can vary quite a bit, in excess of 10%. This is not surprising; digital and lower-frequency analog circuits work just fine if the board is a little thinner or thicker than usual. Some of the board types used in microwave-circuit construction are a generic Teflon PC board, Duroid 5870 and 5880.

TRANSMISSION LINES AND CONNECTORS

From a mechanical accuracy point of view, the most tolerant type of construction is based on waveguide. Tuning is usually accomplished via one or more screws threaded into the waveguide. It becomes unwieldy to use waveguide on the amateur bands below 10 GHz because the dimensions get too large.

Proper connectors are a necessary expense at microwaves. At 10 GHz, the use of the proper connectors is essential for repeatable performance. Do not connect microwave circuits with coax and pigtails. It might work but it probably can't be duplicated. SMA connectors are common because they are small and work well. SMA jacks are sometimes soldered in place, although 2-56 hardware is more common.

At 24 GHz and above, even waveguide becomes small and difficult to work with. At these frequencies, most readily available coax connectors work unreliably, so these higher bands are really a challenge. Special SMA connectors are available for use at 24 GHz.

DEVICE SUBSTITUTION

It is important to copy microwave circuits exactly, unless you really know what you are doing. "Improvements," such as better shielding or grounding can sometimes cause poor performance. It isn't usually attractive to substitute components, particularly with the active devices. It may look possible to substitute different grades of the same wafer, such as the ATF13135 and the ATF13335, but these are really the same transistor with different performance measurements. While two transistors may have exactly the same gain and noise figure at the desired operating frequency, often the impedances needed to maintain stability at other frequencies can be different. Thus, the "substitute" may oscillate, while the proper transistor would work just fine.

You can often substitute MMICs (monolithic microwave integrated circuits) for one another because they are designed to be stable and operate with the same input and output impedances (50 Ω).

The size of components used at microwaves can be critical — in some cases, a chip resistor 80 mils across is not a good substitute for one 60 mils across. Hopefully, the author of a construction project tells you which dimensions are critical, but you can't always count on this; the author may not know. It's not unusual for a person to spend years building just one prototype, so it's not surprising that the author might not have built a dozen different samples to try possible substitutions.

23.7.4 Capacitors for Microwave Construction

Ordinary ceramic chip capacitors cost a few cents while microwave chip capacitors are more than a dollar each. All have them have parasitic resistance and inductance, but the microwave versions use lower-loss materials which make a difference at higher microwave frequencies. Ordinary ceramic capacitors work fine in non-critical applications like blocking and bypass capacitors, even up to 10 GHz. In critical areas, like low-noise or power amplifiers, microwave capacitors are preferred.

For applications requiring high-Q for low loss, like the printed comb-line filter in **Figure 23.37**, two ordinary capacitors in parallel

Figure 23.37 — Printed comb-line filter uses two chip capacitors in parallel to reduce loss.

as shown have lower loss than one expensive microwave capacitor. By paralleling, the parasitic resistances are also paralleled, cutting the resistance in half. An additional advantage is that combinations can be chosen to yield non-standard capacitance values. We might apply this trick to really demanding applications, like high-power solid-state amplifiers, by paralleling microwave capacitors to reduce losses.

23.7.5 Tuning and "No-Tune" Designs

Microwave construction does not always require tight tolerances and precision construction. A fair amount of error can often be tolerated if you are willing to tune your circuits, as you do at MF/HF. This usually requires the use of variable components that can be expensive and tricky to adjust.

Proper design and construction techniques, using high precision, can result in a "no-tune" microwave design. To build one of these no-tune projects, all you need do is buy the parts and install them on the board. The circuit tuning has been precisely controlled by the board and component dimensions so the project should work.

One tuning technique you can use with a microwave design, if you have the suitable test equipment, is to use bits of copper foil or EMI shielding tape as "stubs" to tune circuits. Solder these small bits of conductor into place at various points in the circuit to make reactances that can actually tune a circuit. After their position has been determined as part of the design, tuning is accomplished by removing or adding small amounts of conductor, or slightly changing the placement of the tuning stub. The size of the foil needed depends on your ability to determine changes in circuit performance, as well as the frequency of operation and the circuit board parameters. A precision setup that lets you see tiny changes allows you to use very small pieces of foil to get the best tuning possible.

23.8 Mechanical Fabrication

Most projects end up in some sort of an enclosure, and most hams choose to purchase a ready-made chassis for small projects, but some projects require a custom enclosure. Even a ready-made chassis may require a fabricated sheet-metal shield or bracket, so it's good to learn something about sheet-metal and metal-fabrication techniques.

Most often, you can buy a suitable enclosure. These are sold by most electronics distributors. Select an enclosure that has plenty of room. A removable cover or front panel can make any future troubleshooting or modifications easy. A project enclosure should be strong enough to hold all of the components without bending or sagging; it should also be strong enough to stand up to expected use and abuse.

23.8.1 Cutting and Bending Sheet Metal

Enclosures, mounting brackets and shields are usually made of sheet metal. Most sheet metal is sold in large sheets, 4 to 8 feet or larger. It must be cut to the size needed.

Most sheet metal is thin enough to cut with metal shears or a hacksaw. A jigsaw or band saw makes the task easier. If you use any kind of saw, select a blade that has teeth fine enough so that at least two teeth are in contact with the metal at all times.

If a metal sheet is too large to cut conveniently with a hacksaw, it can be scored and broken. Make scratches as deep as possible along the line of the cut on both sides of the sheet. Then, clamp it in a vise and work it back and forth until the sheet breaks at the line. Do not bend it too far before the break begins to weaken, or the edge of the sheet might bend. A pair of flat bars, slightly longer than the sheet being bent, make it easier to hold a sheet firmly in a vise. Use "C" clamps to keep the bars from spreading at the ends.

Smooth rough edges with a file or by sanding with a large piece of emery cloth or sandpaper wrapped around a flat block.

23.8.2 Finishing Aluminum

Give aluminum chassis, panels and parts a sheen finish by treating them in a caustic bath. (See the information on chemical safety at the beginning of this chapter.) Use a plastic container to hold the solution and wear both safety goggles and protective clothing while treating aluminum. Ordinary household lye can be dissolved in water to make a bath solution. Follow the directions on the container. A strong solution will do the job more rapidly.

Stir the solution with a non-metal utensil until the lye crystals are completely dissolved. If the lye solution gets on your skin, wash with plenty of water. If you get any in your eyes, immediately rinse with plenty of clean, room-temperature water and seek medical help. It can also damage your clothing, so wear something old. Prepare sufficient solution to cover the piece completely. When the aluminum is immersed, a very pronounced bubbling takes place. Provide ventilation to disperse the escaping gas. A half hour to two hours in the bath is sufficient, depending on the strength of the solution and the desired surface characteristics.

23.8.3 Chassis Working

With a few essential tools and proper procedure, building radio gear on a metal chassis is a relatively simple matter. Aluminum is

Repurposing Obsolete Equipment Cabinets

One of the best deals at a hamfest or flea market might not be anything having to do with radio — yet! Obsolete industrial and commercial equipment may not be useable in the ham station but their metal enclosures are top-quality. Purchasing one of these cabinets new would cost hundreds of dollars but the surplus equipment is often sold very cheaply. Reusing the cabinets is easy and stripping the electronics often results in a large collection of hardware and electronic components that can be re-used in ham equipment. The overall process is illustrated in a January/February 2017 *QEX* article by Scott Roleson, KC7CJ included with this book's online supplemental material. Keep an eye out for these bargains everywhere, even at garage sales!

better than steel, not only because it is a superior shielding material, but also because it is much easier to work and provides good chassis contact when used with secure fasteners.

Spend sufficient time planning a project to save trouble and energy later. The actual construction is much simpler when all details are worked out beforehand. Here we discuss a large chassis-and-cabinet project, such as a high-power amplifier. The techniques are applicable to small projects as well.

Cover the top of the chassis with a piece of wrapping paper or graph paper. Fold the edges down over the sides of the chassis and fasten them with adhesive tape. Place the front panel against the chassis front and draw

Figure 23.38 — An enclosure made entirely from PC-board stock.

a line there to indicate the chassis top edge.

Assemble the parts to be mounted on the chassis top and move them about to find a satisfactory arrangement. Consider that some will be mounted underneath the chassis and ensure that the two groups of components won't interfere with each other.

Place controls with shafts that extend through the cabinet first, and arrange them so that the knobs will form the desired pattern on the panel. Position the shafts perpendicular to the front chassis edge. Locate any partition shields and panel brackets next, then sockets and any other parts. Mark the mounting-hole centers of each part accurately on the paper. Watch out for capacitors with off-center shafts that do not line up with the mounting holes. Do not forget to mark the centers of socket holes and holes for wiring leads. Make the large center hole for a socket *before* the small mounting holes. Then use the socket itself as a template to mark the centers of the mounting holes. With all chassis holes marked, center-punch and drill each hole.

Next, mount on the chassis the capacitors and any other parts with shafts extending to the panel. Fasten the front panel to the chassis temporarily. Use a machinist's square to extend the line (vertical axis) of any control shaft to the chassis front and mark the location on the front panel at the chassis line. If the layout is complex, label each mark with an identifier. Also mark the back of the front panel with the locations of any holes in the chassis front that must go through the front panel. Remove the front panel.

MAKING ENCLOSURES WITH PC BOARD MATERIAL

Much tedious sheet-metal work can be eliminated by fabricating chassis and enclosures from copper-clad printed-circuit board material. While it is manufactured in large sheets for industrial use, some hobby electronics stores and surplus outlets market usable scraps at reasonable prices. PC-board stock cuts easily with a small hacksaw. The nonmetallic base material isn't malleable, so it can't be bent. Corners are easily formed by holding two pieces at right angles and soldering the seam. This technique makes excellent RF-tight enclosures. If mechanical rigidity is required of a large copper-clad surface, solder stiffening ribs at right angles to the sheet.

Figure 23.38 shows the use of PC-board stock to make a project enclosure. This enclosure was made by cutting the pieces to size, then soldering them together. Start by laying the bottom piece on a workbench, then placing one of the sides in place at right angles. Tack-solder the second piece in two or three places, then start at one end and run a bead of solder down the entire seam. Use plenty of solder and plenty of heat. Continue with the rest of the pieces until all but the top cover is in place.

In most cases, it is better to drill all needed holes in advance. It can sometimes be difficult to drill holes after the enclosure is soldered together.

You can use this technique to build enclosures, subassemblies or shields. This technique is easy with practice; hone your skills on a few scrap pieces of PC-board stock.

23.8.4 Drilling Techniques

Before drilling holes in metal with a hand drill, indent the hole centers with a center punch. This prevents the drill bit from "walking" away from the center when starting the hole. Predrill holes greater than 1/2 inch in diameter with a smaller bit that is large enough to contain the flat spot at the large bit's tip. When the metal being drilled is thinner than the depth of the drill-bit tip, back up the metal with a wood block to smooth the drilling process.

The chuck on the common hand drill is limited to 3/8 inch bits. Some bits are much larger, with a 3/8 inch shank. If necessary, enlarge holes with a reamer or round file. For very large or odd-shaped holes, drill a series of closely spaced small holes just inside of the desired opening. Cut the metal remaining between the holes with a cold chisel and file or grind the hole to its finished shape. A nibbling tool also works well for such holes.

Use socket-hole punches to make socket holes and other large holes in an aluminum chassis. Drill a guide hole for the punch center bolt, assemble the punch with the bolt through the guide hole and tighten the bolt to cut the desired hole. Oil the threads of the bolt occasionally.

Cut large circular holes in steel panels or chassis with an adjustable circle cutter ("fly cutter") in a drill press at low speed. Occasionally apply machine oil to the cutting groove to speed the job. Test the cutter's diameter setting by cutting a block of wood or scrap material first.

Remove burrs or rough edges that result from drilling or cutting with a burr-remover, round or half-round file, a sharp knife or chisel. Keep an old chisel sharpened and available for this purpose.

RECTANGULAR HOLES

Square or rectangular holes can be cut with a nibbling tool or a row of small holes as previously described. Large openings can be cut easily using socket-hole punches. A portable jig saw with the appropriate cutting blade can be used on thin sheet metal and plastic. The resulting edges will require filing.

23.8.5 Construction Notes

If a control shaft must be extended or insulated, a flexible shaft coupling with adequate insulation should be used. Satisfactory support for the shaft extension, as well as electrical contact for safety, can be provided by means of a metal panel bushing made for the purpose. These can be obtained singly for use with existing shafts, or they can be bought with a captive extension shaft included. In either case the panel bushing gives a solid feel to the control. The use of fiber washers between ceramic insulation and metal brackets, screws or nuts will prevent the ceramic parts from breaking.

PAINTING

Painting is an art, but, like most arts, successful techniques are based on skills that can be learned. The surfaces to be painted must be clean to ensure that the paint will adhere properly. In most cases, you can wash the item to be painted with soap, water and a mild scrub brush, then rinse thoroughly. When it is dry, it is ready for painting. Avoid touching it with your bare hands after it has been cleaned. Your skin oils will interfere with paint adhesion. Wear rubber or clean cotton gloves.

Sheet metal can be prepared for painting by abrading the surface with medium-grade sandpaper, making certain the strokes are applied in the same direction (not circular or random). This process will create tiny grooves on the otherwise smooth surface. As a result, paint or lacquer will adhere well. On aluminum, one or two coats of zinc chromate primer applied before the finish paint will ensure good adhesion.

Keep work areas clean and the air free of dust. Any loose dirt or dust particles will probably find their way onto a freshly painted project. Even water-based paints produce some fumes, so properly ventilate work areas.

Select paint suitable to the task. Some paints are best for metal, others for wood and so on. Some dry quickly, with no fumes; others dry slowly and need to be thoroughly ventilated. You may want to select rust-preventative paint for metal surfaces that might be subjected to high moisture or salts.

Most metal surfaces are painted with some sort of spray, either from a spray gun or from spray cans of paint. Either way, follow the manufacturer's instructions for a high-quality job.

PANEL LAYOUT AND LABELING

There are many ways to layout and label a panel. Some builders don't label any controls or jacks, relying on memory to figure what does what. Others use a marking pen to label controls and inputs. Decals and dry transfers have long been a staple of home brewing. Label makers that print on clear or colored tape are used by many.

With modern computers and available software, it is not hard to lay out professional looking panels. One can use a standard drawing program for the layout. The grids available on these drawing programs are sufficient to make sure that everything is lined up squarely. If the panel label is laid out before the panel is drilled for controls, a copy of the label can be used as a drill template.

Computer-aided design (CAD) programs can also be used to lay out and label panels, although they can have a steep learning curve and may be overkill for many applications.

WB8RCR has written two software programs, *Dial* and *Panel*, that are specifically designed for laying out panels and dials. There are *Windows* versions and platform independent versions available for download at **www.qsl.net/wb8rcr**. These programs output a Postscript file.

These programs can be used in several ways. One can print out a mirror image of the layout on a transparency and then glue that to the front panel with the printing facing towards the panel. In this manner the transparency will protect the label. The panel layout can be printed out on card stock and affixed to the front panel with spray adhesive or self-adhesive contact paper can be used. If the printing is facing outward it can be sprayed with clear acrylic spray to protect it.

Surplus meters often find their way into projects. Unfortunately the meter faces usually do not have an appropriate scale for the project at hand. Relabeling meters has long been a mainstay to make home brew gear look professional. With the advent of computers this job has been made very easy. A software package, *MeterBasic*, by Jim Tonne, W4ENE, available with the downloadable supplemental content, is very easy to use and results in professional looking meters that indicate exactly what you want them to indicate.

Contents

24.1 Fixed Stations
    24.1.1 Selecting a Location
    24.1.2 Station Grounding and Bonding
    24.1.3 Station Power
    24.1.4 Station Layout
    24.1.5 Interconnecting Your Equipment
    24.1.6 Documenting Your Station

24.2 Mobile Installations
    24.2.1 Installation
    24.2.2 Coaxial Cable
    24.2.3 Wiring
    24.2.4 Amplifiers
    24.2.5 Interference Issues
    24.2.6 Operating

24.3 Portable Installations
    24.3.1 Portable AC Power Sources
    24.3.2 Portable DC Power Sources
    24.3.3 Portable Antennas

24.4 Remote Stations
    24.4.1 Introduction to Remote Stations
    24.4.2 Types of Remote Operation
    24.4.3 Remote Networking Basics
    24.4.4 Connecting to Your Remote Station
    24.4.5 Station Automation
    24.4.6 Remote Site Requirements
    24.4.7 Station in Your Hand
    24.4.8 Future of Remote Operating
    24.4.9 Special Events and Demonstrations
    24.4.10 Remote Station Glossary
    24.4.11 Remote Station Resources

Chapter 24

Assembling a Station

Although many hams might not build a major project, such as a transmitter, receiver or amplifier, they do have to assemble the various components into a working station. There are many benefits to be derived from assembling a safe, comfortable, easy-to-operate collection of radio gear, whether the station is at home, in the car or in a field. Configuring and operating a remote-control station is becoming very common. Ken Norris, KK9N, maintains the material on remote control that was originally contributed by K6VVA. Such topics as station location, grounding and bonding, power sources, station layout, and cable routing are also covered.

Chapter 24 — Downloadable Supplemental Content

Portable Stations
- "A Look at Gasoline Powered Inverter Generators," by Bob Allison, WB1GCM
- "Field Day Towers — Doing it Right" by Ward Silver, N0AX and Don Daso, K4ZA

24.1 Fixed Stations

Regardless of the type of installation you are attempting, good planning greatly increases your chances of success. Take the time to think the project all the way through, consider alternatives, and make rough measurements and sketches during your planning and along the way. You will save headaches and time by avoiding "shortcuts." What might seem to save time now may come back to haunt you with extra work when you could be enjoying your shack.

One of the first considerations should be to determine what type of operating you intend to do. While you do not want to strictly limit your options later, you need to consider what you want to do, how much you have to spend and what room you have to work with. There is a big difference between a casual operating position and a "big gun" contest station, for example.

24.1.1 Selecting a Location

Selecting the right location for your station is the first and perhaps the most important step in assembling a safe, comfortable, convenient station. The exact location will depend on the type of home you have and how much space can be devoted to your station. Fortunate amateurs will have a spare room to devote to housing the station; some may even have a separate building for their exclusive use. Most must make do with a spot in the cellar or attic, or a corner of the living room is pressed into service.

Examine the possibilities from several angles. A station should be comfortable; odds are good that you'll be spending a lot of time there over the years. Some unfinished basements are damp and drafty — not an ideal environment for several hours of leisurely hamming. Attics have their drawbacks, too; they can be stifling during warmer months. If possible, locate your station away from the heavy traffic areas of your home. Operation of your station should not interfere with family life. A night of chasing DX on 80 meters may be exciting to you, but the other members of your household may not share your enthusiasm.

Keep in mind that you must connect your station to the outside world. The location you choose should be convenient to a good power source and an adequate ground. If you use a computer, you may need access to the Internert. There should be a fairly direct route to the outside for running antenna feed lines, rotator control cables and the like.

Although most homes will not have an "ideal" space meeting all requirements, the

Figure 24.1 —Scott Redd, K0DQ, operated this station at WW1WW in pursuit of top scores in DX contests. Notice that the equipment on the operating desk is laid out logically and comfortably for long periods "in the chair." [Woody Beckford, WW1WW, photo]

Figure 24.2 — Top RTTY contest operator Don Hill, AA5AU operates with low power from his effective station. RTTY operation emphasizes use of the computer mouse so Don's desk has lots of room for his "mouse hand". [Shay Hill, photo]

Figure 24.3 — Spreading out horizontally, John Sluymer, VE3EJ, has arranged his effective contest and DXing station to keep all of the controls at the same level for easy adjustment. [John Sluymer, VE3EJ, photo]

right location for you will be obvious after you scout around. The amateurs whose stations are depicted in **Figures 24.1** through **24.3** all found the right spot for them. Weigh the trade-offs and decide which features you can do without and which are necessary for your style of operation. If possible pick an area large enough for future expansion.

24.1.2 Station Grounding and Bonding

As discussed in the **Safety** chapter, the station's ground system is very important and serves three purposes: ac safety, lightning protection, and RF management. With some attention to detail and planning, your station can be designed to satisfy all three needs from the start. This section is limited to providing general guidelines for grounding and bonding. Additional information is available from the ARRL's website in the Technology section under the Radio Technology Topics page's group of Safety articles and resources. The ARRL's *Grounding and Bonding for the Radio Amateur* collects a great deal of information into a single book for convenient reference with guidelines for station builders.

AC SAFETY

The **Safety** chapter covers the basic elements of how ac power is configured in residences, including the requirements for grounding and bonding of equipment and earth connections. Make sure your station wiring complies with all ac wiring requirements.

Before building a station or modifying an existing station, start by making sure your existing ac wiring is in good shape. Before you begin, if you are new to ac wiring or uncomfortable around it, get a professional to do the job or have an experienced person show you how to do it. Treated with respect and following simple safety rules, working on ac wiring is safe. This is a good time to read the safety section of any wiring handbook or guide, even if you *think* you know what you're doing.

All branch circuits must have a ground conductor that runs back to the service panel. The ground conductor should be at least as large as the current-carrying conductors so it can handle the same current overloads without causing a fire hazard. The branch circuit ground conductor is almost always one wire in a multi-conductor non-metallic (NM) cable, usually referred to by its trade name, Romex. Inside the cable sheath, the wire is usually bare copper but it can also be have insulation that is green or green-with-yellow-stripes. Make sure the ac service entry ground rod or other earth connection is present and that all wiring to it is sufficiently heavy and that all connecting hardware is in good condition.

Along with the residence's ac service entry ground rod, additional ground rods are often installed for panels where feed lines enter a building, for antennas and towers, and a direct connection to the station's bonding bus. All of these external earth connections must be bonded together using heavy wire or strap.

Although it has been long recommended in Amateur Radio articles and books, do not use a metal cold water pipe as a ground electrode. Those recommendations were made in an era when copper and galvanized pipe were used for all water service plumbing. Plastic pipe is now the standard and mixed systems of copper and plastic pipe are common. Your local building codes will specify how the pipes inside your home should or shouldn't be connected together for electrical grounding purposes.

A bonding bus is a good way for connecting equipment together and also provides a good way to make ac safety grounding connections. Installed behind or under your equipment, the bus can be any heavy metal conductor — copper or aluminum are both available and relatively inexpensive. Strap, pipe, or even heavy wire will do. Connect the bus to the ac safety ground conductor at a power outlet. Only one connection is needed. Then connect the enclosure of each piece of equipment to the bus using a piece of #14 AWG wire, strap, or flat-weave grounding braid.

The typical amateur station includes a lot of accessory equipment that is itself unpowered but which connects to equipment that is connected to the ac line. Your goal in station building should be to insure that any exposed metal will not present a shock hazard. This requires you to provide a safety ground connection for any unpowered equipment with a metal enclosure, such as an SWR bridge, antenna tuner, or antenna switch. Most larger pieces of this type of equipment will have a ground terminal for you to use. If not, add a screw to the enclosure or use a mounting screw for the connection.

LIGHTNING PROTECTION

Begin by reading about and understanding what lightning is and what protection against its effect consists of. Information about lightning and protection plans are available in the 2002 series of *QST* articles by Ron Block, KB2UYT. (The complete set of articles are posted online at **www.arrl.org/lightning-protection**.) Once you have a plan, you can implement it using standard grounding and bonding techniques. The **Safety** chapter covers the basic elements of lightning protection.

Figure 24.4 shows an overview of how

Figure 24.4 — Overview of a station grounding system than incorporates ac safety, lightning protection, and RF management. A single-point ground-panel (SPGP) is used to provide a common bonding connection to equalize voltage during a lightning transient. All ground connections must be bonded together.

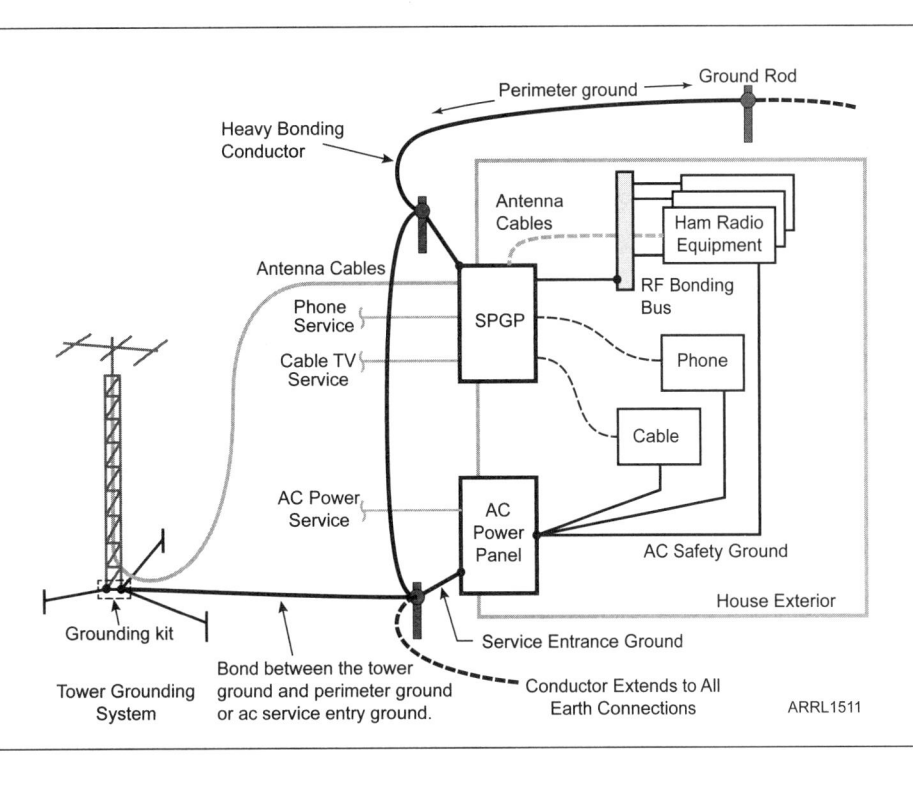

Figure 24.5 — A single-point ground-panel (SPGP) for an active HF station. Mounted on an exterior wall under the station, all filters, switches, and protectors are attached to the aluminum sheet. A heavy ground conductor connects the panel to a ground rod outside. [Kirk Pickering, K4RO, photo]

station grounding and bonding works together to provide lightning protection. All earth connections such as ground rods and buried conductors are connected together. Inside the station, all equipment is bonded together either directly or through a bonding bus.

Devise a lightning protection plan as instructed in the articles by Block. Remember that every conductor entering or leaving your protected zone must have some means of protection against lightning or lightning-induced transients. **Figure 24.5** shows a single-point ground-panel (SPGP) installed on an exterior wall below the station. **Figure 24.6** shows an example of how to mount lightning protectors on an SPGP. Your circumstances are unique and the exact solution is up to you to design and build.

Don't depend on power strips with simple MOV surge protectors to protect your equipment. You can protect one or two branch circuits with a professional/industrial-quality ac surge protector (see **Figure 24.7**), mounted on your ground panel, and connect your ac power distribution system to that. Whole-house surge protectors will not protect your station equipment from lightning since they are only connected to the residence's incoming ac service. You will still need to create an effective ground system in your station.

Make sure all of your equipment is bonded together so that voltage is equalized between pieces of equipment. Bonding can be done directly between pieces of equipment if you do not have too many individual radios and accessories. An alternative is to use the bonding bus approach as illustrated by **Figure 24.8**. Bonding will also serve to provide ac safety if the bonding includes a connection to the ac safety ground.

RF MANAGEMENT

It is typical for a station to begin with one or two radios, a power supply, and some feed lines to antennas outside. Eventually, more accessories are added, along with a computer, possibly and amplifier, and so on. This eventually leads to "RF in the shack" or RFI to various pieces of equipment. The problem is

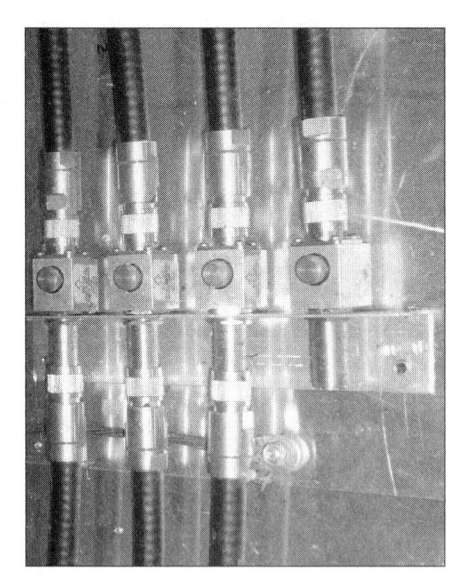

Figure 24.6 — Lightning protectors mounted on a SPGP using an aluminum angle bracket. Some protectors can be mounted directly to panels or as a through-hole using the threaded bulkhead-style connectors. [Ward Silver, NØAX, photo]

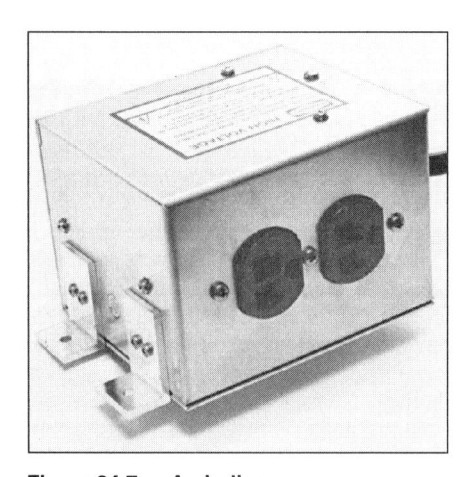

Figure 24.7 — An in-line ac power protector suitable for lightning protection and designed to be mounted on a grounded panel.

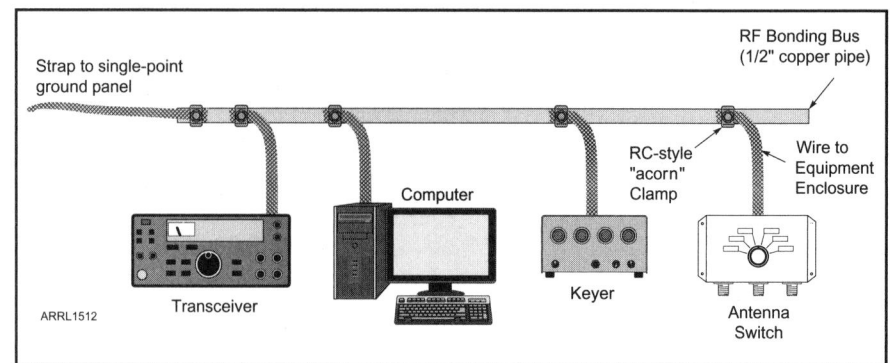

Figure 24.8 — A typical bonding bus for a station with equipment on a table or desk. Connections between the equipment and the bonding bus should be made with heavy wire or strap (#14 AWG is suitable).

Figure 24.9 — A simple RF ground plane made of aluminum roof flashing with a copper pipe bonding bus attached at the rear of the table. Equipment is placed on the flashing and attached to the pipe with short jumpers. The ground plane and bus are attached to the station ground system with a heavy wire. [Ward Silver, NØAX, photo]

caused by the numerous interconnections between pieces of equipment. These pick up transmitted signals as common-mode RF current that can affect amateur equipment, just as it can cause RFI to consumer equipment. (See the **RF Interference** chapter for more information.)

By starting your station with a plan to manage the RF that will be present, you can reduce or eliminate the effects. You will probably not be able to shield your station against RF being picked up by the various cables and enclosures. Instead, use bonding to minimize RF voltage between pieces of equipment so that RF current doesn't flow between them.

Bonding can be done by direct connection or by using a bonding bus.

As an added bonus, good bonding between pieces of equipment also minimizes the small audio buzz and hum voltages caused by leakage current and stray magnetic fields. Many stations use low-level audio signals for digital operation. Bonding helps keep unwanted hum and buzz from contaminating these signal paths. Bonding for RF management can satisfy the requirements for ac safety and lightning protection, too.

One technique for helping to equalize RF voltage around your station is the use of an RF *ground plane* or *reference plane*. **Figure 24.9** shows a simple ground plane made from a sheet of aluminum roof flashing attached to a table top. A bonding bus of copper pipe is clamped to the flashing at the back of the table. Sheet metal screws in the pipe are provided for attaching bonding jumpers to each piece of equipment. The ground plane and bonding bus are then connected to the station ground system. A metal desk or table can serve as the RF ground plane, as well. (The RF ground plane is different than a set of ground radials that provide a return path for RF to the feed point of a vertical antenna.) RF voltage differences are kept low by the ground plane. Extra cable length can be coiled up and placed directly on the ground plane to help keep them from picking up common-mode RF.

Portable and temporary stations pose a challenge for RF management. Station configuration usually has to work around various

24.4   Chapter 29

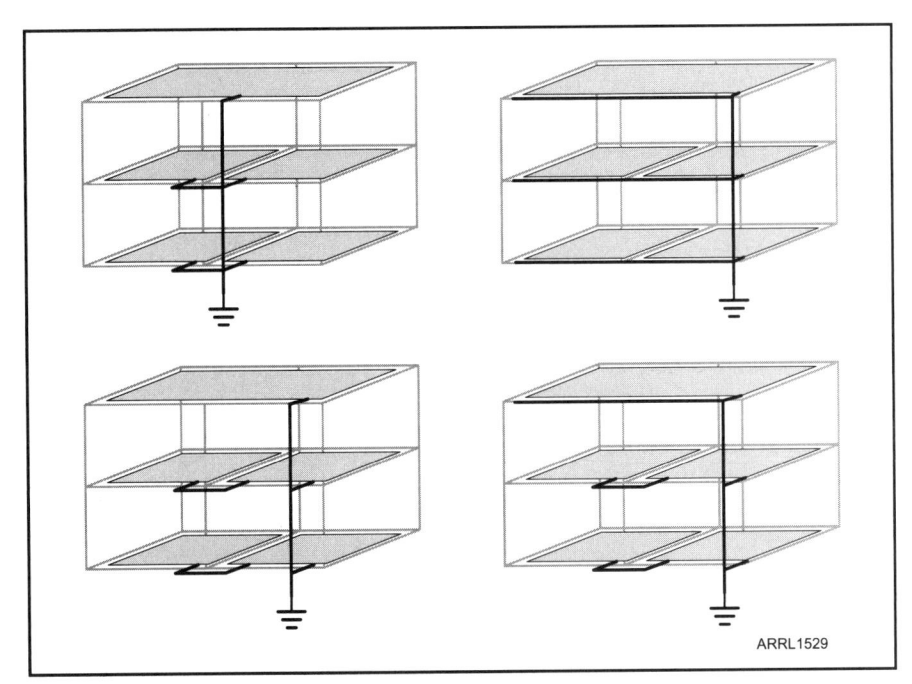

Figure 24.10 — For equipment on shelves, create a ground plane on each shelf. Bond each ground plane segment together (heavy lines) and route cables between the segments along the bonding strap or wire. Several possible examples are shown.

constraints and physical obstacles. Installing a comprehensive ground and bonding system is usually not possible. Under these circumstances, a roll of strap or flexible braid may serve as an effective bonding bus. Screen or even aluminum foil will work as a ground plane. Have plenty of short jumpers and clip leads to connect the equipment enclosures to whatever common connection you can manage.

Many stations have shelving to hold equipment above a desk or table. **Figure 24.10** shows several possible techniques for adding metal sheet or strap to the shelves and connecting it together. You can use metal sheet, screen, or even surplus PC board material as the ground plane. The important thing is to get some metal under the various pieces of equipment to help the bonding connections work at RF.

24.1.3 Station Power

Power supply design and use is covered in the **Power Sources** chapter, and safety issues and station wiring are covered in the **Safety** chapter. A single 20 A, 120 V circuit will provide sufficient power for all of the radio and computer equipment in almost any single-operator amateur station, including most 500 W power amplifiers. A single 20 A, 240 V circuit will provide sufficient power for two legal limit amplifiers that do not transmit simultaneously. A generous number of 120 V outlets should be provided. The 120 V and 240 V outlets should have their equipment grounds bonded together. This simple power arrangement has the major advantage of minimizing problems with audio hum and buzz caused by power system leakage current. Install good quality 20 A outlets and 20 A breakers.

Figure 24.11 shows how you can build your own heavy-duty, high-quality power distribution box. Use metal "back boxes" with high-quality outlets and heavy #12 or #14 AWG wiring. Multiple boxes can be mechanically attached together to support as many outlets as needed. If more than one multi-outlet box is used on the same circuit, use rigid EMT or flexible metal BX conduit between them with all of the metalwork solidly assembled and connected to the ground conductor. A heavy switch can be included to turn the entire package on and off. A GFCI outlet can be included in the box if the branch circuit is not already protected by a GFCI.

Wherever commercial power strips are used in your station, use industrial-quality products with a metal enclosure, heavy wiring, good quality outlets and a built-in switch and circuit breaker (typically rated at 15 A). Avoid inexpensive plastic power strips which cost much less but are of far lower quality.

Using ground fault circuit interrupter (GFCI) circuit breakers or outlets to supply power is not required by the NEC. However, given the many opportunities for stray current in an amateur station and antenna system, GFCI protection is not a bad idea. You can install GFCI breakers in the ac service panel or install GFCI outlets at the station.

24.1.4 Station Layout

Station layout is largely a matter of personal taste and needs. It will depend mostly on the amount of space available, the equipment involved and the types of operating to be done. With these factors in mind, some basic design considerations apply to all stations.

THE OPERATING TABLE

The operating table may be an office or computer desk, a kitchen table or a custom-made bench. What you use will depend on space, materials at hand and cost. The two most important considerations are height and size of the top. Most commercial desks are about 29 inches above the floor. Computer tables are usually a couple inches lower for a more comfortable keyboard and mouse placement. This is a comfortable height for most adults. Heights much lower or higher than this may cause an awkward operating position.

The dimensions of the top are an important consideration. A deep (36 inches or more)

Figure 24.11 — A heavy-duty homemade power distribution box. Several gangable "back boxes" are assembled into a larger box that can hold several duplex outlets. A light switch or GFCI-protected outlet can be included for power control and shock protection. [Jim Brown, K9YC, photo]

Assembling a Station 24.5

top will allow plenty of room for equipment interconnections along the back, equipment about midway and room for writing or a keyboard and mouse toward the front. The length of the top will depend on the amount of equipment being used. An office or computer desk makes a good operating table. These are often about 36 inches deep and 60 inches wide. Drawers can be used for storage of logbooks, headphones, writing materials, and so on. Desks specifically designed for computer use often have built-in shelves that can be used for equipment stacking. Desks of this type are available ready-to-assemble at most discount and home improvement stores. The low price and adaptable design of these desks make them an attractive option for an operating position. An example is shown in **Figure 24.12**.

If possible, arrange your operating desk or table so that it is easy to access the rear of the equipment. You may be able to provide a walkway behind the equipment or the desk or table might be moveable. Either way, you will appreciate being able to work behind the equipment without having to get under a table or work in uncomfortable positions. It also helps avoid wiring errors caused by not having a clear view of the equipment. Equipment can also be left in place while connections are made.

ARRANGING THE EQUIPMENT

No matter how large your operating table, some vertical stacking of equipment may be necessary to allow you to reach everything from your chair. Stacking pieces of equipment directly on top of one another is not a good idea because most amateur equipment needs airflow around it for cooling. A shelf like that shown in **Figure 24.13** can improve equipment layout in many situations. Dimensions of the shelf can be adjusted to fit the size of your operating table.

When you have acquired the operating table and shelving for your station, the next task is arranging the equipment in a convenient, orderly manner. The first step is to provide power outlets and a good ground as described in a previous section. Be conservative in estimating the number of power outlets for your installation; radio equipment has a habit of multiplying with time, so plan for the future at the outset.

Every station is different and each operator has different preferences so giving "cookbook" instructions for station layout is unrealistic. Even so, there are some general principles that make a station layout effective. Start by looking at the photographs of stations in this chapter, in *QST*, and online. Visit stations of other operators to get ideas and try different arrangements. Think about what equipment you use most while operating and make that easy to reach and use. Consider making a temporary arrangement to try out different configurations before you settle on a final layout. Make it easy to update your layout as your habits, tastes, and body change. Configure the station to suit your interests, and keep thinking of ways to refine the layout.

Portable stations have the additional requirement to be lightweight and sturdy, often part of a "go-kit" for emergency communication or other public service.

Figure 24.12 — Mike Adams, N1EN makes the most of his desktop to operate on the HF and VHF+ bands. His laptop and tablet computers are an alternative to the larger desktop systems. He uses a full-size keyboard with the laptop. [Mike Adams, N1EN, photo]

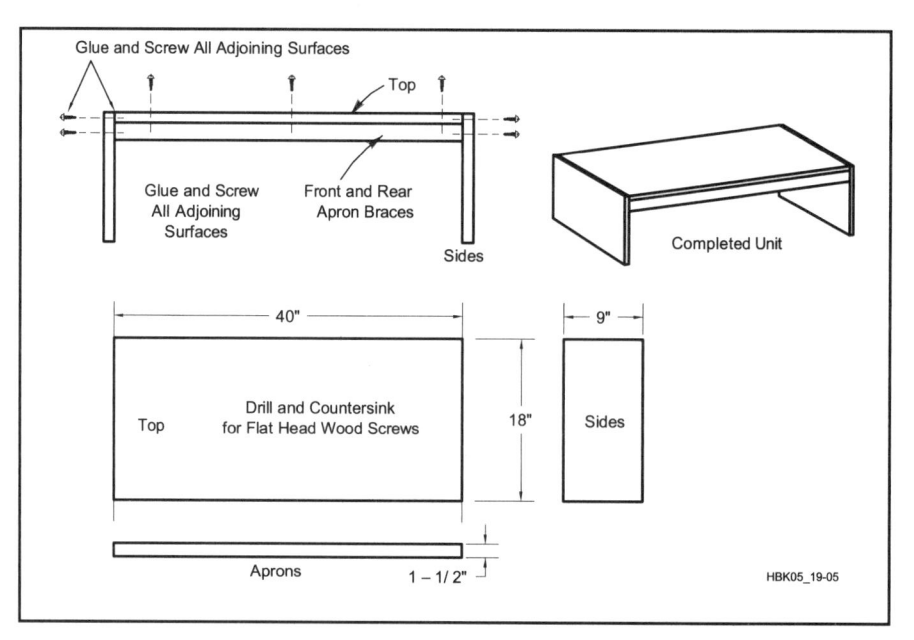

Figure 24.13 — A simple but strong equipment shelf can be built from readily available materials. Use ¾-inch plywood along with glue and screws for the joints for adequate strength.

Figures 24.14 and 24.15 show two different solutions for very different sets of circumstances but both are well-considered and appropriate to the need.

You may find yourself taking advantage of non-traditional materials for your station. **Figure 24.16** shows equipment supported by open metal wire shelving used as commercial or industrial shelving. Not only is the shelving strong, since it is metallic, it serves as an RF ground plane and is open to airflow that provides ventilation to the equipment.

24.6   Chapter 29

Figure 24.14 — This portable 500 W HF station was constructed by W6GJB and K9YC for portable operation during the California QSO Party. [Jim Brown, K9YC, photo]

Figure 24.15 — K1CE adapted this portable metal scaffold as a portable operating desk. The top shelf also serves as a ground plane for the mag-mount VHF/UHF antennas. [Rick Palm, K1CE, photo]

Figure 24.16 — Taking advantage of a good opportunity, NØNI adapted this set of metal wire shelving to hold his equipment. The wire shelves also act as an RF ground plane and provide ventilation. [Bob Lee, WØGXA, photo]

ERGONOMICS

Ergonomics is a term that loosely means "fitting the work to the person." If tools and equipment are designed around what people can accommodate, the results will be much more satisfactory. For example, in the 1930s research was done in telephone equipment manufacturing plants because use of long-nosed pliers for wiring switchboards required considerable force at the end of the hand's range of motion. A simple tool redesign resolved this issue.

Considerable attention has been focused on ergonomics in recent years because we have come to realize that long periods of time spent in unnatural positions can lead to repetitive-motion injuries. Much of this attention has been focused on people whose job tasks have required them to operate computers and other office equipment. While most Amateur Radio operators do not devote as much time to their hobby as they might in a full-time job, it does make sense to consider comfort and flexibility when choosing furniture and arranging it in the shack or workshop. Adjustable height chairs are available with air cylinders to serve as a shock absorber. Footrests might come in handy if the chair is so high that your feet cannot support your lower leg weight. The height of tables and keyboards often is not adjustable.

Placement of computer screens should take into consideration the reflected light coming from windows. It is always wise to build into

Assembling a Station 24.7

your sitting sessions time to walk around and stimulate blood circulation. Your muscles are less likely to stiffen, while the flexibility in your joints can be enhanced by moving around.

Selection of hand tools is another area where there are choices to make that may affect how comfortable you will be while working in your shack. Look for screwdrivers with pliable grips. Take into account how heavy things are before picking them up — your back will thank you.

FIRE EXTINGUISHERS

Fires in well-designed electronic equipment are not common but are known to occur. Proper use of a suitable fire extinguisher can make the difference between a small fire with limited damage and loss of an entire home. Make sure you know the limitations of your extinguisher and the importance of reporting the fire to your local fire department immediately.

Several types of extinguishers are suitable for electrical fires. The multipurpose dry chemical or "ABC" type units are relatively inexpensive and contain a solid powder that is nonconductive. Avoid buying the smallest size; a 5-pound capacity will meet most requirements in the home. ABC extinguishers are also the best choice for kitchen fires (the most common location of home fires). One disadvantage of this type is the residue left behind that might cause corrosion in electrical connectors. Another type of fire extinguisher suitable for energized electrical equipment is the carbon dioxide unit. CO_2 extinguishers require the user to be much closer to the fire, are heavy and difficult to handle, and are relatively expensive. For obvious reasons, water extinguishers are not suitable for fires in or near electronic equipment.

AIDS FOR HAMS WITH DISABILITIES

A station used by an amateur with physical disabilities or sensory impairments may require adapted equipment or particular layout considerations. The station may be highly customized to meet the operator's needs or just require a bit of "tweaking."

The myriad of individual needs makes describing all of the possible adaptive methods impractical. Each situation must be approached individually, with consideration to the operator's particular needs. However, many types of situations have already been encountered and worked through by others, eliminating the need to start from scratch in every case.

An excellent resource is the Courage Handi-Ham System. The Courage Handi-Ham System, a part of the Courage Center, provides a number of services to hams (and aspiring hams) with disabilities. These include study materials and a wealth of useful information on their comprehensive website. Visit **www.handiham.org** for more information.

24.1.5 Interconnecting Your Equipment

Once you have your equipment and get it arranged, you will have to interconnect it all. No matter how simple the station, you will at least have antenna, power and microphone or key connections. Equipment such as amplifiers, computers, TNCs and so on add complexity. By keeping your equipment interconnections well organized and of high quality, you will avoid problems later on.

Often, ready-made cables will be available. But in many cases you will have to make your own cables. A big advantage of making your own cables is that you can customize the length. This allows more flexibility in arranging your equipment and avoids unsightly extra cable all over the place. Many manufacturers supply connectors with their equipment along with pinout information in the manual. This allows you to make the necessary cables in the lengths you need for your particular installation.

Always use high quality wire, cables and connectors in your shack. Take your time and make good mechanical and electrical connections on your cable ends. Sloppy cables are often a source of trouble. Often the problems they cause are intermittent and difficult to track down. You can bet that they will crop up right in the middle of a contest or during a rare DX QSO! Even worse, a poor quality connection could cause RFI or even create a fire hazard. A cable with a poor mechanical connection could come loose and short a power supply to ground or apply a voltage where it should not be. Wire and cables should have good quality insulation that is rated high enough to prevent shock hazards.

Interconnections should be neatly bundled and labeled. Wire ties, masking tape or paper labels with string work well. See **Figure 24.17**. Whatever method you use, proper labeling makes disconnecting and reconnecting equipment much easier. **Figure 24.18** illustrates the number of potential interconnections in a modern, full-featured transceiver.

WIRE AND CABLE

The type of wire or cable to use depends on the job at hand. The wire must be of sufficient size to carry the necessary current. Use the tables in the **Component Data and References** chapter to find this information. Never use underrated wire; it will be a fire hazard. Be sure to check the insulation too. For high-voltage applications, the insulation must be rated at least a bit higher than the intended voltage. A good rule of thumb is to use a rating at least twice what is needed.

Use good quality coaxial cable of sufficient size for connecting transmitters, transceivers, antenna switches, antenna tuners and so on. RG-58 might be fine for a short patch between your transceiver and SWR bridge, but is too

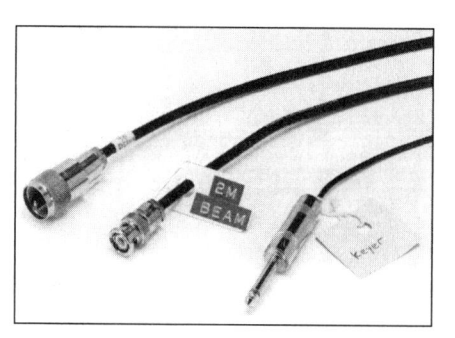

Figure 24.17 — Labels on the cables make it much easier to rearrange things in the station. Labeling ideas include masking tape, cardboard labels attached with string and labels attached to fasteners found on plastic bags (such as bread bags).

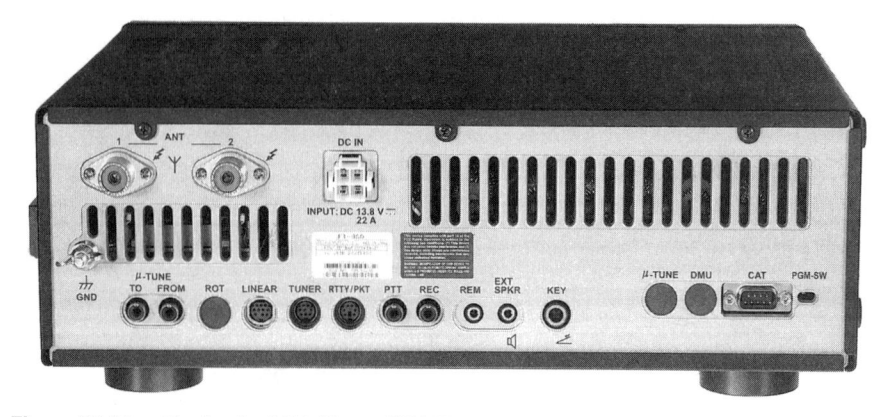

Figure 24.18 — The back of this Yaesu FT-950 transceiver shows some of the many types of connectors encountered in the amateur station. Note that this variety is found on a single piece of equipment.

24.8   Chapter 29

small to use between your legal-limit amplifier and antenna tuner. For more information, see the **Transmission Lines** chapter.

Hookup wire may be stranded or solid. Generally, stranded is a better choice since it is less prone to break under repeated flexing. Many applications require shielded wire to reduce the chances of RF getting into the equipment. RG-174 is a good choice for control, audio and some low-power RF applications. Shielded microphone or computer cable can be used where more conductors are necessary.

For RF connections, #12 – #16 AWG solid or stranded wire or solid strap are preferred. For indoor connections not exposed to the weather, flat-weave tinned braid strap is acceptable. Do not use braid salvaged from coaxial cable for RF connections.

CONNECTORS

Connectors are a convenient way to make an electrical connection by using mating electrical contacts. There are quite a few connector styles, but common terms apply to all of them. Pins are contacts that extend out of the connector body, and connectors in which pins make the electrical contact are called "male" connectors. Sockets are hollow, recessed contacts, and connectors with sockets are called "female." Connectors designed to attach to each other are called "mating connectors." Connectors with specially shaped bodies or inserts that require a complementary shape on a mating connector are called "keyed connectors." Keyed connectors ensure that the connectors can only go together one way, reducing the possibility of damage from incorrect mating.

Plugs are connectors installed on the end of cables and *jacks* are installed on equipment. *Adapters* make connections between two different styles of connector, such as between two different families of RF connectors. Other adapters join connectors of the same family, such as double-male, double-female and gender changers. *Splitters* divide a signal between two connectors.

While the number of different types of connectors is mind-boggling, many manufacturers of amateur equipment use a few standard types. If you are involved in any group activities such as public service or emergency-preparedness work, check to see what kinds of connectors others in the group use and standardize connectors wherever possible. Assume connectors are not waterproof, unless you specifically buy one clearly marked for outdoor use (and assemble it correctly).

Power Connectors

Amateur Radio equipment uses a variety of power connectors. Some examples are shown in **Figure 24.19**. Most low power amateur equipment uses coaxial power connectors. These are the same type found on consumer electronic equipment that is supplied by a wall transformer power supply. Transceivers and other equipment that requires high current in excess of a few amperes often use Molex connectors (**www.molex.com** — enter "MLX" in the search window) with a white, nylon body housing pins and sockets crimped on to the end of wires.

An emerging standard, particularly among

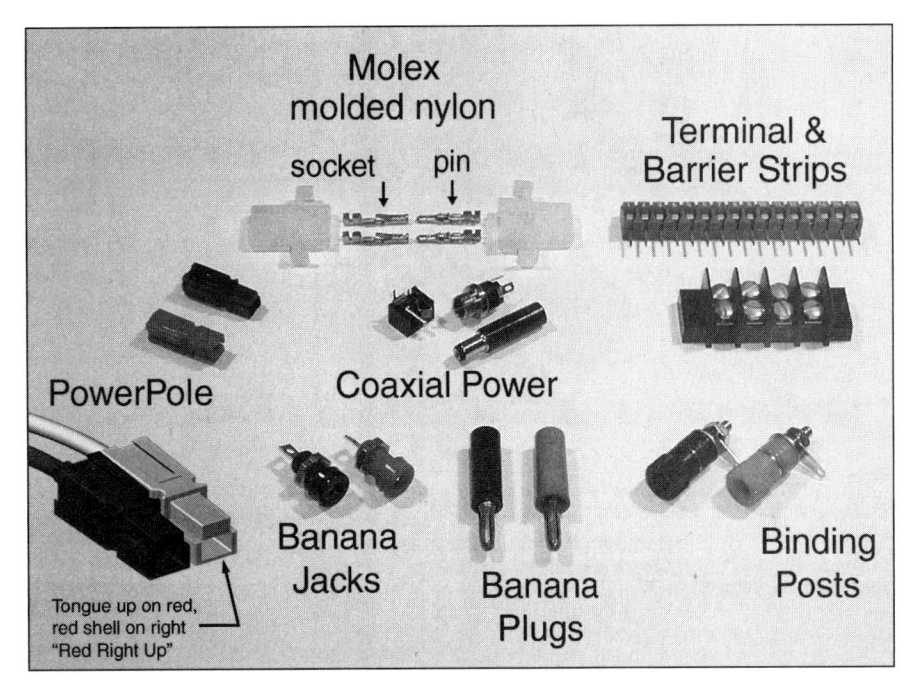

Figure 24.19 — These are the most common connectors used on amateur equipment to make power connections. The proper orientation for paired Powerpole connectors is with the red connector on the right and its tongue on top — "red-right-up". [Courtesy of Wiley Publishing, Ham Radio for Dummies, or Two-Way Radios and Scanners for Dummies]

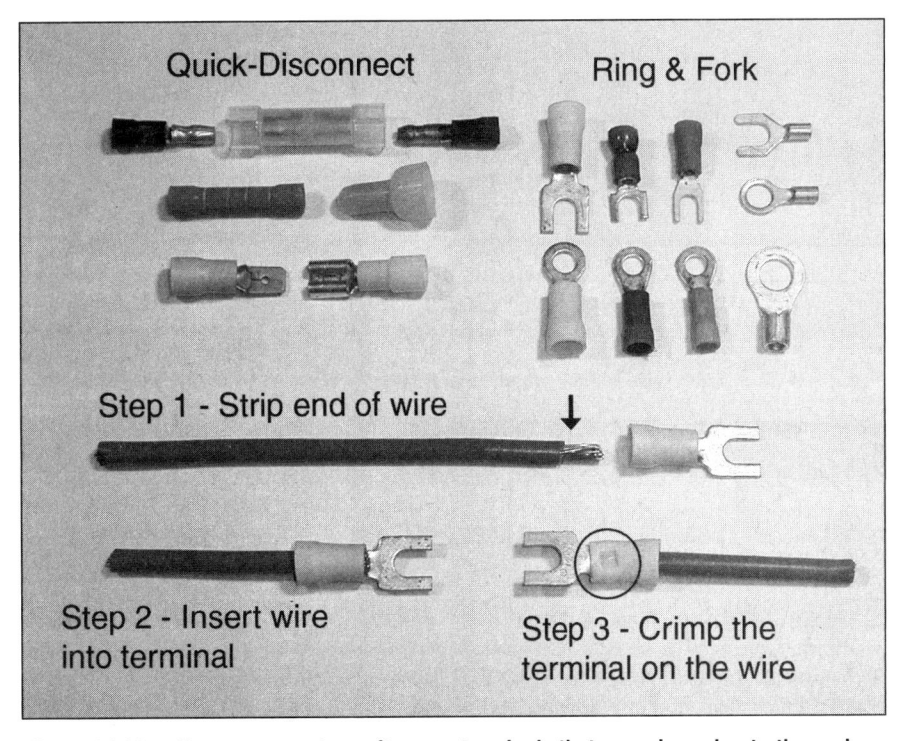

Figure 24.20 — Power connectors often use terminals that are crimped onto the end of wires with special crimping tools. [Courtesy of Wiley Publishing, Ham Radio for Dummies, or Two-Way Radios and Scanners for Dummies]

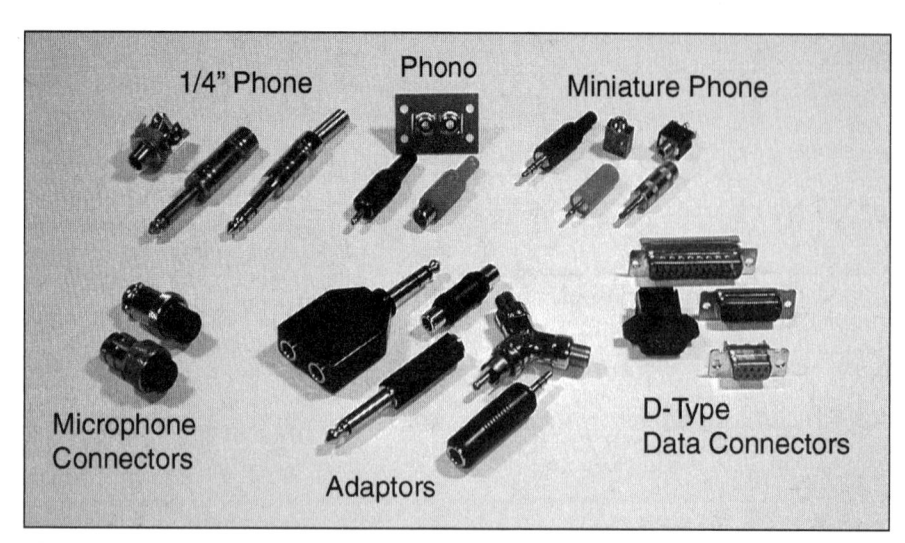

Figure 24.21 — Audio and data signals are carried by a variety of different connectors. Individual cable conductors are either crimped or soldered to the connector contacts. [Ward Silver, NØAX, photo]

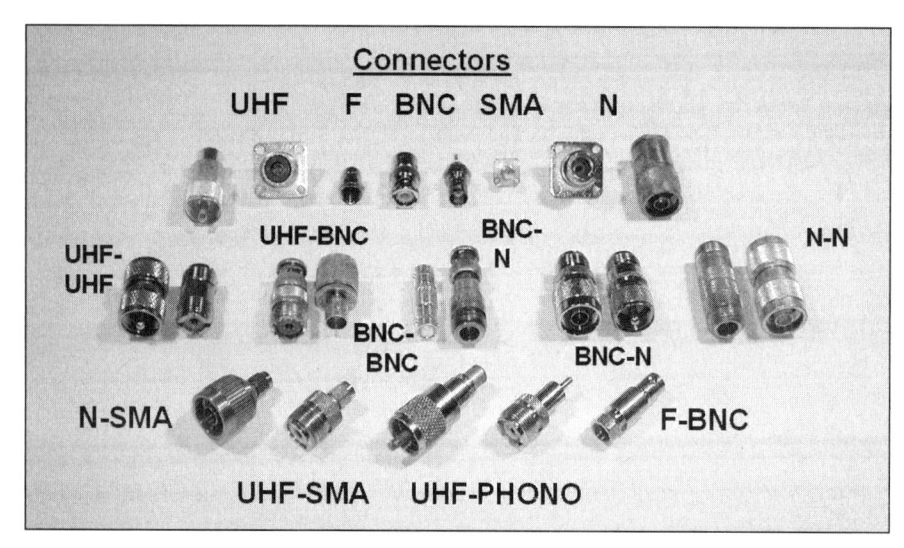

Figure 24.22 — Each type of RF connector is specially made to carry RF signals and preserve the shielding of coaxial cable. Adapters are available to connect one style of connector to another. [Ward Silver, NØAX, photo]

ARES and other emergency communications groups, is the use of Anderson Powerpole connectors (www.andersonpower.com). These connectors are "sexless" meaning that any two connectors of the same series can be mated — there are no male or female connectors. By standardizing on a single connector style, equipment can be shared and replaced easily in the field. The standard orientation for pairs of these connectors is shown in Figure 24.19. Using this orientation increases the compatibility of your wiring with that of other hams.

Molex and Powerpole connectors use crimp terminals (both male and female) installed on the end of wires. A special crimping tool is used to attach the wire to the terminal and the terminal is then inserted into the body of the connector. Making a solid connection requires the use of an appropriate tool — do not use pliers or some other tool to make a crimp connection.

Some equipment uses terminal strips for direct connection to wires or crimp terminals, often with screws. Other equipment uses spring-loaded terminals or binding posts to connect to bare wire ends. **Figure 24.20** shows some common crimp terminals that are installed on the ends of wires using special tools.

Audio and Control Connectors

Consumer audio equipment and Amateur Radio equipment share many of the same connectors for the same uses. Phone plugs and jacks are used for mono and stereo audio circuits. These connectors, shown in **Figure 24.21** come in ¼ inch, ⅛ inch (miniature) and subminiature varieties. The contact at the end of the plug is called the tip and the connector at the base of the plug is the sleeve. If there is a third contact between the tip and sleeve, it is the ring (these are "stereo" phone connectors). Stereo phone connectors are often called TRS (for tip-ring-sleeve) connectors by audio equipment manufacturers.

Phono plugs and jacks (sometimes called RCA connectors since they were first used on RCA brand equipment) are used for audio, video and low-level RF signals. They are also widely used for control signals.

The most common microphone connector on mobile and base station equipment is an 8-pin round connector. On older transceivers you may see 4-pin round connectors used for microphones. RJ-45 modular connectors (see the section on telephone connectors below) are often used in mobile and smaller radios.

RF Connectors

Feed lines used for radio signals require special connectors for use at RF frequencies. The connectors must have approximately the same characteristic impedance as the feed line they are attached to or some of the RF signal will be reflected by the connector. Inexpensive audio and control connectors cannot meet that requirement, nor can they handle the high power levels often encountered in RF equipment. Occasionally, phono connectors are used for HF receiving and low-power transmitting equipment.

By far, the most common connector for RF in amateur equipment is the UHF family shown in **Figure 24.22**. (The UHF designator has nothing to do with frequency.) A PL-259 is the plug that goes on the end of feed lines, and the SO-239 is the jack mounted on equipment. A "barrel" (PL-258) is a double-female adapter that allows two feed lines to be connected together. UHF connectors are typically used up to 150 MHz and can handle legal-limit transmitter power at HF.

UHF connectors have several drawbacks including lack of weatherproofing, poor performance above the 2 meter band and limited power handling at higher frequencies. The Type-N series of RF connectors addresses all of those needs. Type-N connectors are somewhat more expensive than UHF connectors, but they require less soldering and perform better in outdoor use since they are moisture resistant. Type-N connectors can be used to 10 GHz.

For low-power uses, BNC connectors are often used. BNC connectors are the standard for laboratory equipment, as well, and they are often used for dc and audio connections. BNC connectors are common on handheld

Coax Connectors — Not as Simple as They Appear
by Hal Kennedy, N4GG

"You get what you pay for" was never more true than when it comes to common UHF connectors, including PL-259s, SO-239s, adapters, and related parts. Every hamfest seems to have at least one vendor selling "mystery" UHF connectors, sometimes for as little as a dollar each. What are you buying when you buy the cheapest PL-259? It's pretty much a guess. For the difference of a dollar or two, "mystery" UHF connectors are a very poor investment.

PL-259s have four parts: the outer sleeve called the "knurled nut," the connector body, the insulator/dielectric and the center pin. All four components can be compromised to the point of making a bargain connector useless.

Problems frequently encountered:

- Finish: Bargain connectors sometimes have a finish you can't solder to! They may have a chrome-like appearance, but the plating may not take solder well and has to be filed down for a good connection.
- Threading: The internal threads at the rear of the body are there to accept a UG-style insert that narrows the connector barrel to accept smaller diameter coax such as RG-8X or RG-58. The threads may be metric! UG inserts also sometimes appear in the US market with metric threads. Either way, the insert will not screw into the body.
- Dielectric: Good connectors use quality phenolic or Teflon insulation between the center pin and the body. Bargain connectors might use anything, including materials such as polystyrene, which will melt when the center pin is soldered.
- Center pin diameter: This is one of the most common and insidious problems in mystery PL-259s. The center pin outer diameter (OD) is almost always slightly smaller than it should be and it's hard to notice. The center pin connection between a PL-259 and an SO-239 or barrel connector depends on the male side pin OD being correct and the matching fingers on the female side being the correct diameter and made of the proper spring material.
- Center socket spring tension: If the SO-239 socket metal relaxes over time and/or temperature, an intermittent connection will be created that can be very hard to track down.
- Mating indentions: The indentations on the end of the SO-239 that mate to a PL-259 (the annulus flange) may only have four indentations to match up with the short prongs on the body of the male connector. A quality SO-239 or barrel connector has indentations all the way around. If the PL-259 and SO-239 don't seat completely, an intermittent connection is likely to develop.
- Tee and right-angle (elbow) UHF adapters: The center conductor has to make a right-angle turn inside the shell. In poor-quality adapters the right-angle connection is done with a spring contact — these do not hold up. Quality tee and right-angle adapters are reliable because the internal conductors are tapped and threaded — the conductors are screwed together within the body at the right angle junction.

How can we tell the good connectors? If the price is too good to be true — well, it is. PL-259s with good silver plating have a dull appearance. Good connectors have a part number and manufacturer's name stamped into them. You can look up the connector's specifications if it's marked. An example is the connectors made by Amphenol — all of which have parts numbers such as 83-1SP (PL-259) or 83-1R (SO-239) stamped into or onto the connector body.

radios for antenna connections. The newest handheld transceivers often use small, screw-on SMA type connectors for their antennas, though.

The type of connector used for a specific job depends on the size of the cable, the frequency of operation and the power levels involved. More information on RF connectors may be found in the **Component Data and References** chapter.

Data Connectors

Digital data is exchanged between computers and pieces of radio equipment more than ever before in the amateur station. The connector styles follow those found on computer equipment.

D-type connectors are used for RS-232 (COM ports) and parallel (LPT port) interfaces. A typical D-type connector has a model number of "DB" followed by the number of connections and a "P" or "S" depending on whether the connector uses pins or sockets. For example, the DB-9P is used for PC COM1 serial ports.

USB connectors are becoming more popular in amateur equipment as the computer industry has eliminated the bulkier and slower RS-232 interface. A number of manufacturers make USB-to-serial converters that allow devices with RS-232 interfaces to be used with computers that only have USB interfaces.

Null modem or *crossover* adapters or cables have the same type of connector on each end. The internal connections between signal pins are swapped between ends so that inputs and outputs are connected together. This allows interfaces to be connected together directly without any intermediary equipment, such as an Ethernet switch or an RS-232 modem.

Pinouts for various common computer connectors are shown in the **Component Data and References** chapter. Several practical data interface projects are shown in the **Station Accessories** and **Digital Communications** chapters in the downloadable supplemental content.

Telephone and Computer Network Connectors

Modular connectors are used for telephone and computer network connections. Connector part numbers begin with "RJ." The connectors are crimped on to multiconductor cables with special tools. The RJ11 connector is used for single- and double-line telephone system connection with 4 or 6 contacts. The RJ10 is a 4-contact connector for telephone handset connections. Ethernet computer network connections are made using RJ45 connectors with 8 contacts.

24.1.6 Documenting Your Station

An often neglected but very important part of putting together your station is properly documenting your work. Ideally, you should diagram your entire station from the ac power lines to the antenna on paper and keep the information in a special notebook with sections for the various facets of your installation. Having the station well documented is an invaluable aid when tracking down a problem or planning a modification. Rather than having to search your memory for information on what you did a long time ago, you'll have the facts on hand.

Besides recording the interconnections and hardware around your station, you should also keep track of the performance of your equipment. Each time you install a new antenna, measure the SWR at different points in the band and make a table or plot a curve. Later, if you suspect a problem, you'll be able to look in your records and compare your SWR with the original performance.

In your shack, you can measure the power output from your transmitter(s) and amplifier(s) on each band. These measurements will be helpful if you later suspect you have a problem. If you have access to a signal generator, you can measure receiver performance for future reference.

24.2 Mobile Installations

Solid-state electronics and miniaturization have allowed mobile operators to equip their vehicles with stations rivaling base stations. Indeed, it is possible to operate from 160 meters through 70 cm with one compact transceiver. Adding versatility, most designed-for-mobile transceivers are set up so that the main body of the radio can be safely tucked under a seat, with the operating "head" conveniently placed for ease of use as shown in **Figure 24.23**.

Common power levels reach 100-150 W on HF, and 50-75 W on VHF. With proper antenna selection and placement (see the **Antennas** chapter), mobile stations can work the world, just like their base station counterparts. The only real difference between them is that you're trying to drive at the same time you are operating, and safe operating requires attention to the details.

For some of us living in antenna-restricted areas, mobile operating may offer the best solution for getting on the air. For others it is an enjoyable alternative to home-station operation. No matter which category you're in, you can enjoy success if you plan your installation with safety and convenience in mind.

There is a considerable amount of information about mobile operation, both HF and VHF+, online. Many contributions to this section have come from the website of Alan Applegate, KØBG, at **www.k0bg.com**. Specialty groups, such as RVers and off-road groups will have additional perspectives. Your vehicle dealer also has service bulletins regarding the installation of radio equipment. Although the bulletins mainly apply to VHF equipment, they are a valuable source of information about convenient routes and access points for power and other wiring.

There is a considerable amount of information about mobile operation, both HF and VHF+, online. Many contributions to this section have come from the website of Alan Applegate, KØBG, at **www.k0bg.com**. Specialty groups, such as RVers and off-road groups will have additional perspectives. Your vehicle dealer also has service bulletins regarding the installation of radio equipment. Although the bulletins mainly apply to VHF equipment, they are a valuable source of information about convenient routes and access points for power and other wiring.

24.2.1 Installation

Installing Amateur Radio equipment in modern vehicles can be quite challenging, yet rewarding, if basic safety rules are followed. All gear must be securely attached to the vehicle. Unsecured cup holder mounts, mounts wedged between cushions, elastic cords, hook-and-loop tape, magnets, or any other temporary mounting scheme *must be avoided*! Remember, if it isn't bolted down, it will become a missile in the event of a crash. The radio mounting location must avoid SRS (airbag) deployment zones — virtually eliminating the top of the dash in most modern vehicles — as well as vehicle controls (see the sidebar "Air Bags and Mobile Installations).

If you're not into building a specific mount for your vehicle, there are many no-holes-needed mounts available from Amateur Radio dealers. Some mounts are even designed for a specific transceiver make and model. **Table 24.1** lists some suppliers.

Two other points to keep in mind when choosing a mounting location are convenience and lack of distraction. Microphone and power cabling should be placed out of the way and properly secured. The transceiver's controls should be convenient to use and to view. See **Figure 24.24** for examples.

Mounting radios inside unvented center consoles and overhead bins should also be avoided. Modern mobile transceivers designed for remote mounting allow the main body to be located under a seat, in the trunk, or in another out-of-the-way place (**Figure 24.25**) but be sure there is plenty of ventilation.

If you drive off-road or on rough roads, you may also wish to consider using shock mounts, also known as "Lord Mounts" for their original manufacturer. For more information, see the product information on "Plateform Mounts" from the Astrotex Company at **www.astrotex.com/lord.htm**.

24.2.2 Coaxial Cable

Cable lengths in mobile installations seldom exceed 15 feet, so coax losses are not a major factor except on the 70 cm and higher-frequency bands. Good quality RG-58A or RG-8X size coax is more than adequate for HF and VHF. While there is nothing wrong with using RG-8 size coax (0.405 inch), it is stiffer and has a larger bending radius, making it harder to work with in most mobile applications.

There are some caveats when selecting coax. Avoid solid center conductors such as in standard RG-58. It has a propensity to kink, is susceptible to failure from vibration and can be difficult to solder properly. Both RG-58A and RG-8X use foam dielectric, and care is needed when soldering PL-259 connectors — especially when reducers are being used. The **Component Data and References** chapter illustrates the correct installation procedure.

24.2.3 Wiring

Proper wiring is an essential part of any mobile installation. Consider the following points when selecting materials and planning the cable routing.

• Wire needs to be correctly sized and fused stranded wire.

Figure 24.23 — In this mobile installation, the transceiver control head is mounted in the center console, next to a box with switches for adjusting the antenna.

Table 24.1
Mobile Mount Sources
Gamber Johnson — www.gamberjohnson.com
Havis-Shields — www.havis.com
Jotto Desk — www.jottodesk.com
PanaVise Products — www.panavise.com
RAM Mounting Systems — www.ram-mount.com

Figure 24.24 — At A, the transceiver control head is attached to one of many available mounts designed for this purpose. Mounts are typically highly adjustable, allowing the control head or radio to be positioned close to the operator. An antenna controller is mounted below the microphone. At B, HF and VHF transceiver control heads and the microphone are all mounted to the dashboard, within easy reach.

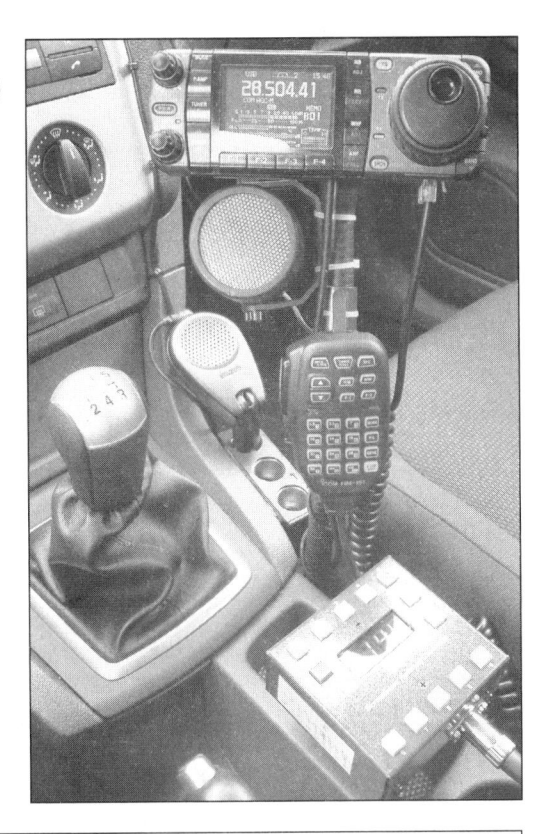

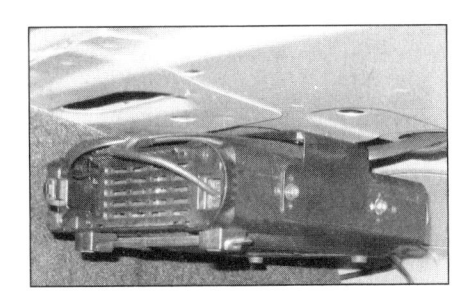

Figure 24.25 — The main body of the radio may be mounted in the vehicle's trunk or other out-of-the-way spot. Allow for plenty of ventilation.

- All cables need to be protected from abrasion, heat, and chemicals.
- Wiring needs to be shortened and/or bundled with appropriate wire ties to avoid interaction with passengers and mechanical devices.. **Figure 24.26** shows a typical vehicle wiring tray.

Power cables should be connected directly to the battery following manufacturers' recommendations, with the requisite positive and negative lead fuses located close to the battery. **Figure 24.27** shows a typical fuse block. Accessory (cigarette lighter) sockets and power taps shouldn't be used except for very low current loads (<5 A), and then only with care. It pays to remember that a vehicle fire is both costly and dangerous! More information may be found at **www.fordemc.com/docs/download/Mobile_Radio_Guide.pdf** and **service.gm.com/techlineinfo/radio.html**.

The fuses supplied with most mobile transceivers are ATC style. Most automotive fuses are ATO. The ATC fuse element is completely sealed in plastic and the ATO is not. Since the power cable fuse holders are not waterproof, only an ATC fuse should be used if the fuse holder is exposed to the weather or located anywhere in the engine compartment. If an ATO is used, and water gets into the fuse, the fuse element corrodes and eventually fails.

Proper wiring also minimizes voltage drops and helps prevent ground loops. Modern solid-state transceivers will operate effectively down to 12.0 V dc (engine off). If the voltage drops below 11.6 V under load, some transceivers will reduce power, shut down or operate incorrectly. The vehicle chassis should not be used for ground returns; paint or other insulation can isolate different chassis sections and using a chassis return can create a ground loop.

Running cables through the engine firewall can be easy in some vehicles and nearly impossible in others. Using factory wiring grommets should be avoided unless they're not being used. In some cases, the only alternative is to drill your own hole. If you have any questions or concerns, have your local mobile sound shop or two-way radio dealer install the wiring for you.

Power for ancillary equipment (wattmeters, remotely tuned antennas and so on) should follow the same wiring rules. The use of a multiple outlet power distribution panel such as a RigRunner (**www.westmountainradio.com**) is also recommended. They're convenient, and offer a second level of protection.

WIRE SIZE

The **Component Data and References** chapter lists the current-handling capabilities of various gauges of wire and cable. The correct wiring size is one that provides a low voltage drop (less than 0.5 V under full load). Don't use wire at its maximum current-current carrying capacity.

Here's the formula for calculating the cable assembly voltage drop (V_d):

$$V_d = [(R_W \times 2 \ell \times 0.001) + 2k] \times I$$

where

R_W = resistance value (Ω per 1000 feet) from the **Component Data and References** chapter.

Assembling a Station 24.13

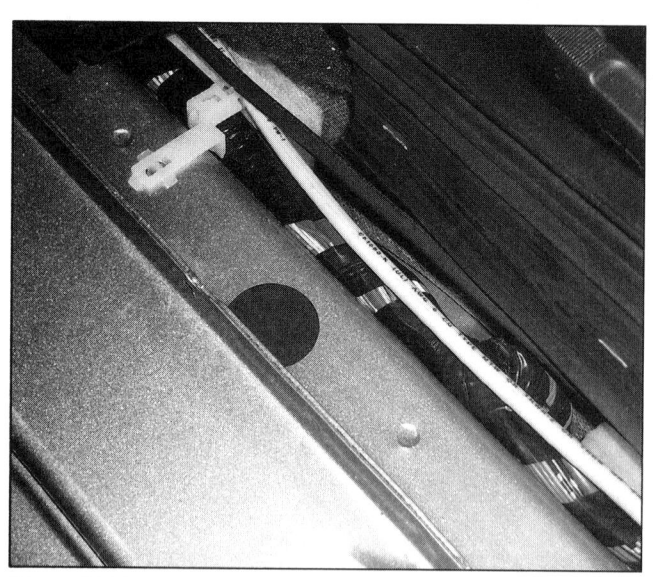

Figure 24.26 — Most vehicles have wiring troughs hidden behind interior body panels.

Figure 24.27 — Wiring attached to a fuse block.

ℓ = overall length of the cable assembly including connectors, in feet.

k = nominal resistive value for one fuse and its holder. Note: Most power cables have two fuses. If yours doesn't, use 1 k in the formula. If you don't know the fuse and holder resistance, use a conservative value of 0.002 Ω.

I = peak current draw in amperes for a SSB transceiver, or steady state for an FM radio.

For example, the peak current draw for a 100 W transceiver is about 22 A, and a typical power cable length is 10 feet. Using the resistive values for 1000 feet of #10 AWG wire (0.9987 Ω), and a conservative value for the fuse resistances (0.002 Ω each), the calculated drop will be 0.527 V.

It's important to reiterate that the wire size should be selected for minimum voltage drop, not maximum power handling capability. The voltage drop is often referred to as "I-squared-R loss" — the current in amperes, squared, times the resistance — and should be held to a minimum whenever possible. In cabling, excessive I²R losses can cause the wire to overheat with predictable results.

The insulation material of wire used in mobile installations should have a temperature rating of at least 90 °C, and preferably 105 °C. It should be protected with split-loom covering whenever possible, especially under-hood wiring.

Selecting the correct size fuse is also important. The average current draw for any given fuse should not exceed 60% of its rating. Thus, the correct fuse rating for a 22-A load is 30 A. That same 30-A fuse will handle a 40-A load for about 120 seconds, and

Battery Connections

For many years, connecting mobile station power leads directly to the battery (or to the battery positive and ground tie-point) has been the standard recommendation. In vehicles equipped with EIS (Engine Idle Shutoff), however, additional sensing modules in the vehicle electrical system may require alternate connections.

With EIS, as soon as the vehicle stops for a short time, the engine shuts off and the battery voltage drops. To support the additional starting cycles, starters and batteries are more robust, but so are the sophistication of the electrical devices supporting them. The most important device is the ELD (Electronic Load Detector), typically located within the main fuse panel.

ELDs have been in use for many years to measure the current drawn by the accessories (air conditioning, lights, and so on), which allow the engine CPU to more accurately adjust the air/fuel mixture. However, on vehicles equipped with EIS, the ELD is located in battery's negative lead or its connector. (See your vehicle's service manual for the exact location of the ELD.) The ELD is used for *coulomb-counting* to estimate the battery's State of Charge (SoC). Measuring current during starting provides an estimate of the battery's Reserve Capacity (RC). This ensures the battery has enough reserves to restart the engine when the engine has to start again. (See the **Power Sources** chapter for more information on vehicle batteries.)

During engine shutdown, most EIS systems use a dc-to-dc converter to assure that the accessories have a constant voltage source for electric motors that power brakes, air conditioning, transmission servo pressure, fuel pumps, and engine cooling systems. A second trunk-mounted battery may be used, or even super-capacitors (low-voltage capacitors with many farads of capacitance). The converter and accessory operation is under the control of the Battery Monitoring System (BMS) and amateur transceiver wiring must avoid circumventing its operation.

Connecting the transceiver directly to the battery would bypass the BMS which is not recommended, nor is connecting the radio to the dc-to-dc converter, to the trunk-mounted accessory-power battery, or to existing vehicle wiring. In vehicles equipped with a BMS and/or ELD the correct method of connecting the radio is to connect the positive lead directly to the battery, and the negative lead to the battery's chassis grounding point. The negative lead fuse should not be removed! This avoids damage caused by a loose or broken battery connection, which could cause a Load Dump Transient (LDT) to occur. Should an LDT occur, the fuse might blow depending on the location of the battery lead failure. Without the fuse, damage to the transceiver could be the result.

If there is any doubt, check with your dealer about how the Battery Monitoring System (BMS) is connected and the recommended connection points for your radio's power leads. Be sure the connections you make are to points adequately rated for the load your radio presents. More information on batteries, alternators, and the newer vehicle power systems is available online at **www.k0bg.com**. — *Alan Applegate, KØBG*

24.14   Chapter 29

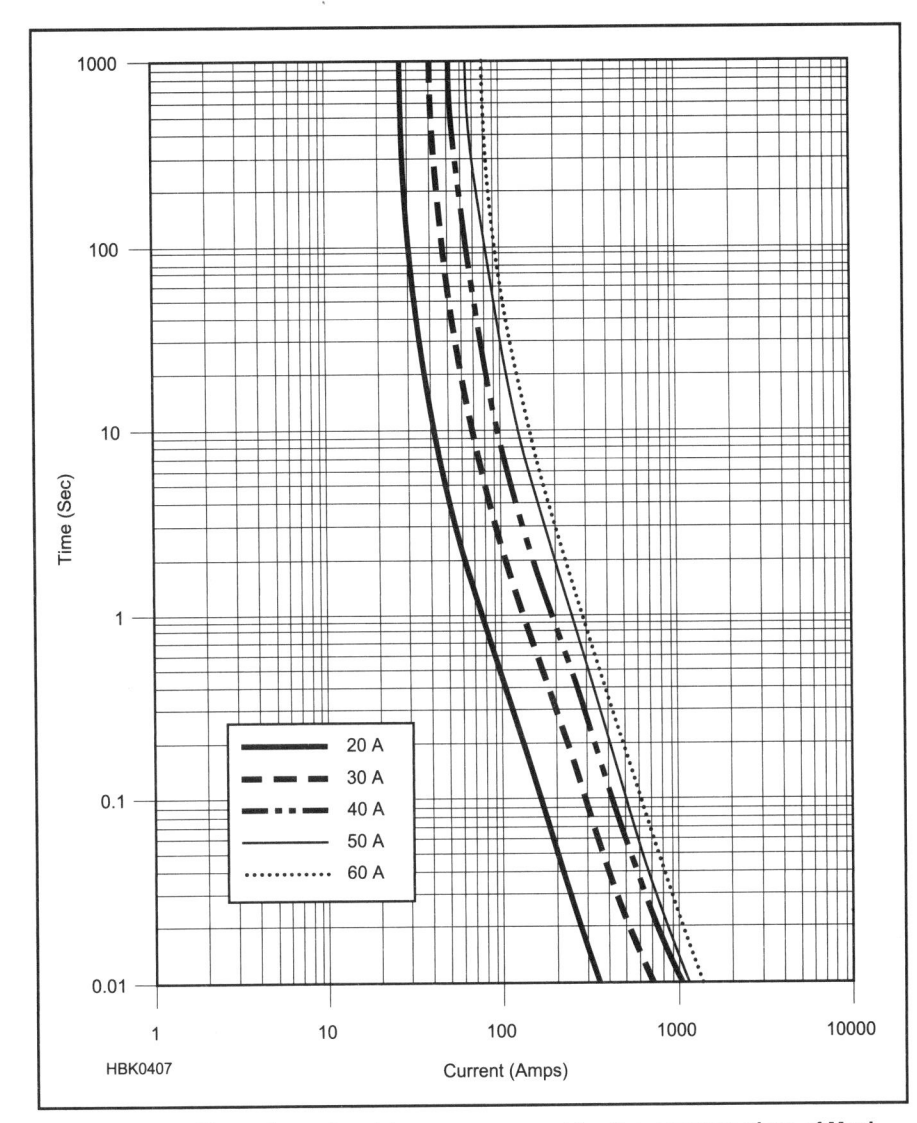

Figure 24.28 — Chart of opening delay versus current for five common sizes of Maxi fuses, the plastic-body high-current fuses common in vehicles. [Based on a chart from Littelfuse Corp]

a 100-A load for about 2 seconds. Therefore, it pays to be conservative when selecting the carrying capacities of both wire and fuses. **Figure 24.28** shows the characteristics of several sizes of automotive fuses.

24.2.4 Amplifiers

Mobile HF amplifiers have been around for many years, and with the advent of high-power solid state devices they are common. However, running high power in a mobile environment requires careful planning. Considerations include, but are not limited to:

• alternator current ratings and battery capacity

• wiring (in addition to safe current ratings, excessive voltage drop will create distortion of the output signal)

• antenna and feed line power ratings

• placement and secure mounting in the vehicle

• wiring and placing of remote controls

See **www.k0bg.com/amplifiers.html** for more information on these topics.

Before purchasing an amplifier, take a close look at your antenna installation and make sure it is operating efficiently. Using an amplifier with a poor antenna installation is counterproductive. Here's a rule of thumb appli-cable to any type of antenna: If the *unmatched* input SWR is less than 1.7:1 on 17 meters or any lower frequency band, then it isn't mounted correctly, and/or you need a better antenna. Whatever antenna you use, it must be capable of handling the amplifier power level — 500 W or more. More information on HF mobile antennas and installation tech-niques may be found in the **Antennas** chapter.

Mobile amplifiers for VHF/UHF operation are not as popular as they once were because most mobile transceivers have adequate output power (about 50 W). Boosting this to 150-300 W or more should be done with caution. Mobile VHF/UHF antennas for high power (>100 W) are rare, so check antenna ratings carefully. Those that are available need to be permanently mounted, and preferably on the roof to avoid inadvertent contact.

With any high-power mobile installation, pay careful attention to RF safety. More information on RF exposure can be found in the **Safety** chapter.

24.2.5 Interference Issues

In a mobile installation, radio frequency interference falls under two basic categories: *egress* (interference from the vehicle to your amateur station) and *ingress* (from your amateur gear to the vehicle). Most hams are familiar with ignition interference as it is the most common form of egress. RF interference to an auto sound system is a common form of ingress.

Both types of interference have unique solutions but they have at least one in common and that is *chassis bonding*. Chassis bonding refers to connecting accessory equipment or assemblies to the frame or chassis of the vehicle. For example, the exhaust system is isolated from the structure of the vehicle and acts like an antenna for the RFI generated by the ignition system. It should be bonded to the chassis in at least three places. **Figure 22.29** shows an example of bonding. More on these techniques is available at **www.k0bg.com/bonding.html**.

Other RFI egress problems are related to fuel pumps, HVAC and engine cooling fans, ABS sensors, data distribution systems and control system CPUs. These are best cured at the source by liberal use of snap-on ferrite cores on the wiring harnesses of the offending devices. Snap-on cores come is a variety of sizes and formulations called mixes. The best all-around ferrite core material for mobile RFI issues is Mix 31. Suitable cores are available from most Amateur Radio dealers. Unknown surplus units typically offer little HF attenuation and should be avoided. See the **RF Interference, RF Techniques,** and **Component Data and References** chapters for more information on ferrite cores.

Alternator whine can be another form of RFI egress. It is typically caused by an incorrectly mounted antenna resulting in a ground loop, rather than a defective alternator diode or inadequate dc power filtering as has been the traditional solution. Attempting to solve alternator whine with a dc filter can mask the problem and increases I^2R losses. Additional information on proper antenna mounting is in the **Antennas** chapter.

RFI ingress to the various on-board elec-

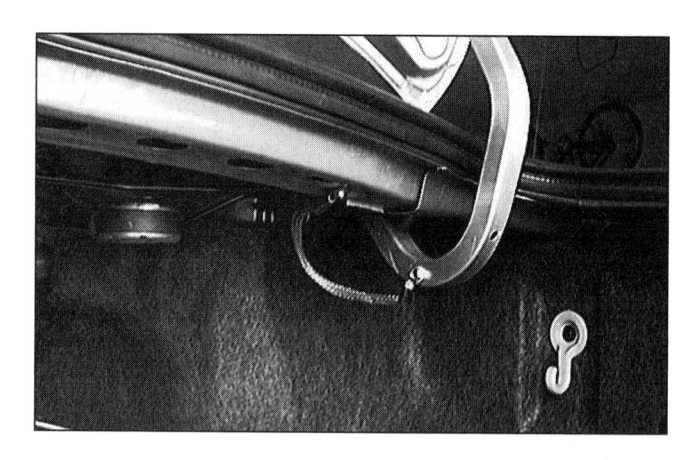

Figure 24.29 — Bonding vehicles parts — in this case, the trunk lid to the main body — can help reduce interference.

tronic devices is less common. The major causes are unchecked RF flowing on the control wires and common mode currents flowing on the coax cable of remotely-tuned HF antennas. Again, this points out the need to properly mount mobile antennas.

For more information on RFI issues, see the **RF Interference** chapter, *The ARRL RFI Handbook*, and the ARRL Technical Information Service (**www.arrl.org/tis**).

24.2.6 Operating

The most important consideration while operating mobile-in-motion is safety! Driver

---

Air Bags and Mobile Installation

Since 1998 all passenger vehicles are required to have Supplemental Restraint Systems (SRS), better known as *airbags*. Side airbags and airbags for rear seat passengers have become commonplace. When used in conjunction with seat belts, they've become a great life saving device, but they do have a drawback — they literally explode when they deploy!

Airbags deploy within 200 ms, expanding at about 200 mph, driven by gas from a controlled explosion. **Figure 24.A** drawing shows a typical vehicle with several air bags deployed in the passenger compartment. Any radio gear within range of an airbag will be ripped free with great force and flung about the interior. This should eliminate from consideration any dash-top mounting scheme including windshield suction cup (mobile phone) mounts, so often employed.

Figure 24.B shows the passenger compartment of a vehicle with airbags deployed after a minor collision that caused less than $300 damage to the bumper. Note the loose piece of dashboard on top of the deflated air bag and the broken windshield. These are typical effects of a deploying airbag, whether from the top or center of the dash. Knowing how airbags deploy, avoid mounting radio gear anywhere near them.

It is always a difficult task finding a suitable mounting location for a transceiver and/or control head that is out of airbag range yet easily seen and operated. One workaround is a gooseneck mount (see **Table 24.1** for a list of suppliers). These attach via a seat belt (no hole needed). They're a good alternative as long as they're placed away from the passenger airbag deployment area (the whole right side of the dashboard). The dealer for your make and model may have additional guidelines for mounting radios and control heads in the car.

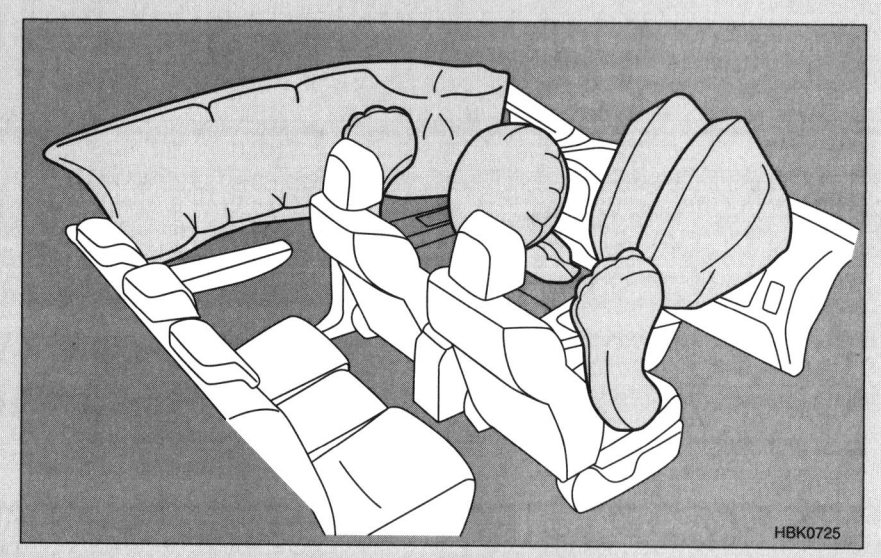

Figure 24.A — Airbag deployment zones in a modern vehicle.

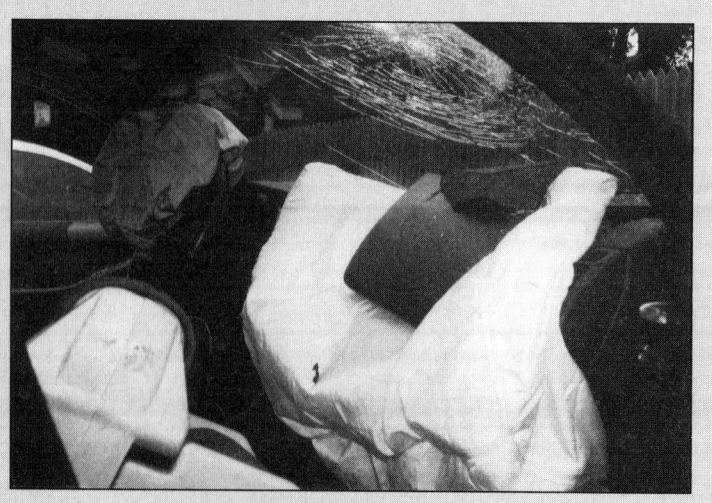

Figure 24.B — Airbag deployment following a minor collision caused significant disruption inside the passenger compartment.

24.16   Chapter 29

distraction is a familiar cause of vehicle crashes. While Amateur Radio use is far less distracting than mobile phones or texting, there are times when driving requires all of our attention. When bad weather, excessive traffic, or a construction zone require extra care, play it safe — hang up the microphone and turn off the radio!

In addition to properly installing gear, a few operating hints can make your journey less distracting. One of those is familiarization with your transceiver's menu functions and its microphone keys (if so equipped). Even then, complicated programming or adjustments are not something to do while underway.

Logging mobile contacts has always been difficult. Compact digital voice recorders have made that function easy and inexpensive. Units with up to 24 hours of recording time are available for less than $50.

For maximum intelligibility at the other end, avoid excessive speech processing and too much microphone gain. Don't shout into the microphone! It's human nature to increase your speaking level when excited or when the background level increases. In the closed cabin of a vehicle, your brain interprets the reflected sound from your own voice as an increase in background level. Add in a little traffic noise and by the end of your transmission you're in full shout mode! One solution is to use a headset and the transceiver's built-in monitor function. Doing so gives you direct feedback (not a time-delayed echo), and your brain won't get confused. Note that headset use is not legal in some jurisdictions and never legal if both ears are covered.

Overcoming vehicle ambient noise levels often requires the use of an external speaker and all too often it is an afterthought. Selecting a speaker that is too small accentuates high frequency noise which makes reception tiresome. Using adapters to interface with vehicle stereo systems isn't productive for the same reason. For speakers that are too large, mounting becomes a safety issue.

For best results, use at least a 4-inch speaker. Rather than mount it out in the open, mount it out of the way, under the driver's seat. This attenuates the high frequency noise, and enhances the mid-range response which increases intelligibility.

Many vehicle audio systems now support audio input from external sources including analog (headphone audio), USB, and Bluetooth. You may be able to route your mobile rig's audio through the vehicle audio system using one of these methods. The audio sounds far better than through a small speaker!

Most modern transceivers contain some form of DSP (digital signal processing) noise reduction as covered in the **DSP and SDR Fundamentals** chapter. Some are audio based and some are IF based, with the latter being preferred. But both types do a decent job of reducing high-frequency hiss, static spikes, and even ignition hash.

24.3 Portable Installations

Many amateurs experience the joys of portable operation once each year in the annual emergency exercise known as ARRL Field Day. Setting up an effective portable station requires organization, planning and some experience. For example, some knowledge of propagation is essential to picking the right band or bands for the intended communications link(s). Portable operation is difficult enough without dragging along excess equipment and antennas that will never be used.

Some problems encountered in portable operation that are not normally experienced in fixed-station operation include finding an appropriate power source and erecting an effective antenna. The equipment used should be as compact and lightweight as possible. A good portable setup is simple. Although you may bring lots of gear to Field Day and set it up the day before, during a real emergency speed is of the essence. The less equipment to set up, the faster it will be operational.

24.3.1 Portable AC Power Sources

There are three popular sources of ac power for use in the field: batteries, dc-to-ac inverters, and gasoline powered generators. Batteries and inverters are covered in detail in the **Power Sources** chapter. This section will focus on gasoline powered generators. The book *Emergency Power for Radio Communications* by Mike Bryce, WB8VGE is another good resource for generator application information.

Essentially, a generator is a motor that's operating "backward." When you apply electricity to a motor, it turns the motor's shaft (allowing it to do useful work). If you need more rotational power, add more electricity or wind a bigger motor. Take the same motor and physically rotate its shaft and it generates electricity across the same terminals used to supply power when using the motor as a motor. Turn the shaft faster and the voltage and frequency increase. Turn it slower and they decrease. To some degree, all motors are generators and all generators are motors. The differences are in the details and in the optimization for specific functions.

A "motor" that is optimized for generating electricity is an alternator — just like the one in your car. The most basic generators use a small gas engine to power an ac alternator, the voltage and frequency of which depends on rotational speed. Because the generator is directly coupled to the engine, the generator's rotational speed is determined by the speed of the engine. If the engine is running too fast or too slow, the voltage and frequency of the output will be off. If everything is running at or near the correct speed, the voltage and frequency of the output will be a close approximation of the power supplied by the ac mains — a 120 V ac sine wave with a frequency of 60 Hz. These are referred to as *constant-speed generators*. Most consumer models use two pole armatures that run at 3600 RPM to produce a 60 Hz sine wave.

Inverter generators produce high-voltage, multiphase ac that is rectified to dc — similar to an automobile alternator. The dc power is then converted back to very clean and consistent ac power by a solid state power inverter controlled by a microprocessor. Unlike the constant-speed generators, inverters can run at idle while still providing power, increasing speed to meet additional demand. This improves economy and reduces emissions. The most common models are available with capacities to approximately 2000 W output and some can be paralleled with special cables for higher capacity. The June 2012 *QST* Product Review "A Look at Gasoline Powered Inverter Generators" compares several popular models available at that time and is provided on the CD-ROM accompanying this book.

VOLTAGE REGULATION

There are several electronic and mechanical methods used to "regulate" the ac output — to keep the voltage and frequency values as stable as possible as generator and engine speeds vary because of current loads or other factors. Remember, a standard generator *must* turn at a specific speed to maintain output regulation, so when more power is drawn from the generator, the engine must supply more torque to overcome the increased physical/magnetic resistance in the generator's core — the generator *can't* simply spin faster to supply the extra power.

Most generators have engines that use mechanical or vacuum "governors" to keep the generator shaft turning at the correct speed. If the shaft slows down because of increasing generator demand, the governor "hits the gas" and draws energy stored in a heavy rotating flywheel, for example, to bring (or keep) the shaft speed up to par. The opposite happens if the generator is spinning too fast.

In addition to mechanical and vacuum speed regulating systems, generators that are a step up in sophistication additionally have electronic automatic voltage regulation (AVR) systems that use special windings in the generator core (and a microprocessor or circuit to monitor and control them) to help keep things steady near 120 V and 60 Hz. AVR systems can respond to short term load changes much more quickly than mechanical or vacuum governors alone. A decade ago AVR generators were the cream of the crop. Today, they're mostly used in medium to large units that can't practically employ inverters to maintain the best level of output regulation. You'll find them in higher quality 5 to 15 kW "home backup systems" and in many recreational vehicles.

Isolate Source and Load

Basic, inexpensive generators are intended to power lights, saws, drills, ac motors, electric frying pans and other devices that are not dependent on clean sine-wave power. If you want the highest margin of safety when powering computers, transceivers and other sensitive electronics, a portable *inverter generator* is the best way to go. Some popular examples are shown in **Figure 24.30**, and their key specifications are shown in **Table 24.2**. Available in outputs ranging from 1 to 5 kW, these generators use one or more of the mechanical regulation systems mentioned previously, but their ultimate benefit comes from the use of a built-in ac-dc-ac inverter system that produces beautiful — if not perfect — 60 Hz sine waves at 120 V ac, with a 1% to 2% tolerance, even under varying load conditions.

Instead of using two windings in the generator core, an inverter generator uses 24 or more windings to produce a high frequency ac waveform of up to 20 kHz. A solid state inverter module converts the high frequency ac to smooth dc, which is in turn converted to clean, tightly regulated 120 V ac power.

And that's not all. Most inverter generators are compact, lightweight and quiet.

GENERATOR CONSIDERATIONS

In addition to capacity and output regulation, other factors such as engine type, noise level, fuel options, fuel capacity, run time, size, weight, cost or connector type, may factor in your decision. Consider additional uses for your new generator beyond Field Day or other portable operation.

Capacity

Your generator must be able to safely power all of the devices that will be attached to it. Simply add up the power requirements of *all* the devices, add a reasonable safety margin (25 to 30%) and choose a suitably powerful generator that meets your other requirements.

Some devices — especially electric motors — take a lot more power to start up than they do to keep running. A motor that takes 1000 W to run may take 2000 to 3000 W to start. Many items don't require extra start-up power, but be sure to plan accordingly.

Always plan to have more capacity than you require or, conversely, plan to use less gear than you have capacity for. Running on the ragged edge is bad for your generator *and* your gear. Some generators are somewhat overrated, probably for marketing purposes. Give yourself a margin of safety and don't rely on built-in circuit breakers

Figure 24.30 — Modern inverter generators from McCullough, Honda, Yamaha and Subaru/Robin. See Table 24.2 for a partial list of specifications.

Table 24.2
Specifications of the Inverter Generators Shown in Figure 24.30

Make and Model	Output (W) (Surge/Cont)	Run Time (h) Full / 25% Load	Noise Range (dBA @ 21 feet)	Engine Type	Weight (Pounds)	Notes*
McCulloch FDD210M0	N/A / 1800	4 / N/A	60-70	105.6 cc, 3 HP	65 (shipping)	a,b
Honda EU2000i	2000 / 1600	4 /15	53-59	100 cc, OHC	46	a,b,c
Yamaha EF2400iS	2400 / 2000	N/A / 8.6	53-58	171 cc, OHV	70	a,b,c
Subaru/Robin R1700i	N/A / 1650	N/A / 8.5	53-59	2.4 HP, OHV	46	a,b,c

*a — has 12 V dc output; b — has "smart throttle" for better fuel economy; c — has low oil alert/shutdown

to save your gear during overloads. When operating at or beyond capacity, a generator's frequency and voltage can vary widely before the current breaker trips.

Size and Weight

Size and weight vary according to power output — low power units are lightweight and physically small, while beefier models are larger, weigh more and probably last longer. Watt for watt, however, most modern units are smaller and lighter than their predecessors. Models suitable for ham radio typically weigh between 25 and 125 pounds.

Engines and Fuel

Low end generators are typically powered by low-tolerance, side valve engines of the type found in discount store lawnmowers. They're noisy, need frequent servicing and often die quickly. Better models have overhead valve (OHV) or overhead cam (OHC) engines, pressure lubrication, low oil shutdown, cast iron cylinder sleeves, oil filters, electronic ignition systems and even fuel injection. These features may be overkill for occasional use but desirable for more consistent power needs.

Run Time

Smaller generators usually have smaller gas tanks, but that doesn't necessarily mean they need more frequent refueling. Some small generators are significantly more efficient than their larger counterparts and may run for half a day while powering small loads. As with output power, run times for many units are somewhat exaggerated and are usually specified for 50% loads. If you're running closer to max capacity, your run times may be seriously degraded. The opposite is also true. Typical generators run from three to nine hours on a full tank of gas at a 50% load.

Noise

Except for ham-friendly inverter units — which are eerily quiet thanks to their high tech, sound dampening designs — standard generators are almost always too loud. Noise levels for many models are stated on the box, but try to test them yourself or talk to someone who owns the model you're interested in before buying. Environmental conditions, distance to the generator and the unit's physical orientation can affect perceived noise levels.

Generators housed in special sound dampened compartments in large boats and RVs can be much quieter than typical "outside" models. However, they are expensive and heavy, use more fuel than compact models, and most don't have regulation specs comparable to inverter models.

Regulation

For hams, voltage and frequency regulation are the biggies. AVR units with electronic output regulation (at a minimum) and inverter generators are highly desirable and should be used exclusively, if only for peace of mind.

Unloaded standard generators can put out as much as 160 V ac at 64 Hz. As loads increase, frequency and voltage decrease. Under full load, output values may fall as low as 105 V at 56 Hz. Normal operating conditions are somewhere in between.

Some hams have tried inserting uninterruptible power supplies (UPSs) between the generator and their sensitive gear. These devices are often used to maintain steady, clean ac power for computers and telecommunication equipment. As the mains voltage moves up and down, the UPS's Automatic Voltage Regulation (AVR) system bucks or boosts accordingly. The unit's internal batteries provide power to the loads if the ac mains (or your generator) go down.

In practice, however, most UPSs can't handle the variation in frequency and voltage of a generator powered system. When fed by a standard generator, most UPSs constantly switch in and out of battery power mode — or don't *ever* switch back to ac power. When the UPS battery goes flat, the unit shuts off. Not *every* UPS and *every* generator lock horns like this, but an inverter generator is a better solution.

RF Noise

Some generators create RF noise in the HF bands as common-mode current on connected power cords. Glen Brown, W6GJB, built and Jim Brown, K9YC, designed the choke in **Figure 24.31** to suppress the noise. The assembly consists of a pair of chokes in series, each consisting of 8 turns of #14 AWG Romex-type cable wound on Type 31, 2.4-inch OD ferrite toroids. One choke is wound on two cores for 80- and 40-meter coverage. The second choke is wound on one core for 10 MHz and above. (Figure 24.31A) The chokes are attached directly to a duplex outlet installed in an electrical enclosure (Figure 24.31B). A heavy-duty extension cord connects the choke to the generator.

DC Output

Some generators have 12 V dc outputs for charging batteries. These range from 2 A trickle chargers to 100 A powerhouses. Typical outputs run about 10 to 15 A. As with the ac outputs, be sure to test the dc outputs for voltage stability (under load if possible) and ripple. Car batteries aren't too fussy about a little ripple in the charging circuit, but your radio might not like it at all!

Miscellaneous

Other considerations include outlets (120 V, 240 V and dc output), circuit breakers (standard or ground fault interrupter type), fuel level gauges, handles (one or two), favorite brands, warranties, starters (pull or electric), wheels, handles or whatever you require.

SETUP, SAFETY AND TESTING

Before starting the engine, read the user manual. Carefully follow the instructions regarding engine oil, throttle and choke settings (if any). Be sure you understand how the unit operates and how to use the receptacles, circuit breakers and connectors.

Make sure the area is clean, dry and unobstructed. Generators should *always* be set up *outdoors*. Do not operate gas powered engines in closed spaces, inside passenger vans, inside covered pickup beds, etc. If rain is a possibility, set up an appropriate canopy or other *outdoor protective structure*. Operating generators and electrical devices in the rain or snow can be dangerous. Keep the generator and any attached cords dry!

Exhaust systems can get hot enough to ignite certain materials. Keep the unit several feet away from buildings, and keep the gas can (and other flammable stuff) at a safe distance. Don't touch hot engines or mufflers!

Figure 24.31 — A heavy-duty common-mode RF choke wound on Type 31 ferrite cores for ac generators. K9YC and W6GJB use this choke during portable operating. See the text for construction details.

When refueling, shut down the generator and let things cool off for a few minutes. Don't smoke, and don't spill gasoline onto hot engine parts. A flash fire or explosion may result. Keep a small fire extinguisher nearby. If you refuel at night, use a light source that isn't powered by the generator and can't ignite the gasoline.

Testing

Before starting (or restarting) the engine, *disconnect* all electrical loads. Starting the unit while loads are connected may not damage the generator, but your solid state devices may not be so lucky. After the engine has warmed up and stabilized, test the output voltage (and frequency), if possible, *before* connecting loads.

Because unloaded values may differ from loaded values, be sure to test your generator under load (using high wattage quartz lights or an electric heater as appropriate). Notice that when you turn on a hefty load, your generator will "hunt" a bit as the engine stabilizes. Measure ac voltage and frequency again to see what the power conditions will be like under load. See your unit's user manual or contact the manufacturer if adjustments are required.

Safety Grounds and Field Operation

The NEC addresses safety grounding for this type of generators in section 250.34. The NEC considers "portable" to describe a generator that is easily carried from one location to another by a person. "Mobile" applies to generators that are capable of being moved on wheels or rollers and includes generators mounted in a vehicle.

A ground rod or other direct earth connection is not required for portable generators as long as the generator has receptacles mounted on the generator panel and the receptacles have equipment grounding terminals (i.e. the third ground pin of an ac receptacle) that are bonded to the frame of the generator. Equipment must be connected to the generator through a suitable cord and plug, such as the usual extension cord. Any exposed metal surface of the equipment must be connected through the ground wire of the power cord to the receptacle ground terminal, as well. If the generator is mounted in a vehicle the same rules apply as long as the equipment supplied by the generator is mounted on the vehicle and the frame of the generator is bonded to the frame of the vehicle. In both cases, it is OK to use a ground rod connected to the generator frame but you don't have to.

Ground rods may be used if desired. If the generator is more than a short distance from the station or if more than one separate station is powered by the same generator, a ground rod at the generator and at each station may be prudent (with all ground rods bonded together).

Regardless of the grounding method you choose, a few electrical safety rules remain the same. Your extension cords *must* have intact, waterproof insulation, three "prongs" and three wires, and must be sized according to loads and cable runs. Use #14 to #16 AWG, three wire extension cords for low wattage runs of 100 feet or less. For high wattage loads, use heavier #12 AWG, three-wire cords designed for air compressors, air conditioners or RV service feeds. If you use long extension cords to power heavy loads, you may damage your generator or your radio gear. When it comes to power cords, think *big*. Try to position extension cords so they won't be tripped over or run over by vehicles. And don't run electrical cords through standing water or over wet, sloppy terrain.

During portable operations, try to let all operators know when the generator will be shut down for refueling so radio and computer gear can be shut down in an orderly manner. Keep the loads disconnected at the generator until the generator has been refueled and restarted.

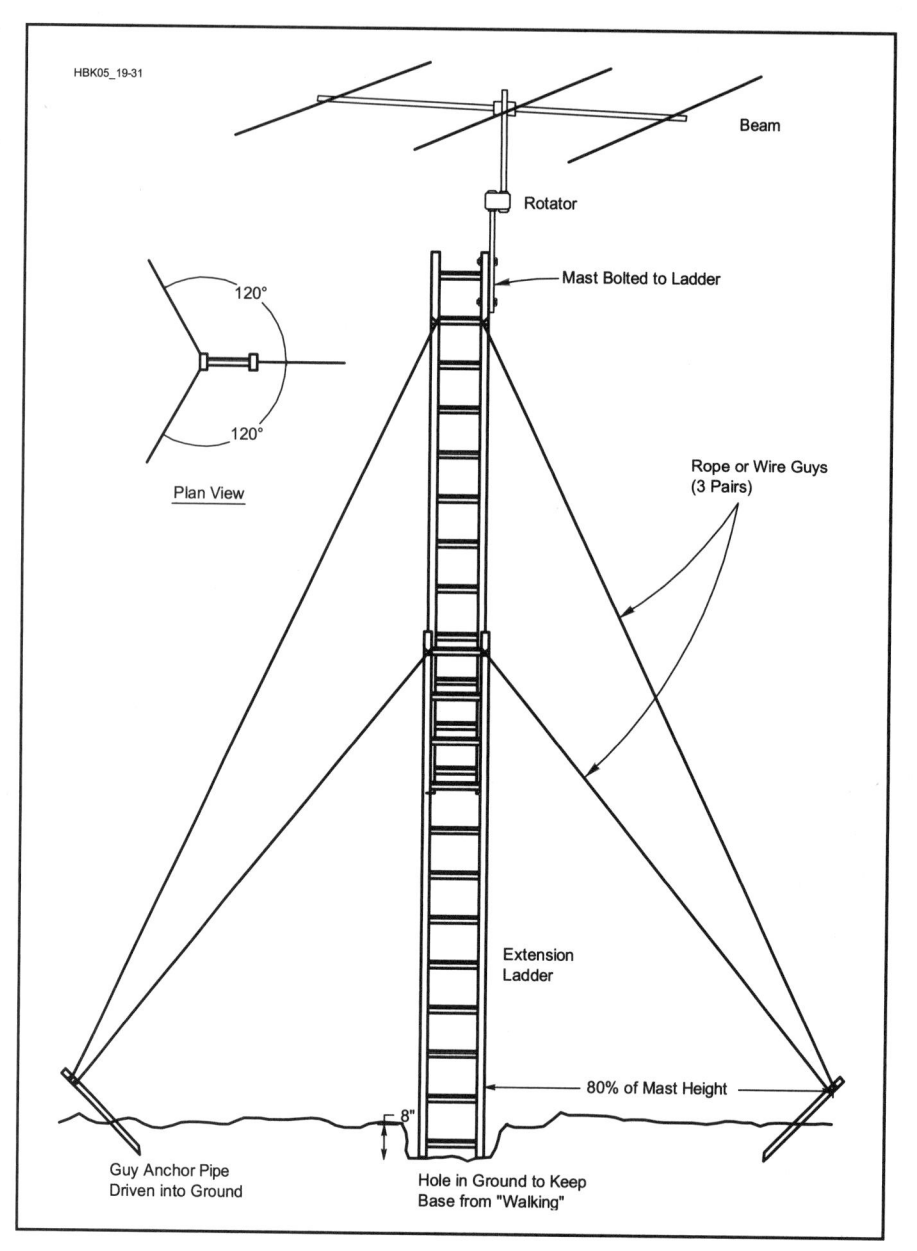

Figure 24.32 — An aluminum extension ladder makes a simple but sturdy portable antenna support. Attach the antenna and feed lines to the top ladder section while it is nested and lying on the ground. Secure the base, push the ladder vertical, attach the bottom guys and extend the ladder. Attach the top guys. Do not attempt to climb this type of antenna support.

24.20   Chapter 29

this case). As the battery's state of charge (SoC) is reduced, so is the voltage, especially under load. (See the **Power Sources** chapter for complete information on batteries, including charging.) As voltage falls, transmit signal quality begins to drop, sometimes drastically, and output power drops off as well. Further, most transceivers will simply shut themselves off once their input voltage drops to approximately 11.6 V. There are two popular workarounds to the problem.

First, multiple batteries wired in parallel may be used to extend operating time. But their terminal voltage when not being charged is still around 12 – 12.2 V, well below what the radio wants to see. Several manufacturers and distributors sell "battery boosters" that provide a regulated output of 13.8 V as battery voltage varies. Booster efficiency varies with the input voltage and current draw, but hovers around 80%.

Another workaround in some cases is a dc-to-dc converter which runs from a nominal input of 24 or 48 V, providing a regulated output of 13.8 V. In this case, two (or more) 12 V batteries are wired in series or in series-parallel to extend operating time. Converter efficiency is typically greater than 88%. Both ground-isolated and non-isolated models are available. The latter units use a common bus for the negative connection between power source batteries and output connections.

Whichever method is used, battery voltage should be monitored to assure long battery charge-cycle life. For example, a nominal 12 V lead-acid battery is considered 100% discharged when the voltage under load reaches 10.5 V. Below this level the charge-cycle life is reduced. Other battery types have similar SoC (discharge) level ratings.

24.3.3 Portable Antennas

An effective antenna system is essential to all types of operation. Effective portable antennas, however, are more difficult to devise than their fixed-station counterparts. A portable antenna must be light, compact and easy to assemble. It is also important to remember that the portable antenna may be erected at a variety of sites, not all of which will offer ready-made supports. Strive for the best antenna system possible because operations in the field are often restricted to low power by power supply and equipment considerations. Some antennas suitable for portable operation are described in the **Antennas** chapter.

ANTENNA SUPPORTS

While some amateurs have access to a truck or trailer with a portable tower, most are limited to what nature supplies, along with simple push-up masts. Select a portable site that is as high and clear as possible. Elevation is especially important if your operation involves VHF. Trees, buildings, flagpoles, telephone poles and the like can be pressed into service to support wire antennas. Drooping dipoles are often chosen over horizontal dipoles because they require only one support.

An aluminum extension ladder makes an effective antenna support, as shown in **Figure 24.32**. In this installation, a mast, rotator and beam are attached to the top of the second ladder section with the ladder near the ground. The ladder is then pushed verti-

Figure 24.33 — Telescoping fiberglass poles can be used to support a variety of wire antennas or small VHF/UHF Yagis. The one shown in A is 40 feet long, yet collapses to 8 feet for storage. At B, a typical twist-lock mechanism secures the sliding sections in place.

24.3.2 Portable DC Power Sources

If a generator is not available to supply ac voltage for portable operation, starter or marine deep-cycle batteries are often used for portable or Field Day operation. Battery-only dc operation has its own unique set of problems, not the least of which is voltage stability.

Most solid-state transceivers are designed to operate at a nominal 13.8 V from a battery being charged by a vehicle's engine. Depending on the battery type, resting voltage may be as low as 12.2 V (lead-acid in

Figure 24.34 — The portable tower mounting system by WA7LYI. At A, a truck is "parked" on the homemade base plate to weigh it down. At B, the antennas, mast and rotator are mounted before the tower is pushed up. Do not attempt to climb a temporary tower installation.

Assembling a Station   24.21

Figure 24.35 — The portable mast and tripod by WA7LYI. At A, the tripod is clamped to stakes driven into the ground. The rotator is attached to a homemade pipe mount. At B, rocks piled on the rotator must keep the rotator from twisting and add weight to stabilize the mast. At C, a 10 foot mast is inserted into the tripod/rotator base assembly. Four 432 MHz Quagis are mounted at the top.

cal and the lower set of guy wires attached to the guy anchors. When the first set of guy wires is secured, the ladder may be extended and the top guy wires attached to the anchors. Do not attempt to climb a guyed ladder.

Telescoping fiberglass poles (**Figure 24.33**) are popular for supporting wire verticals, inverted Vs and small VHF/UHF antennas. These poles can extend up to 40 feet in length, yet retract to 4 to 8 feet for easy transport. They typically weigh less than 20 pounds, and some are much lighter.

Figures 24.34 and **24.35** illustrate two methods for mounting portable antennas described by Terry Wilkinson, WA7LYI. Although the antennas shown are used for VHF work, the same principles can be applied to small HF beams as well.

In Figure 24.34A, a 3 foot section of Rohn 25 tower is welded to a pair of large hinges, which in turn are welded to a steel plate measuring approximately 18 × 30 inches. One of the rear wheels of a pickup truck is "parked" on the plate, ensuring that it will not move. In Figure 24.34B, quad array antennas for 144 and 222 MHz are mounted on a Rohn 25 top section, complete with rotator and feed lines. The tower is then pushed up into place using the hinges, and guy ropes, anchored to heavy-duty stakes driven into the ground, complete the installation. This method of portable tower installation offers an exceptionally easy-to-erect, yet sturdy, antenna support. Towers installed in this manner may be 30 or 40 feet high; the limiting factor is the number of "pushers" and "rope pullers" needed to get into the air. A portable station located in the bed of the pickup truck completes the installation.

The second method of mounting portable beams described by WA7LYI is shown in Figure 24.35. This support is intended for use with small or medium-sized VHF and UHF arrays. The tripod is available from any dealer selling television antennas; tripods of this type are usually mounted on the roof of a house. Open the tripod to its full size and drive a pipe into the ground at each leg. Use a hose clamp or small U-bolt to anchor each leg to its pipe.

The rotator mount is made from a 6-inch-long section of 1.5-inch-diameter pipe welded to the center of an "X" made from two 2-foot-long pieces of concrete reinforcing rod (rebar). The rotator clamps onto the pipe, and the whole assembly is placed in the center of the tripod. Large rocks placed on the rebar hold the rotator in place, and the antennas are mounted on a 10 or 15 foot tall mast section. This system is easy to make and set up.

TIPS FOR PORTABLE ANTENNAS

Any of the antennas described in the **Antennas** chapter or available from commercial manufacturers may be used for portable operation. Generally, though, big or heavy antennas should be passed over in favor of smaller arrays. The couple of decibels of gain a 5-element, 20 meter beam may have over a 3-element version is insignificant compared to the mechanical considerations. Stick with arrays of reasonable size that are easily assembled.

Wire antennas should be cut to size and tuned prior to their use in the field. Be careful when coiling these antennas for transport, or you may end up with a tangled mess when you need an antenna in a hurry. The coaxial cable should be attached to the center insulator with a connector for speed in assembly. Use RG-58 for the low bands and RG-8X for higher-band antennas. Although these cables exhibit higher loss than standard RG-8, they are far more compact and weigh much less for a given length.

Beam antennas should be assembled and tested before taking them afield. Break the beam into as few pieces as necessary for transportation and mark each joint for speed in reassembly. Hex nuts can be replaced with wing nuts to reduce the number of tools necessary.

24.4 Remote Stations

The following section was updated by Ken Norris, KK9N, from material originally contributed by Rick Hilding, K6VVA. Although this section focuses on "remoting" HF equipment, the same considerations apply to most remotely-operated stations, with the exception of repeater installations.

24.4.1 Introduction to Remote Stations

Remote stations (stations operated by remote control) have been a part of Amateur Radio for decades, but usually in the form of VHF/UHF repeaters. In the past, a few remote stations operating on HF have been developed in impressive locations with significantly more land, equipment and expense than for a repeater installation. Prior to the expansion of Internet technologies, some of these remote pioneers utilized VHF/UHF links, dialup, or commercial microwave equipment for connectivity between the remote and home stations. There has been a significant increase in the number of remote stations over the last 10 years and the trend is accelerating rapidly.

Since this section was originally written, there have been several new developments and refinements of the technology available to access your home or remote station. As latency across the Internet has been reduced, operating in fast-paced contests over very long links — even between continents — is now commonplace.

You may want to monitor your home station while you're away, avoid homeowner restrictions on outdoor antennas, or fight interference issues from electrical power lines, plasma TVs, network routers, and the like. With today's technology your home station or a remote HF station may be as simple as a 100-W HF radio and all-band dipole or vertical, or a fully automated contest station, with connectivity to the operator via the Internet. There is a flavor of remote station to meet almost every taste and budget.

This overview of remote station operation looks at different methods of remote operation and how they are each unique in equipment and technologies. There is no cookbook approach to creating a remote station. This discussion is intended to introduce topics to be considered in the circumstances encountered by each station builder.

Two important definitions that will be used throughout this chapter are the naming of the locations of equipment. The location for your radio, host computer, amplifier and antennas is your *station site* whether this is at your house or at a distant site. The other end of the connection is the *remote client* location. This location consist of the computer in front of you with the remote computer running client software and possibly a remote radio head (front panel) connected to the station site.

LICENSING AND REMOTE OPERATION

Before discussing the technical details, it must be emphasized that operating a remote station also carries with it an extra responsibility to be properly licensed and to identify your station correctly. Because the transmissions are made from the location of the remote station, you must follow the regulations that apply at the remote location. This is particularly important when the station is outside the jurisdiction of the regulatory authority that granted your license, such as a US ham operating a station in South America or a European ham operating a station in the US You must be properly licensed to transmit from the remote station! This may require a separate license or reciprocal operating permission from the country where the remote station is located. FCC rules require the control operator of a remotely-controlled station to have a US license, regardless of where the operator is located.

Don't assume that because you have a US license, you automatically have a corresponding license to operate a remote station outside the US. For instance, CEPT agreements generally do not apply to operators who are not physically present in the country of the transmitter and you may be required to be physically present at the transmitter, as well. There may also be contest or award rules that apply to remote stations — be sure to know and follow all rules that apply.

24.4.2 Types of Remote Operation

REMOTE RECEIVERS

There are several different options for remote operation today. The most basic is the many remote receivers that are available online. These receivers are maintained by other amateurs and communication hobbyists and can be used by anyone with a computer, web browser, and the Internet. Websdr and GlobalTuner are just two examples of remote monitoring sites and there are many more. (See this section's Resources list for URLs of these and other websites.) These websites give you the opportunity to be able to monitor radio activities in other countries or your own signal from another location.

Amateurs are also using the Raspberry Pi microcomputers, USB SDR receivers, and a long wire to build remote radio servers. The technologies available on these microcomputers allow remote access through a WiFi or cellular modem, connectivity by VPN (Virtual Private Network) or VNC (Virtual Network Computing) software and RDP (Remote Desktop Protocol), or use the operating system's built-in web publisher to produce the screen of the radio software. The best part is that all the components are low-powered enough to be powered by a solar cell on top of a mountain or at a friend's farm.

REMOTING YOUR HOME STATION

With the availability of high speed internet through cell phones or hotel room and office WiFi, operating your Amateur Radio station while at work, traveling, vacationing, or just visiting the family has become an enjoyable part of the hobby. Your remote connection, referred to as "remoting," can be as simple as a computer or cell phone monitoring the audio from your radio for the frequency you left it on, to full automated control and a remote radio control head so you can catch that last needed DX country to fulfill your DXCC award. Some Amateur Radio operators have removed their HF equipment from their vehicles and installed remote connections to their home stations.

DEDICATED REMOTE STATION

There are many Amateur Radio operators who are handicapped by homeowners' association requirements or living in a temporary location, apartment, or retirement home that restricts the installation of outdoor antennas. Other operators live in areas where noise from electrical utilities and electronic devices render an HF receiver almost useless. For these reasons, setting up a station away for the restrictions and noise can be very appealing.

Some contesters build a remote station in another country in order to be the DX while operating from home. Setting up a remote station in another country does not add any more equipment than a station a few miles out of town. It does add different rules and regulations to your operating that must be followed.

Maintenance is also more difficult. If you want to find out why the amplifier is alarming when operating on 40 meters, a 6-hour flight to a remote site is no trivial matter. Technology is available for remote monitoring the remote site. As long as you have Internet connectivity to the remote site, there are ways of troubleshooting your problems.

24.4.3 Remote Networking Basics

Today, the Internet has become the preferred source for connectivity of your remote station. Landline telephones can still be used for remote DTMF control of your equipment or as a source for transferring the audio to and from your remote radio.

With the availability of high-speed Internet at your home, at the office, or on the road from WiFi and mobile phones, reliable connectivity to your remote station has become easier. This ease of connectivity does come with the need to understand more about networking and how computers and other TCP devices communicate with each other. This section has been included to expose you to terminologies and technology that will aid in getting your Internet equipment connected and operational. (See this section's Glossary for definitions of terms, abbreviations, and acronyms.)

ROUTER AND PORT FORWARDING

When you turn on your computer at home to browse the Internet, it does not connect directly to the Internet. As seen in **Figure 24.36** the computer first connects to a gateway most commonly known as a *router*. The router then allows the computer to connect to it and awaits to see what the computer wants to do with the connection. When you open your Internet browser on the computer, the router then assigns a numeric *port* within the router for the computer's IP address to route data to the IP address your Internet Service Provider (ISP) has assigned to the router.

This is basically how computers in your private home or work network communicate with the World Wide Web, public computer servers and devices throughout the world. The router is the guardian that controls what information comes in and goes out of your private network.

Port forwarding is an option in most routers that enables you to create a permanent translation table that maps an incoming protocol port from your ISP to a specific IP address on your private network. It is a transparent process, meaning Internet clients cannot see that port forwarding is being performed. This process enables you to remotely connect to TCP/IP-enabled equipment and TCP servers on a computer on your private network that are otherwise hidden from the Internet by your router.

STATIC OR DDNS IP ADDRESSING

When you sign up with an Internet service, the ISP provides you with a modem to connect their network with the network in your house. Normally when the modem is activated, it will request an IP from the ISP's *Dynamic Host Configuration Protocol* (DHCP) servers. Even though you can find out what the IP address is, you have no control over what IP address is assigned and how often it changes. Because it can be changed, this is a *dynamic IP address*.

For the best connection to the Internet to provide access to your station remotely, a *static IP address* from your ISP is the preferred option. With a static IP address you will be able to easily connect remotely to your remote station without the IP address changing periodically. ISPs are currently assigning more static IP addresses due to better management of active IP addresses and larger companies moving to the new IPv6 routing which has more addresses available. This means the old static IPv4 IP addresses they were using must be changed, as well.

If you are unable to get a static IP address, there are avenues for finding out what your assigned dynamic IP address is. WhatisMyIPAddress, MyIPAddress and other websites can tell you the current dynamic IP address you have been assigned from the ISP.

A better way to manage the ISP dynamic IP address is to use a service known as *Dynamic Domain Name System* (DDNS). This service will maintain an external connection to your computer through the modem/router and *firewall*, providing a named address for you to connect to your equipment at home. This requires a small piece of software to run on your computer at home and an external DDNS service provider. Most DDNS service providers charge a fee to maintain and support this connection.

INTERNET BANDWIDTH

How much Internet bandwidth do you need? How you set up your station, what devices and protocols you use, and what means you use for connecting to the Internet determine if you get a reliable connection or one that freezes or delays when you are copying the call of a DX station.

If you are using a mobile connection for your roaming client station, you need *high-speed* or *high-bandwidth* service, the same as required for a streaming music service. 3G cellular service is the minimum service you can use at 144 kbits/s transfer rate. Mobile network services such as 4G or LTE vary in most areas, but will give you network speeds and reliability closer to what most ISP networks can provide.

Speed is advertised by download speed (the bit rate from the ISP to your computer). *Upload speed* (from your computer to the ISP) may be only ⅓ of the download speed, but is important for getting your audio and control to the transmitter. Using Internet sites such as Speakeasy can give you a good indication of the download and upload speeds on your computer.

It is important to realize that sharing an Internet connection can also cause reduction in bandwidth. If others in your home are online at the same time, their activity will consume some of the bandwidth available to your network devices. A dedicated line or service upgrade to support remote station operation may be required unless you can account for all the concurrent household bandwidth requirements and determine that your service is capable of handling it all. A router with *quality of service* (QoS) prioritizing capabilities might solve or at least minimize multi-user problems on a single-line Internet connection.

Rural ISPs usually consist of a wireless network over large areas. Network speeds can vary depending on the time of day or day

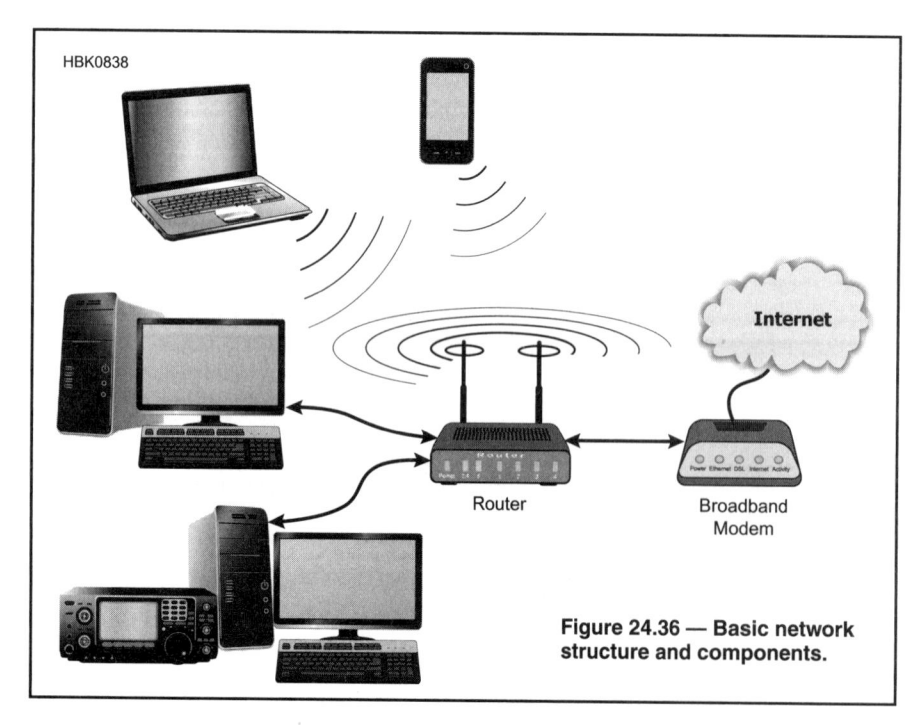

Figure 24.36 — Basic network structure and components.

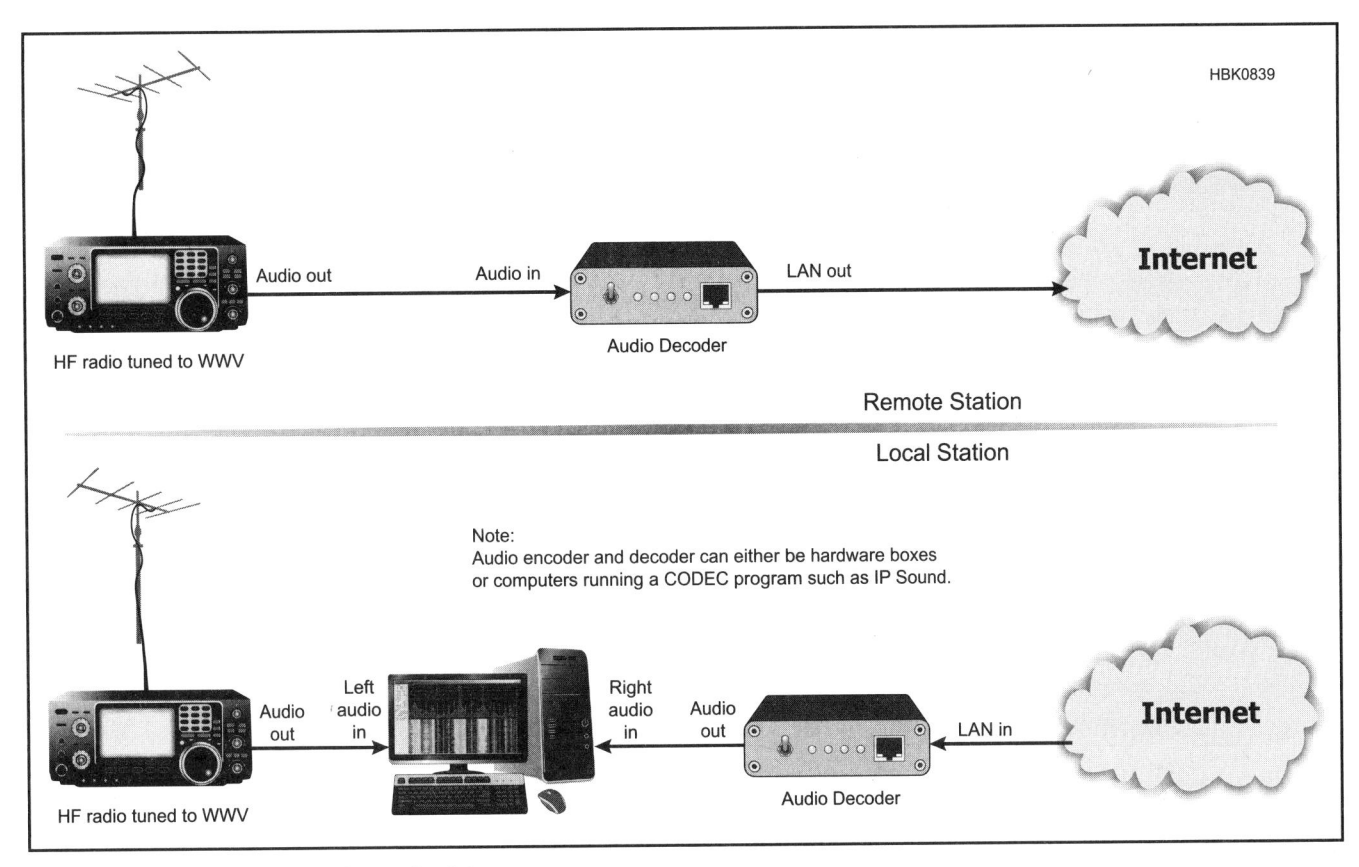

Figure 24.37 — N6RK's method for testing latency.

of the week. This can be important, especially when you are trying to operate in a contest over a weekend when everyone is home streaming a movie. If you plan to use a webcam for monitoring and security purposes, or stream a panadapter/waterfall type display, you must account for that bandwidth in your overall connectivity needs as well.

Hotels are known to vary network speeds depending on how many guests are in the hotel that night. You can check with the hotel staff to see if there is a secondary WiFi system that can give you more bandwidth.

INTERNET LATENCY

You need *low delay* (latency) to operate remote, the same as any online game player. For casual operating, you may be able to tolerate a latency of 250 ms or 300 ms. Serious contesters and DXers will most likely find this much delay frustrating, especially on CW. If you are a high-speed CW contest operator, very low latency is required to be competitive. Below 200 ms is adequate, below 100 ms is better. Otherwise, tuning "lags" and you will experience poor timing in the pileups. Voice and digital operating are more tolerant of delay.

You can easily evaluate basic Internet latency yourself using the computer. In a *Windows 7* (PC) environment, under START | ALL PROGRAMS | ACCESSORIES you will find COMMAND PROMPT, or in a *Windows 8* and newer system, select START and type CMD. From within this DOS-like window you can run the *ping*, *tracert* and or *pathping* commands to access a particular IP address at the station site and average the response times to measure the latency. By adding the -t command to the ping command (for example, "ping 192.168.0.1 –t"), you will get continuous ping results until you use the CTRL-C keys to stop the ping process. This is critical to know in advance or to troubleshoot connectivity issues once you are operational.

For the purposes of conducting Internet system audio latency tests, N6RK's method illustrated in **Figure 24.37** is very effective. Using a receiver at the remote site and one at the control point, the recorded latency can easily be determined. **Figure 24.38** shows a latency of 40 ms for the return audio over K6VVA's private control link using a

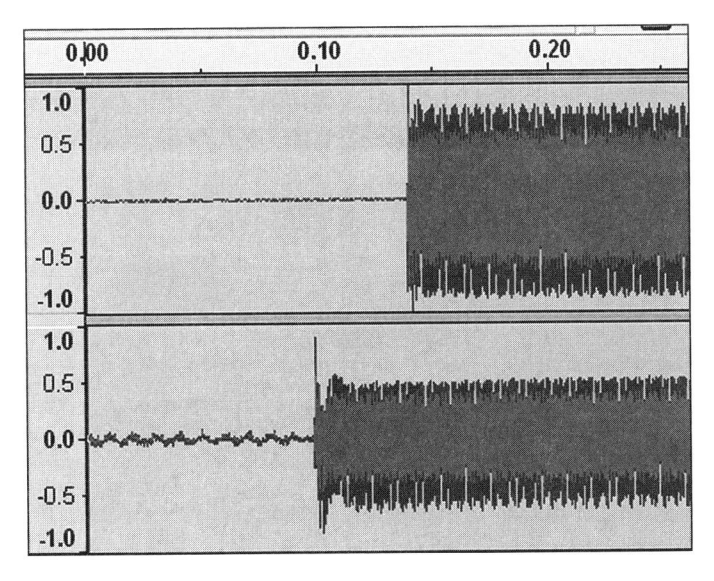

Figure 24.38 — K6VVA's latency test results.

RemoteRig audio interface that requires a network speed of about 180 kbps. The audio is crystal clear and at 40 ms, little difference is noticed from the remote site than from having the radio control head connected directly to the radio at home.

24.4.4 Connecting to Your Remote Station

There are many ways to connect, control, and monitor a remote station. What equipment, communications medium to connect them, and how you use your remote station is only limited by time, money, and resources available. The following methods are to be used as guidance as you plan and build your remote Amateur Radio station.

BASIC MONITORING

The basic remote monitoring station shown in **Figure 24.39** can consist of very few components. If you just want to set your HF radio on a specific frequency, let's say a 40 meter net, and monitor it from work during your lunch break, then all you need is an audio cable connected from the headphone/speaker jack on your radio to the microphone jack on your computer. On your computer you will need audio software to provide a connection to your mobile phone or work computer. Using the *Autoanswer* function on the host computer will give you unmanned audio connect. Simply connect the computer/handheld device to the audio software account on your home computer and listen in on the net.

Many remote station operators have found *Skype* to be a workable solution for remote audio routing as well as *IP-Sound*. Another way to completely avoid Internet latency and bandwidth issues for audio is to use a POTS (Plain Old Telephone System) connection with a dedicated analog phone line that might also be shared with a DSL data service for control.

One of the newest technologies available to give you basic remote monitoring is the ability to use a Raspberry Pi as a TCP server for a SDR receiver. There are a few different versions of RTL-SDR TCP servers available that makes it possible for programs like Airspy's *SDR#* to remotely connect to a Raspberry Pi/SDR receiver through the internet.

VNC CONNECTIONS

If you enjoy listening to your HF radio and would like to be able to tune remotely through the bands for different conversations, start with an audio cable from your radio's headphone /speaker jack to the microphone input on the computer. Your radio will need to have *computer aided transceiver* (CAT) control capabilities. Radios with CAT control will have a serial, USB, or Ethernet port available for the computer to be able to connect and send control data to the radio. Icom radios have a CI-V control port which require an COM-to-CI-V or USB-to-CI-V interface.

You will then need radio control software installed on the computer. Several radio manufactures have radio control software available. There are several software companies that have software to control just about any radio with CAT control. Two examples are *Ham Radio Deluxe* and *TRX-Manager*.

Once you have installed the radio control software and connected the computer to the radio, you will need remote access to the host computer. A simple scenario, shown in **Figure 24.40**, uses *Virtual Network*

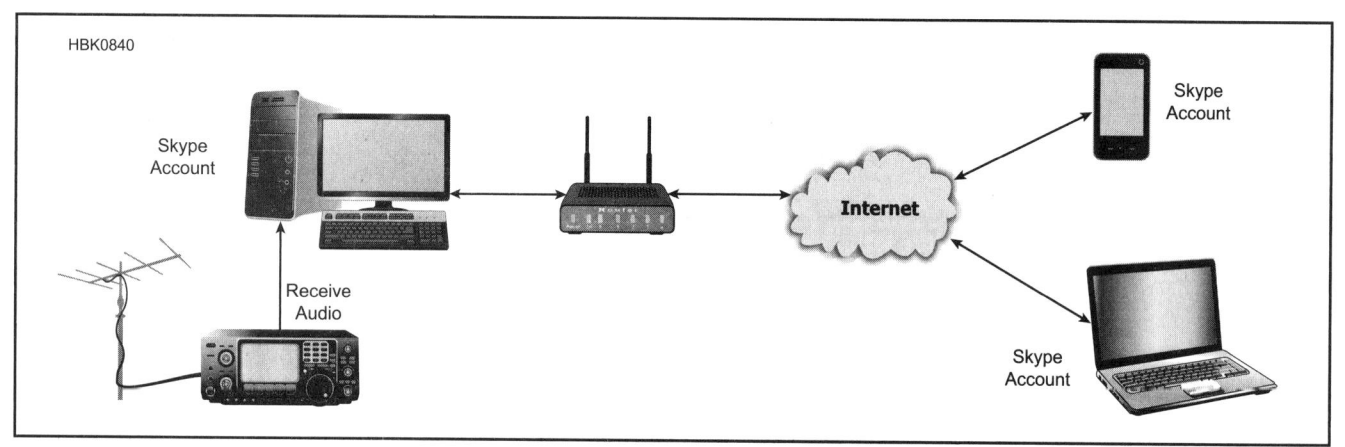

Figure 24.39 — Basic remote monitoring.

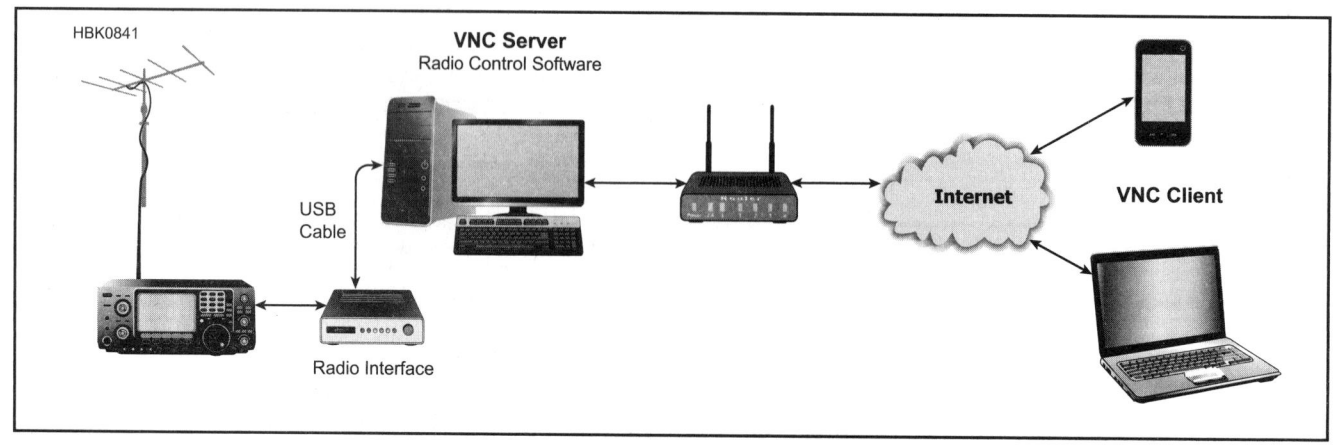

Figure 24.40 — VNC software connection.

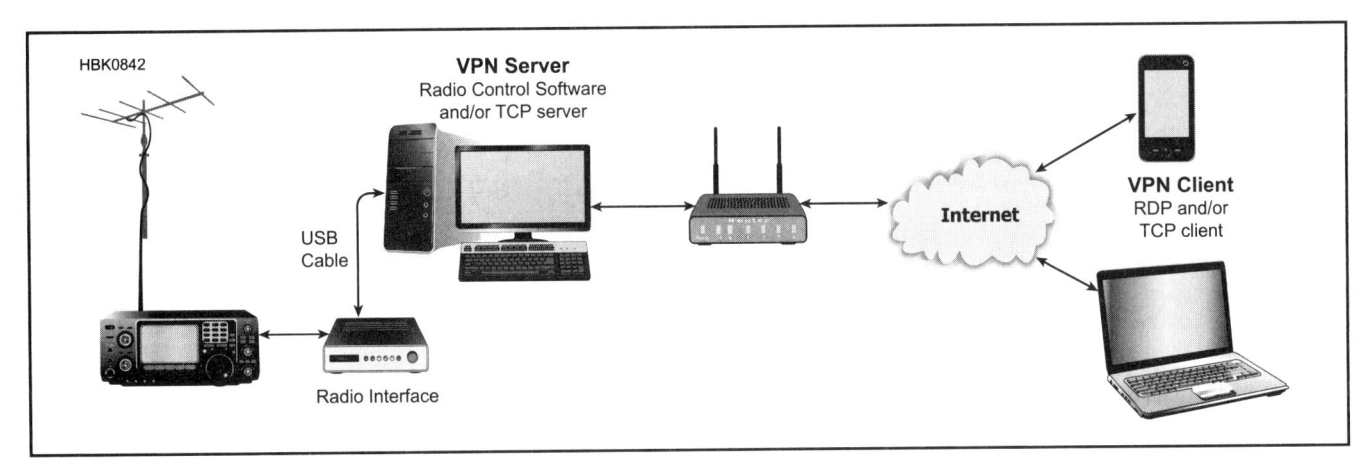

Figure 24.41 — VPN software connection.

Computing (VNC) software, such as *Chrome Remote Desktop*, *TightVNC*, *TeamViewer* or *LogMeIn*, that allows users to take remote control of the host computer running the radio software. VNC software allows full control of the host computer, with some software including the sound interface and others requiring additional software for monitoring for the audio. Audio server software like *Skype* and *IP-Sound* can also be used. Be aware that some VNC software packages charge extra for access to the remote sound. This software does take a lot of bandwidth to pass the screens and control between the connected computers/handheld devices.

All of the VNC software options mentioned here can be accessed with an iPhone, iPad, Android phone or tablet. Once you have connected to your station with the VNC software, you will be able to change frequency and bands using the radio control software on the host computer.

VPN CONNECTIONS

A virtual private network (VPN) is like a tunnel through public Internet access to connect to a private network, such as your station network. There are a number of VPN software packages and hardware options that enable you to create the Internet connection for transporting data between the computer in front of you and the computer/devices at your home or remote station. A VPN uses encryption and other security mechanisms to ensure that only authorized users can access the network and that the data cannot be intercepted.

The VPN server at the station end can be either on the host computer or in the network router. It depends on if you need connectivity to only the host computer or the whole station network. Microsoft has included VPN servers and clients in recent versions of their operating systems and some network routers include VPN servers. Other VPN software packages include *OpenVPN* and LogMeIn *Hamachi*.

Once you have established a VPN connection to the host computer or router from your client computer, shown in **Figure 24.41**, you will be able to connect your TCP client software to the radio control TCP server software and/or accessories at your station. Another option is connecting to the radio control software on the host computer with a *Remote Desktop Protocol* (RDP) connection to view your radio control software on the screen and use *Skype* or *IP-Sound* for the audio connection. This will give you a secure connection to your station.

Using a VPN connection can be combined with a remote radio head. This will give you secure access to the equipment connected to your radio, and allow you to operate the radio from the remote radio head.

TCP SERVER/CLIENT

TCP server/client software is two programs that provide a connection over the Internet between your host computer and the client computer you have in front of you. Each piece of equipment can have its own TCP server/client software installed at both ends.

The TCP server software is installed on a computer that will be connected to your radio, tuner, rotator, or other station equipment, where it communicates with the station equipment by serial, Ethernet, or USB connections. Most of the TCP server software allows you to be able to control the equipment locally on this computer when you are at the station, as well as through a remote Internet connection.

The TCP client software is installed on the computer that will connect to the TCP server software through your Internet connection. This provides you access to the station equipment with a dedicated TCP network connection to each device you connected to a TCP server computer.

There are advantages to using dedicated TCP server/client connections to your station. They use very small data packets, multiple

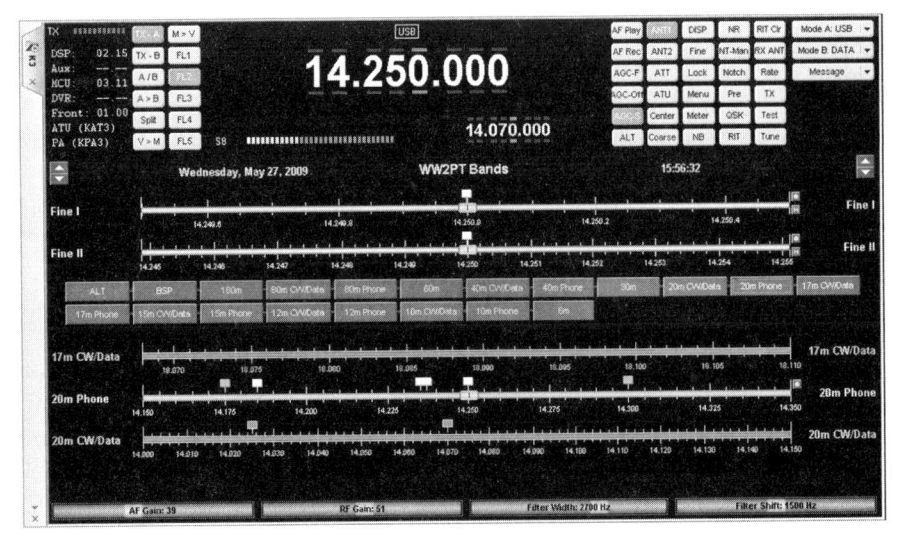

Figure 24.42 — Ham Radio Deluxe.

TCP servers can be run in parallel for each device, and they can be connected only when you really need to see the data from the remote piece of equipment.

There are several radio manufacturers that have radio control software available utilizing TCP server/client technology. There are also software companies that provide software to control just about any radio with a CAT interface. Examples of this software are *Ham Radio Deluxe* (shown in **Figure 24.42**) and *TRX-Manager*.

REMOTE RADIO HEADS

Operating remotely from a computer or tablet can be fun and exciting, but it is not the same as turning a VFO or tweaking a bandpass filter knob to dig out the weak DX station. Manufacturers have developed Internet-based interfaces to remotely connect a detachable radio head to the base section of the radio, hundreds of miles away.

One company to advance this idea is Microbit. Their RemoteRig standalone interfaces use separate *Session Initiation Protocol* (SIP), VoIP, and control channels to connect the two parts of the radio over Ethernet. Passing of the audio and control signals, along with CW paddle signals is transparent to the remote radio head. Elecraft even makes the K3/0 remote head for the K3 transceiver that is identical to the front of the radio, giving you full functionality of your K3 station wherever you have Internet access. The W4AAW multi-multi contest station uses the K3/RemoteRig combination at one of the operating positions for off-site operators during contests.

These remote radio interfaces work with several other radios. Remoting the Icom IC-706 and Kenwood TS-480 transceivers is very popular among amateurs. There are groups that have installed the base part of the Icom IC-706 in different locations and have the ability to connect to any one of them from the radio head. They have the capability to change the profile in the RemoteRig at the radio head for it to connect to the different remote site base units.

Figure 24.43 shows the Elecraft K3/0 remote head with the RemoteRig interface installed in a tool case for easy transport and setup. One major advantage to using these interfaces with the remote radio heads is the audio and control signals have been streamlined and optimized to best performance between the two interfaces. This makes operating over low bandwidth and weak cellular network possible.

HAM RADIO ONLINE

If you are unable to invest in the equipment to be able to operate remotely and really want to experience the rush of operating a contest or DX from a station with large antennas and lots of power, there are options available online.

The websites for RemoteHams and RemoteHamRadio offers you a chance to operate world-class Amateur Radio stations around the world from your home. You can either lease a K3/0 remote head or install a TCP client software on your computer, then connect a microphone and/or paddle. Now you have access to a community of stations accessible through the Internet, offering an experience not available through most stations.

The VY1JA remotely controlled contest station in the Yukon Territory is an ongoing work in progress. When the station becomes fully operational, guest operators will be allowed to remotely operate in contests from this unique station in the Canadian north.

24.4.5 Station Automation

Automation is key to having a fully functional remote station. The ability to control your rotator, antennas, and amplifier from your computer has been around for some time. Now several manufactures have added remote TCP server/client software to control your station from off-site. The following section describes software and hardware to enable automation and remote control of your station.

SWITCHING ANTENNAS

To automate your antenna system, one of the first pieces of hardware you will need is a band decoder. A band decoder detects what band your radio is on and passes this information to the antenna switching network. The band decoders can detect the band either by a binary coded decimal (BCD) output from the radio, through a CI-V interface on an Icom radio, or reading the frequency data from the radio. Band decoding can be accomplished with standalone units, such as the Array Solutions BandMaster or Elecraft KRC2, or a decoder built into an antenna switching controller, as with the Ameritron RCS-12, EA4TX RemoteBox, or Hamation integrated controllers.

An alternative to using a band decoder takes advantage of station control or logging software with the capability to send band data to antenna switching units via Ethernet or serial connections. The Green Heron Engineering antenna switches can be controlled by local software, as well as through TCP server/client software. Snaptekk offers a 4-port antenna switch with WiFi and a TCP server built in.

Additional advantages of Hamation antenna switches and EA4TX RemoteBox is the availability of USB connections to the host computer and TCP server/client software. With this software you can reconfigure your automatic antenna selection remotely or manually control what antenna you want to use.

You can simplify your remote station by using one antenna for all the bands. Using a multiband dipole or vertical antenna will eliminate the need for antenna switching. Using the SteppIR BigIR vertical antenna with its controller, for example, gives you a versatile antenna that follows the frequency from your radio.

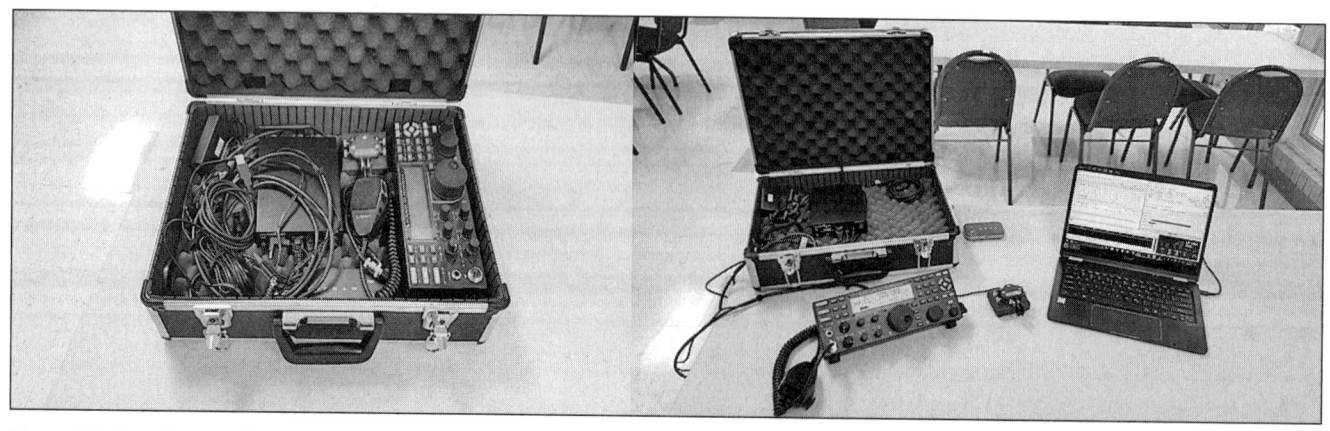

Figure 24.43 — Remote Station Go Box.

Figure 24.44 — PSTRotator software.

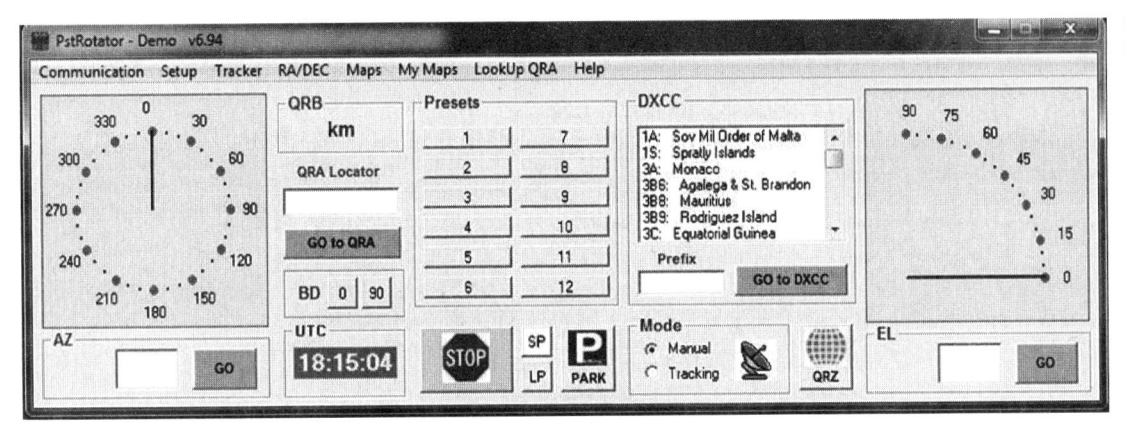

ROTATORS

Automating your rotator system usually starts with installing an interface in the rotator control box to give your computer control of the rotator. Electronic Rotator Control (ERC) interface kits from Vibroplex or EA4TX give you the capability of connecting to your computer via USB or serial connections.

Most logging and contesting software, either directly or indirectly, gives you control of your rotator as you enter a call sign into the call field of your logging software. *PSTRotator* control software (see **Figure 24.44**) can interface with several logging software packages. It also has built-in TCP server/client software to tie it into your logging software on your remote client computer for automated rotator control from an offsite operating location.

RF AMPLIFIERS

Several modern amplifiers have the capability of full automation by detecting and following the frequency the radio's output signal. Add this to the automatic antenna switching and tuners found in some of today's high end amplifiers, such as the SPE Expert series, automation of your station has become much easier. Connecting these amplifiers to your host computer only takes a single USB or serial cable, giving you monitoring and control of half your station.

A remote VPN connection and an RDP session will give you remote access to configure and monitor the amplifier. Combine this with the RemoteRig RC-1216H interface and you will have the ability to remotely configure and operate ACOM and SPE Expert amplifiers.

Another option is to use separate amplifier and tuner/antenna switches. Equipment such as the Elecraft K3 line can be combined to read the frequency data from the K3 transceiver, set the band on the amp, set the tuner to a preset memory location, and select the appropriate antenna. The Elecraft KPA500 amplifier and KAT500 tuner both have serial connections for the host computer, as well as TCP server/client software for control and monitoring from the remote client computer as seen in **Figure 24.45**. Combine this with a remote head radio connection and you have no need for a VPN or VNC connection to your station, providing you with a clean, low bandwidth connection.

STATION MONITORING

It's important to know that a remote station is operating correctly when in a contest or trying to snag that rare DX station. There are a few manufacturers of power and SWR meters that include serial ports and software to monitor the meter on the host computer. The TelePost LP-100A power meter includes an RS-232 serial port for connection to the host computer. This software can be monitored via a VPN or VNC connection. TCP server/client software from Wizkers will allow remote access to the LP-100A through your host computer.

Several other RF power meters have built-in Ethernet connections and TCP server/client software for direct connection to the meter from a remote site without going through a host computer. The SMΩRF meter from MicroHam shown in **Figure 24.46** is one such example that gives the operator a full range of information about how the station is operating and evaluates the antenna system in the event of a problem.

POWER AND RELAY CONTROL

There are a lot of ways to remotely turn devices on and off in your shack. If you want

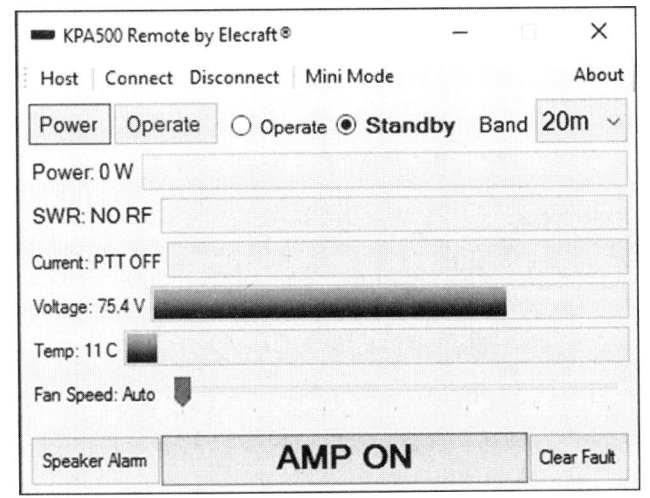

Figure 24.45 — Elecraft KPA500 TCP server/client.

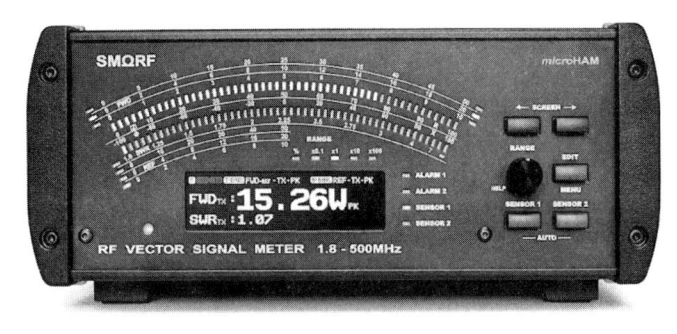

Figure 24.46 — MicroHAM SMΩRF power meter.

Assembling a Station   24.29

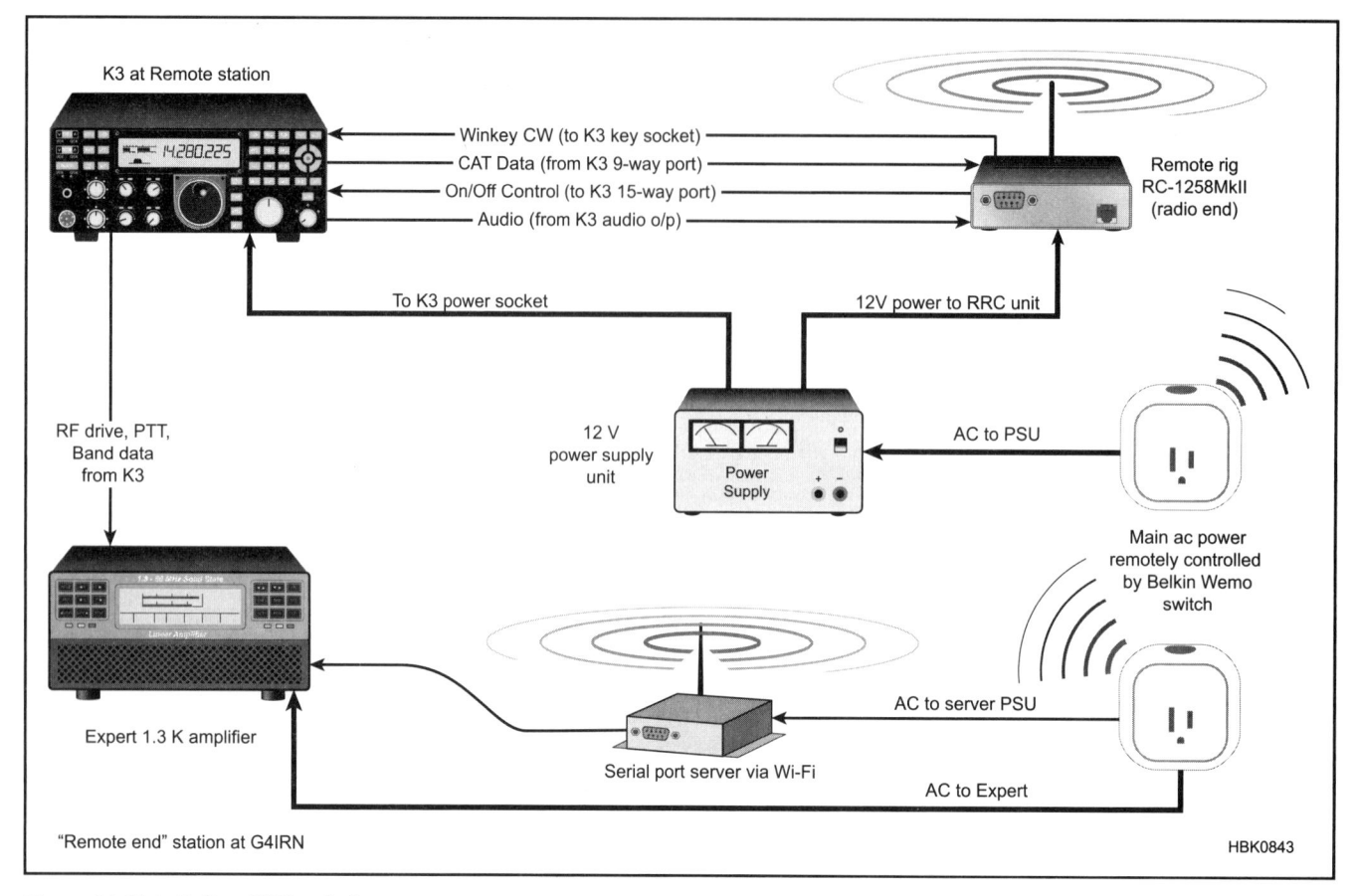

Figure 24.47 — Belken WiFi switches.

Figure 24.48 — MicroHAM microKEYER II interface.

to turn your radio, amplifier, and computer on and off, or switch between antennas, there is equipment available to do this.

Using your phone line to control devices is as simple as using the DTMF keypad on a phone. Several manufactures produce equipment to connect to the phone line with onboard relays that are turned on and off by DTMF tones. You can buy units with 1 to 8 relays from Velleman and Viking Electronics.

Using the Internet to control relays is also possible. Digital Loggers and Belken produce Ethernet-enabled power strips that can be turned on and off by an app on your Android or iPhone. **Figure 24.47** shows how G4IRN uses a pair of WiFi units to turn his amplifier and 12 V power supply on and off. This works great for turning on a power supply or switching between two antennas. For a lower cost option, Velleman makes a relay kit that connects to your host computer by USB and provides software that runs on the computer with an app to control the relays from your phone.

RADIO INTERFACES

Connecting the radio to the computer can be as simple as running serial cables and audio cables from the radio to the computer, but serial connections can be difficult to configure and the audio connections can allow noise to get into the receive and transmit audio. It is recommended that an interface between the radio and the computer be installed. Several manufactures make interface for most radio models that have CAT control in them, such as the ones offered from MicroHAM (see **Figure 24.48**), Tigertronics, and West Mountain Radio. Using interfaces simplifies connections and configurations. They also provide higher quality analog-to-digital audio converters than what most computers come with.

Several newer radios have the interface built in. A USB cable is all that's required for audio and CAT between the radio and the computer.

SERIAL PORT SERVERS

Serial port servers, such as the Moxa Nport or Digi Connect series, are interfaces that connect a RS-232/422/485 device to an Ethernet port. These port servers can act as a gateway between two protocols or pass

24.30   Chapter 29

encapsulated serial traffic between a serial device and a remote computer over Ethernet networks. Unless your software on the client computer is designed to communicate with the serial device over Ethernet, redirect software such as the Digi RealPort is required to manage the encapsulated serial traffic. Serial port servers are used when you do not want to use a computer at the station to connect the serial port on a piece of remote station equipment.

24.4.6 Remote Site Requirements

PURCHASE VS RENT OR LEASE

Although having direct control over every aspect of what you want to do is most desirable, you may want to consider a rental or lease with a cooperative land owner. In either case, having a detailed agreement or contract prepared by a competent attorney is a must. Be sure to include every contingency you can think of, and especially what happens if the land owner decides to sell. Leasing or renting with an option to purchase allows you to fully evaluate the site before making a long-term commitment to it.

RELIABLE ACCESS BY ROAD

If your remote site is not on developed property, will you be able to get there safely, rain or shine? What happens if any problems develop that require immediate attention at the remote site? Pavement or a good all-weather, well-maintained gravel road should be available. Having more than one means of getting in or out should emergencies arise while you are at the site is also an important consideration. These concerns must be addressed before agreeing to purchase, rent, or lease a remote site.

GEOLOGICAL AND OTHER HAZARDS

Evaluate the geological factors involved. In a hilltop or mountaintop site, is there evidence of soil movement that could affect access or damage your equipment shelter or tower installations? Does the property sit near an earthquake fault? Is there a significant risk of fire during fire season? Is the site exposed to high wind or storms? In flat-land sites, is there a risk of flooding or drainage problems? Remember, you won't be there to rescue your equipment! In consideration of both your initial construction activities and ongoing maintenance tasks, are there any wildlife hazards from animals or insects? What about allergies or reactions to plants such as poison ivy or poison oak? Diligently investigate all aspects of a potential remote site *before* you end up with bad surprises down the line. For a reasonable fee, there are companies from which you can secure a Geological and Property Hazards report to aid in your assessment.

RAW SITE PREPARATION

It you are fortunate enough to locate suitable property, be sure to evaluate the site preparation needs. How much time and money will be necessary to develop the remote site to meet your specific needs? Is there brush and vegetation to be dispensed with? Will trees need to be cut down? Will bulldozers, excavators, and trenchers need access to the site? Concrete trucks? Service vehicles? Diligent evaluation of all costs involved will reduce unnecessary stress.

SITES WITH EXISTING FACILITIES

Finding a site with a self-supporting tower or two in place that can accommodate your needs, along with a building large enough for your equipment and operational needs can be like finding a pot of remote gold. However, unless you are experienced with towers and construction, hire professionals to evaluate everything. If you are considering co-locating at a remote site with existing antennas and equipment in use, consider hiring a professional to help you evaluate the likelihood of problems. Birdies and intermodulation could end up being a source of potential conflict and stress if problems can't be resolved.

TERRAIN CONSIDERATIONS

Evaluate the terrain on the bands you wish to operate. For HF, Dean Straw, N6BV, has developed a very useful program called *HFTA — High Frequency Terrain Assessment*. (See the *ARRL Antenna Book*.) Use *HFTA* to assist you in placement of your antennas. Don't expect excellent ground/soil conductivity if your remote site is on top of a rocky mountaintop.

If you plan to use vertical antennas, make sure there is sufficient room on the property to place the radials, whether on a mountaintop or flat area. Placing verticals near water, especially saltwater, is the most desirable way to achieve the low takeoff angles for long-haul DX. Remember that exposure to salt air or spray will create significant maintenance issues.

NOISE LEVELS

Since one of the reasons for building a dedicated remote station away from your home is to lower noise levels, you'll want to carefully evaluate existing and potential noise sources. Start by visiting the site with a receiver in several different types of weather and listening on all the bands you intend to use with a full-size dipole antenna. If noise levels are low, this is no guarantee that problems won't crop up in different seasons or from hardware failures. You should avoid nearby substations or high-voltage and power distribution lines. If you will be sharing a site with other users, coordinate with them to test intermodulation and adjacent channel interference before you go into full operation.

ELECTRICAL POWER

Having electrical power already available at your remote site can certainly save a lot of money. The most ideal situation is to have underground power to the remote site. Be sure to evaluate the full costs of installing ac power if it is not already present at the site or on the property. Truly remote sites may require wind, solar, or generator power systems like that shown in **Figure 24.49**.

If your remote site will require solar/wind/battery power, it is critical that you properly assess sunlight path and duration, wind patterns, and provide sufficient battery storage to meet your intended operating needs during lengthy periods of inclement weather. The article "Designing Solar Power System for FM Translators" is a valuable resource for planning of remote HF station off-grid power. (See the Resources section below.) You must thoroughly account for the power requirements of each and every piece of equipment.

There are various estimates for the duty cycle of transceivers. A conservative duty cycle of 50% for CW/SSB is recommended for power capacity evaluation. (RTTY/digital/AM/FM duty cycles will likely be higher.) Internet switches, routers, rotators, computers and anything electrical will also consume power. A supplementary diesel or propane remote-start generator to a basic off-grid system may be an appropriate option, particularly if you plan on using an amplifier. If your remote site is in a rugged terrain rural area, make sure a diesel or propane service provider vehicle can get to the location *before* you make final plans! It may be possible to use smaller propane tanks you can haul in a truck, but any manifold-type system necessitates insuring that the proper BTU requirements can be met based upon the propane generator manufacturer's ratings. Installing a solar and wind remote battery monitor system is advisable.

When you have made an accurate assessment of your complete system needs, add a generous additional contingency factor. It is also advisable to get quotes on your proposed system from at least two different "green power" equipment suppliers, and to make sure they fully understand your requirements and intended use *before* you purchase anything.

Figure 24.49 — Solar panels can be used to charge a bank of batteries to supply power. Effective off-grid power requires an accurate and conservative estimate of power needs and available energy sources. [Rick Hilding, K6VVA, photo]

INTERNET ACCESS

If you are planning to operate your remote station via the Internet, be sure that broadband service such as cellular, rural wireless, DSL or cable TV can reach your site by asking the local service provider to do a site evaluation. Satellite Internet downlink speed may be fast, but uplink speed is often quite a bit slower. Be sure the minimum link speed is adequate in both directions.

If your control point is close enough to the remote site, another option is to implement your own private wireless "bridge" system. Even if multiple "hops" are involved, with the right equipment you can potentially have better results than using even broadband Internet. Hamnet technologies (see the **Digital Modes and Protocols** chapter) may be an option to connect a remote station that's not too far away.

INSURANCE AND SECURITY

You've heard the expression "Stuff Happens." Unless you have blanket coverage in an existing homeowner's insurance policy that includes your remote site equipment, look into the ARRL "All-Risk" Ham Radio Equipment Insurance Plan. If you will be hiring others to do work at your remote site, be sure that liability coverage issues are addressed. The same applies to any guests or visitors such as fellow hams. Have a competent attorney draw up a "Liability Release" agreement with strong "Hold Harmless" language.

If your remote site is yours alone and not a co-habitation arrangement with other services, be sure and evaluate all security needs (a necessity even if co-located). You might need one or more security gates, webcam surveillance and auto-remote notification of security breaches.

PERSONAL SAFETY

Regardless of your age, it is prudent to have someone with you at the site. You could severely cut yourself, or fall and break a leg. If there are wildlife hazards in the area, take appropriate steps to protect yourself.

Carry a first aid kit and have one readily available at your remote site. Keep some emergency supplies such as various sealed food items in a varmint-proof container and a case of bottled water in the event you find yourself stranded.

If your remote site is within the coverage area of a local repeater, take along a handheld radio (with batteries charged) as part of your SOP (Standard Operating Procedure). This is especially important for rural and remote operating sites.

24.4.7 Station in Your Hand

Operating or just monitoring band conditions from your mobile phone or tablet is almost as easy as from your computer. With today's smartphone technologies, Skype, VPN, RDP, and VNC connections to your station are quite possible.

There are several apps available or being developed for connections directly to your radio or radio interface. *RRC-Nano* is an app for Android devices from RemoteRig (see **Figure 24.50**), which makes it possible to remote your station. It uses the RemoteRig interface at the station site to provide remote access to the radio through your phone. Another option available is the *SmartSDR* app for the iPhone or iPad to remotely connect to the FlexRadio Systems 6000-series SDR radios.

24.4.8 Future of Remote Operating

The Future is Boundless! With upcoming advancements in hardware technologies and software development, operating remotely will soon become second nature. Several Amateur Radio equipment manufacturers have turned their attention to providing remote access to their equipment.

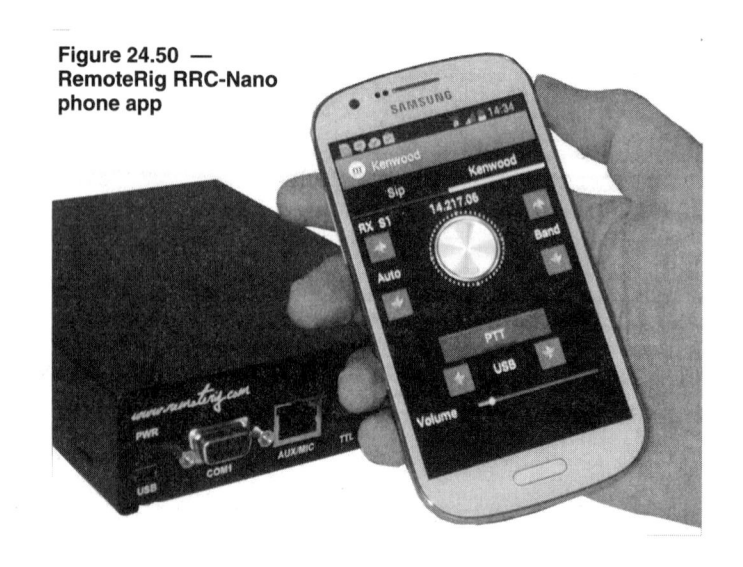

Figure 24.50 — RemoteRig RRC-Nano phone app

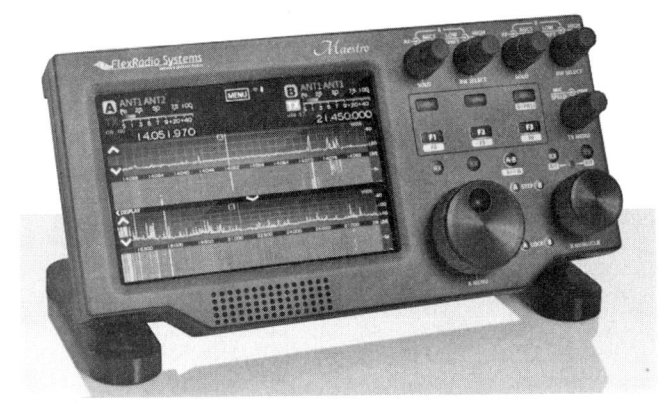

Figure 24.51 — FlexRadio Maestro.

Someday in the not too distant future you will be able to make changes to the amplifier, select a different antenna, or test an antenna to see if severe weather has affected it. All this through the screen on the Maestro-like control console as seen in **Figure 24.51**, while sitting in a coffee shop.

The Raspberry Pi has become a versatile and powerful microcomputer for the radio amateur. There are projects available for band decoding for control of antennas, VPN server interfaces for radios, and USB SDR's for remote monitoring. For more information on project with the Raspberry Pi, view the presentation by Ed James, KA8JMW and Mike Pendley, K5ATM on "Raspberry Pi: A Low Cost Platform for Amateur Radio Projects." The ARRL's *Raspberry Pi Projects for Dummies* is a great book to start with if you have not played with one yet and want to learn how to use them.

24.4.9 Special Events and Demonstrations

Remote stations come in very handy during special events. If you are putting on a demonstration of Amateur Radio, setting up an effective antenna may not always be viable, and you may not be able to communicate very far. Local noise levels or RFI problems may present significant challenges.

Setting up a remote link to your home or dedicated remote station will give you a definite advantage and make the experience more enjoyable for the audience. For example, a remote client station was used at a Boy Scout Jamboree-On-The-Air event. Young scouts were given the chance to communicate with other scouts around the world with the help of a capable station without the usual compromises associated with portable stations. This makes for a more effective demonstration of what Amateur Radio can do.

24.4.10 Remote Station Glossary

App — An application (program) installed on a cellular smartphone.

Band decoder — An interface device that reads frequency data from a modern transceiver and facilitates automatic control switching of other equipment such as a bandpass filter.

Bandwidth — Typically expressed in Mbps or kbps, this is used to represent both the capability of an Internet connection for data transfer as well as the amount of data that can be transferred.

CAT — Computer Aided Transceiver. Used for interface between modern Amateur Radio transceiver and computer. Provides radio control and audio interfacing.

Cellular Modem — Also known as a "hot spot", allows an Internet connection through the cellular phone network.

CEPT — European Conference of Postal and Telecommunications Administrators. US amateurs are permitted to operate from member nations without the requirement of obtaining additional licensees or permits.

CI-V — Proprietary communications medium for interfacing Icom transceivers to computers and associated equipment.

DDNS — Dynamic Domain Name System. Internet services provided to associate domain names with Dynamic IP addresses.

DHCP — Dynamic Host Configuration Protocol. This functionality is incorporated into most routers and provides automatic assignment of IP addresses to computer devices on a LAN where fixed or static IP addresses are not required.

DSL — Digital Subscriber Line. A technology for bringing high-bandwidth data to homes and small businesses over ordinary copper telephone lines.

DTMF — Dual-Tone Multi-Frequency signaling. Keypad signaling system using the voice-frequency band over telephone lines between telephone equipment and other communications devices. Also known by the trade name Touch-Tone.

Duty cycle — A device which is constantly "on" would normally be considered to have a 100% duty cycle. Morse code keying has spaces between the elements and the characters, therefore the duty cycle would be less.

ERC — Easy Rotator Control. Electronic interfaces for controlling rotators from a computer.

Firewall — Firmware or software capabilities in computers and routers that can be configured to minimize or completely block unauthorized users from access.

HAMNET — Broadband-Hamnet (BBHN). A high speed wireless computer network using commercial WiFi equipment with custom firmware on Amateur Radio frequencies.

Internet Service Provider (ISP) — An organization that provides services for accessing and using the Internet.

IP — Internet Protocol. The communications protocol used to route packets of information between devices on the Internet. (see also *TCP*)

IPv4 — The fourth version of the Internet Protocol (IP), based on 32-bit (four-byte) decimal addressing.

IPv6 — The sixth and most recent version of the Internet Protocol (IP), based on 128-bit addressing, using eight groups of four hexadecimal digits.

IP Address — Every computer or device accessible via the Internet or a LAN has a unique numeric address, such as 192.168.1.1 assigned to it. The IP address is associated to the fixed MAC address of the device.

kbps — Kilobits per second (one thousand bits per second). Typically used as a reference to bandwidth data rate capability or actual usage.

LAN — Local Area Network. A home LAN enables multiple computers to connect to a single Internet service.

Latency — The delays involved in data routing from one point to another, but also a factor in A/D conversion processes.

Assembling a Station 24.33

MAC address — Media Access Control address. A unique address given to network interface devices such as Ethernet or WiFi interface cards.

Mbps — Megabits per second (one million bits per second). Typically used as a reference to bandwidth data rate capability or actual usage.

ms — Milliseconds. The unit of time typically used for measuring latency.

Netbook — A portable computer smaller than a traditional laptop or notebook. Many netbooks now use solid-state instead of rotating hard drives.

Packet — A formatted set of digital information. All information sent via the Internet is first converted into packets for transmission.

Panadapter — A device similar to a spectrum analyzer that allows you to visually see the RF spectrum received by the radio.

Pathping — A hybrid utility of the *path* and *tracert* functions which requires more time for analysis between two Internet connection points, but results in a more detailed analysis.

Ping — A utility used to ascertain the availability of another computer device over the Internet or LAN and also measure the round trip time required for the connection.

Port forwarding — Functionality most commonly used in routers to direct or re-direct incoming Internet traffic to specific destinations on a local network.

POTS — Plain Old Telephone Service. This generally refers to the use of a regular analog telephone system for purposes of remote audio and control signal routing in lieu of the Internet.

QoS — Quality of Service. The overall performance of a telephony or computer network. Performance can be enhanced by prioritizing services on the network.

RDP — Remote Desktop Protocol. A proprietary protocol developed by Microsoft, which provides a user with a graphical interface to connect to another computer over a network connection.

Remote Client — The remote location from which the operator will be controlling the host station site. This could be a home location or hotel room, but can be anywhere connectivity to the host station site is available.

Router — A device that allows traffic on a single Internet service line to be selectively distributed to multiple computer devices on a LAN. Many routers provide for assignment of local IP addresses as well as automatically via DHCP.

SDR — Software Defined Radio. A radio communication system where components that have been typically implemented in hardware (e.g. mixers, filters, amplifiers, modulators/demodulators, detectors, etc.) are instead implemented by means of software on a personal computer or embedded system.

Serial Port Server — A device that transfers data between a computer or device serial port (COM port) and an Ethernet local area network (LAN).

Smartphone — A generic term for portable cellular phones with integrated computer capabilities.

Static IP — A fixed IP address in a computer or device.

Station site — The actual physical location of the transmitter, host computer, antennas and related equipment necessary to generate an RF signal on the HF bands. Some have used the term *Remote Base*.

Switch — A network device that allows multiple computers or devices to share the same Internet or LAN connection.

TCP — Transport Control Protocol. An Internet protocol, usually combined with IP (see *Internet Protocol*) to transfer data between devices over networks.

TCP Client — Software designed for remotely connecting to and processing data from equipment through a TCP Server over a home network or the Internet.

TCP Server — Host software used for providing TCP Client software remote access to a computer or device.

Tracert — A utility for tracing the path taken by packets across the Internet and latency assessing analysis along the route.

VNC — Virtual Network Computing. A graphical desktop sharing system that uses the Remote Frame Buffer protocol (RFB) to remotely control another computer.

VPN — Virtual Private Network. Allows you to create a secure connection to another network over the Internet.

Waterfall — A graphical display that shows a continually updating sequence of RF spectra.

WiFi — A form of network connectivity without a physical wired connection, although with limited range. Also known by its controlling standard, IEEE 802.11.

Wireless bridge — Low powered transmitter-receiver devices for providing point-to-point digital communications, usually Ethernet, such as for interfacing Internet services to areas without traditional means.

24.4.11 Remote Station Resources

For other great resources on how to set up a remote station, see the following articles or books:

Aaker, Mark, K6UFO, "Remote Operating for Amateur Radio: Ten Things to Know" see **k6ufo.com/attachments/Remote_Op_Ten_Things.pdf**

Aaker, Mark, K6UFO, "Remote Access — Six Ways to Implement" see **k6ufo.com/attachments/K6UFO_Visalia_2016.pdf**

Aaker, Mark, K6UFO, "Remote RTTY Contesting" see **k6ufo.com/attachments/K6UFO_Dayton_RTTY.pdf**

ARRL Website Radio and Technology Topics, Link and Remote Control, **www.arrl.org/link-remote-control**

Craft, Brock; Evans, Jonathan, and Cook, Mike, *Raspberry Pi Projects for Dummies*

Ford, Steve, WB8IMY, *Remote Operating for Amateur Radio*, published by ARRL.

Hilding, Rick, K6VVA, "How Not to Build a Remote Station — Part 1," *National Contest Journal*, Jan/Feb 2010, pp 8-10.

Hilding, Rick, K6VVA, "How Not to Build a Remote Station — Part 2," *National Contest Journal*, Mar/Apr 2010, pp 19-23.

James, Ed, KA8JMW and Pendley, Mike, K5ATM, "Raspberry Pi: A Low Cost Platform for Amateur Radio Projects" see **www.nm5hd.com/documents/PRESENTATIONS/RaspberryPi.pdf**

Lodewyck, Ron, N6EE, "Remote Contesting" see **n6ee.net84.net/Articles/Remote.pdf**

Sepmeier, Bill, "Designing Solar Power System for FM Translators," Radio Guide, Sep 2008, pp 6, 8; see **www.k6vva.com/remotestuff/radioguidesolararticle.pdf**

Yerger, Alfred T., WA2EHI, "Remote Control Your Rig via the Internet," see **www.arrl.org/files/file/Technology/LinkRemoteControl/RemoteControl.pdf**

Web URLs for Companies and Websites in this Section

ACOM — **www.acom-bg.com**
Airspy — **www.airspy.com**
Ameritron — **www.ameritron.com**
Array Solutions — **www.arraysolutions.com**
Belken — **www.belkin.com/us**
Chrome Remote Desktop — **chrome.google.com/webstore/detail/chrome-remote-desktop**

Digi — **www.digi.com**
Digital Loggers — **www.digital-loggers.com**
EA4TX — **ea4tx.com/en**
Elecraft — **www.elecraft.com**
FlexRadio — **www.flexradio.com/amateur-products**
Global Tuner — **www.globaltuner.com**
Ham Radio Deluxe — **www.ham-radio-deluxe.com**
Hamation — **hamation.com**
HAMNET — **www.broadband-hamnet.org**
Icom — **www.icomamerica.com/en**
IP Sound — **www.iw5edi.com/software/ip-sound**
Kenwood — **www.kenwood.com/usa/com/amateur**
LogMeIn — **secure.logmein.com/home/en**

LogMeIn Hamachi — **www.vpn.net**
MicroHAM — **microham-usa.com**
Moxa — **www.moxa.com**
MyIPAddress — **www.myipaddress.com/show-my-ip-address**
OpenVPN — **openvpn.net**
PSTRotator — **www.qsl.net/yo3dmu/index_Page346.htm**
Raspberry Pi — **www.raspberrypi.org**
RealVNC — **www.realvnc.com/index.html**
RemoteHamRadio — **www.remotehamradio.com**
RemoteHams — **www.remotehams.com**
Skype — **www.skype.com**
Snaptekk — **www.snaptekk.com**
SPE Expert — **www.linear-amplifier.com**
Speakeasy — **www.Speakeasy.net/speedtest**

SteppIR — **www.steppir.com**
Teamviewer — **www.teamviewer.com/en**
TelePost (N8LP) — **www.telepostinc.com/n8lp.html**
Tigertronics — **www.tigertronics.com**
TightVNC — **www.tightvnc.com**
TRX Manager — **www.trx-manager.com/demoe.htm**
Velleman — **www.vellemanusa.com/home**
Vibroplex — **www.vibroplex.com**
Viking Electronics — **www.VikingElectronics.com**
Websdr — **www.Websdr.org**
West Mountain Radio — **www.westmountainradio.com**
WhatisMyIPAddress — **whatismyipaddress.com**
Wizkers — **www.wizkers.io**

Assembling a Station   24.35